# Navigating Genesis

"Few from the biblical or scientific communities have done more to further the conversation between these two communities—and from a perspective that simultaneously respects the high claims of Scripture and has handled the continuing stream of new data on an ongoing basis that comes from the research of the various sectors of the scientific world. I read with delight how Hugh Ross integrated these two supposedly antithetical realms of inquiry into a harmonious reading of the creation narrative in Genesis 1 and the contributions from all segments of the scientific endeavor. A careful reading of *Navigating Genesis: A Scientist's Journey through Genesis 1–11* will be one filled with rich rewards on almost every page. This book is destined to become a classic in the correlation of science and Scripture for the twenty-first century. It will profit not only believers who have been bewildered by the plethora and diversity of opinions of the creation narrative in Genesis by the friends of Scripture, but it will also go a long way to giving those who, like the new atheists, think there was no possible way to adequately explain the Genesis 1–11 account with the emerging evidences and research from the real world of scientific fact. This book will demonstrate that such a suspicion is altogether without any grounding."

–Walter C. Kaiser Jr.
President Emeritus, Gordon-Conwell Theological Seminary

"Dr. Ross offers an in-depth literal historical biblical approach to the text of Genesis that addresses both its scientific and interpretative issues. Readers will discover an intelligent look that addresses the ways Scripture and the scientific evidence complement one another, revealing the integrity and accuracy of God's Word in the process."

–Dr. John Ankerberg
Founder and president of *The John Ankerberg Show*

"In *Navigating Genesis*, Hugh Ross clearly shows how the early chapters of the Bible and modern scientific findings seamlessly mesh together, telling a consistent story about the origin of the universe and the early history of humans, without compromising either the biblical text or the scientific discoveries. Such a picture is crucial if Christians are to make the case that the Bible is inspired by God and relevant to our current culture. Dr. Ross's respect for, and understanding of, both the biblical record and the scientific facts should be a model for theologians and scientists, and gives continued support that the Christian Scriptures and the natural realm were sculpted by the same Artist."

–Dr. Michael G. Strauss
David Ross Boyd Professor of Physics, University of Oklahoma

H U G H   R O S S

# NAVIGATING
# GENESIS

*A Scientist's Journey through Genesis 1–11*

Cover design by Morgan Lawrence and Grüv Creative Communications

Unless otherwise identified, all Scripture quotations in this publication are taken from the HOLY BIBLE: NEW INTERNATIONAL VERSION ® (NIV®). Copyright ©1973, 1978, 1984 by International Bible Society. Used by permission of Zondervan Publishing House. All rights reserved. Another version used is the King James Version (KJV).

   Ross, Hugh (Hugh Norman), 1945-
      Navigating Genesis: a scientist's journey through
   Genesis 1–11 / Hugh Ross.
      pages cm
      Includes bibliographical references and index.
      ISBN 978-1-886653-86-3

      1. Bible. Genesis, I-XI--Criticism, interpretation,
   etc. 2. Bible. Genesis, I-XI--Evidences, authority,
   etc. 3. Bible and science.  I. Title.

   BS1235.52.R67 2013        222'.1106
                         QBI13-600170

Printed in the United States of America

# CONTENTS

# PREFACE

Since the publication of my book *The Genesis Question*, 2nd edition, in 2001, scientists have made many new discoveries that substantially strengthen the case for the scientific and historical accuracy of the first eleven chapters of Genesis. This book describes many of these discoveries, including: the dating of early plant species; determination of Earth's continental growth and atmospheric oxygenation histories; a profile of the Sun's luminosity history; details about the Avalon and Cambrian explosions; research into the cognitive and relational capacities of birds and mammals; DNA evidence elucidating the time, place, and manner of humanity's origin; and archaeological and geological finds relevant to Eden's location. Several new discoveries support a theistic explanation for three origins of life— physical, soulish, and spiritual—and for supernatural speciation. Readers will also find fresh discussion of the extent and characteristics of the "worldwide," but not global, flood.

The twenty-first century has brought many new challenges to belief in the accuracy and authority of the Bible, Genesis 1–11 in particular. Well-publicized ridicule has come from the new atheists and Darwinian evolutionists. Evolutionary creationists and young-earth creationists have also weighed in with some new arguments for their particular Genesis interpretations. This book responds to such perspectives on Genesis 1–11.

In this book I've attempted to convey my own perspective, that of a research scientist, a student of Scripture, and an evangelical pastor. If my words help you recognize the uniqueness of the biblical record and the accuracy that points to its supernatural Source, my purpose in writing will have been achieved. Most importantly, may you find in these pages a more captivating glimpse of the Creator's glory, power, wisdom, and love.

# 1

# PERSONAL JOURNEY

*The Holy Bible*, the best-selling book of all time, makes a compelling claim for itself: divine inspiration.[1] Given the high respect this book has been accorded over many centuries, this claim would seem dangerous to ignore. Yet the Bible *is* ignored more and more in popular culture, as people have moved on to more "sophisticated" conceptions of spirituality and divine revelation.

The justification I hear more often than any other for leaving the Bible behind is that "everyone knows" it is antiquated and full of scientific nonsense, if not blatant errors and contradictions. Amazingly, when I ask people to cite examples, many cannot bring to mind even one. Apparently, they base their opinion on hearsay and repeat a widespread misconception.

Among those who do answer my question, one Bible portion draws more vigorous attack than all others combined: the first few chapters of Genesis. This attack opens a wonderful door of opportunity for me—and for every believer who knows something about the scientific discoveries of the past few decades. Instead of offering an excuse for disbelief and rejection, these chapters present some of the most persuasive evidences ever assembled for the supernatural authorship, accuracy, and authority of the Bible.

The language of these chapters is remarkably clear and specific. The words repeatedly associate spiritual events with physical events, and physical events are, in a word, testable.

As a scientist I would say these events beg to be tested. However, as if the implied invitation here in Genesis to test were not enough, the apostle Paul exhorted his readers to "test everything,"[2] to see what holds water and what does not, and to keep only what does. For Genesis 1–11, the content is largely natural history. So many of the appropriate tests will come from relevant disciplines of science.

## Scientific Testing

Genesis chapters 1–11 present a history of the universe, Earth, life, and early humanity. With the help of many remarkable advances in astronomy, physics, geophysics, chemistry, paleontology, biochemistry, and anthropology, the words of the first eleven chapters can be subjected point by point to rigorous investigation. They can be verified or refuted with greater precision and to a greater depth than previous generations might have imagined possible.

Of course, not all biblically described events can be subjected to scientific testing. But those we cannot test are not necessarily invalidated. Rather, if the Genesis 1–11 miraculous interventions can be validated, they indicate the reality and availability of the power and the love to account for the nontestable miracles: the virgin's pregnancy, Lazarus's resurrection, and the water's transformation into wine, for example. While Mary, Lazarus, and the wine consumed at the wedding feast are not available for scientific analysis, the universe, Earth, Earth's fossils, and living creatures certainly are, and they can be subjected to the degree of scientific scrutiny needed to confirm or deny the creation, flood, and postflood events reported in Genesis 1–2 and 6–11.

## Biblical Testing

In Acts 17:11 we read that "the Bereans were of more noble character than the Thessalonians, for they received the message with great eagerness and examined the Scriptures every day to see if what Paul said was true." Dozens of biblical texts parallel or overlap the content of Genesis 1–11. Consequently, interpretations of these chapters can be tested by how well they integrate with the rest of the Bible. Since "the Scripture cannot be broken,"[3] understandings of Genesis 1–11 that contradict any other part of the Bible must be rejected.

The apostle John in his first letter commands all believers to "test the spirits to see whether they are from God."[4] That is, the spirit within a human being may cause that person to distort the truth. The desire for autonomy of thought and freedom from God's authority combined with peer pressure from the surrounding culture typically results in people's testing by *their* standards and according to *their* notions rather than God's.

Biblical language also must be considered. A precise understanding of the text is crucial for interpreting the scientific and historical details as well as the theological context. Such an understanding includes knowledge of word definitions in the original language, usage of certain words throughout the Bible, grammatical context, cultural context, range of theological lessons the text aims to communicate, and the intended audiences.

**My Own Inquiry**

The scientific content of Genesis 1–11 holds special significance for me because it revolutionized my thinking and changed my life's direction.[5] Until I was in my late teens, my singular passion was science, astronomy in particular. My life's purpose was to learn more and more about the universe. By the time I turned sixteen, I had studied enough cosmology to become convinced that of all the origins models ever proposed, the big bang model best fit the observational data. Soon after my sixteenth birthday, the implications of that model began to dawn on me.

Without consciously doing so, I took a huge philosophical and spiritual step—actually, a series of steps. I understood that the big bang meant an ever-expanding universe and that a continuously expanding universe could be traced back to a beginning. If the universe had a beginning, it must have a cause. The big bang theory implied that a Creator exists. That much seemed clear, but the rest of the picture seemed less clear. Who was this Creator, or God? What was God like? Had God communicated to humanity through some means other than the creation itself?

Millions of people through the ages have lived and died by their "holy books." But if all the holy books came from the same source and said pretty much the same thing, as my teachers suggested, why did the followers of each book criticize, condemn, and even kill the followers of the others? I began to suspect that all religions were humanly crafted fronts for people's psychological desire to dominate others.

In the universe's physics I saw harmony, consistency, freedom from contradiction, a pervading beauty, and an elegance of design. If God had spoken to humanity through a book or books, I reasoned, God's communication would manifest the same qualities as did the cosmos. Science had convinced me that the God of the universe was neither capricious nor careless. People, on the other hand, even the most "objective" scientists I had met or read, were prone to at least some weaknesses and inconsistencies and to making some errors, particularly the kind of "errors" arising from limited knowledge and understanding. And, when it came to predicting the future, human imperfection and imprecision seemed abundantly (and forgivably) obvious.

On these premises I began—and ended—my investigation of the world's sacred writings. While I found words of interest and beauty and truth in these works, each reflected the limited (now known to be incorrect) scientific knowledge of its time and place—each except one. This particular book stood apart, and dramatically so.

## A Surprising Discovery

From its first page I could see the Bible's distinctions. The quantity and detail of scientific content far exceeded what I found in any of the other books. To my surprise, the scientific method was as clearly evident in Genesis 1 as in a modern research paper. Most impressive of all, the four initial conditions and the sequence of major creation events—not just one or two, but nearly a dozen—all matched the established scientific record. As I pondered how this accuracy could have been achieved, noting that the book was written at least three thousand years ago, I calculated the odds that the writer could have guessed the initial conditions and correctly sequenced the events (ignoring for the moment the questions about how the writer could have known what they were), and I discovered that the odds are utterly remote. Only one conclusion made sense to me, the conclusion that the Creator of the universe had something to do with the words of Genesis 1.

When I turned the page, I discovered more of the same documentary-type communication. By the time I came to the flood chapters, I realized I could not dismiss this book, at least not yet. I decided to spend an hour a day (or more), in addition to my homework time, studying the Bible until I reached the end or found a provable error.

Eighteen months later I arrived in Revelation 22. During those months I had read every page and failed to discover anything I could label as a verifiable error or contradiction. Some parts I had trouble understanding, but that didn't bother me. I understood enough, just as I understood enough of physics and astronomy to trust what I was learning in my university courses. I was so astonished by the Bible's consistent and frequent anticipation of future scientific discoveries that I decided to attempt a probability calculation. My notepad scribbles showed me the numbers, based on conservative estimates for a small sampling of biblical predictions: the Bible matched the best-established laws of physics in its degree of trustworthiness. I knew how implicitly I trusted the laws of physics. How could I not trust this book's message and the One who sent it with such supernatural precision through fallible human messengers?

With some delays and more than a little wrestling with personal pride, I did make a transfer of trust, inviting God, the Creator of the vast cosmos, to be my God, the Master of my destiny, through Jesus Christ, His Son.[6]

## What Controversy?

Because I didn't really know anyone at that time who had actually read the Bible, I had no idea about all the conflict and debate surrounding these opening chapters of Genesis. Only later did I encounter the misperceptions about the Bible's beginning among nonbelievers, as well as the differences and debates among Christians over how to interpret this portion of Scripture. When I did find out, I recognized the need to address the controversies.

How could the two "books" of revelation from the same Source—that is, the book of nature and the Bible—tell anything other than the same message? They will always match up when we come to understand them more fully and interpret them responsibly. There is nothing to fear—for either believer or skeptic—in searching out the truth.

What you'll find in the pages that follow is my attempt to navigate Genesis with you. Some would call such a trek an ill-advised foray through a minefield. I prefer to view it as a rewarding excursion with surprise discoveries along the way that ultimately satisfy intellectual curiosity.

I will address a multitude of questions—about the beginning of time, matter, and life, and what the latest research tells us about them—I've been asked again and again about my understanding of the Bible's first chapters. This goal seems ambitious enough. I have not written this book as a commentary on the Bible's first eleven chapters. I purposely limited the book's scope to addressing those portions of Genesis 1–11 that overlap the record of nature and to addressing challenges raised by skeptics, both inside and outside the Christian community, to understanding Genesis 1–11 as the inerrant, inspired Word of God. We will begin, in the next chapter, by clearing some obstructions that often end the journey before it can begin.

# 2

# REASONS FOR RESISTANCE

**W**hile scientific developments of the nineteenth century seemed to undermine confidence in the truth of Genesis, advances of the twentieth century breathed new vitality into belief in the biblical Creator. Evidence of a cosmic beginning in the finite past—only 13.8 billion years ago[1] rather than the virtually infinite past of prior naturalistic scenarios—steadily accumulated, in agreement with Genesis 1:1. Thus, the standard naturalistic origin-of-life model, which rested on the assumption of an eternal (or nearly so) cosmos, lost its footing.

Meanwhile, as researchers for the first time measured the far reaches of the solar system, the Milky Way Galaxy, and deep space, they uncovered a growing list of features that appear to have been "designed for life." They found multiple physical characteristics that required narrowly defined limits for any kind of life to be possible. These discoveries yielded a new scientific proposition: the anthropic principle, the observation that all the physical features of the universe, including the characteristics of the solar system, are "just right" to suit the needs of life, and especially human life.[2]

In 1992, science historian Frederic Burnham commented that belief in God is "more respectable today" among scientists than at any time in the last hundred years.[3] Simultaneously, however, our society (at least here in the Western world) seems to have shifted toward a *less* respectful view of the Judeo-Christian worldview. Beliefs in the Bible as God's Word and in the deity of Jesus Christ increasingly are considered naïve and passé.

### Case Closed?
Reasons for resistance to Christian beliefs abound. As I speak to university, business, and professional groups across the nation and as I read survey results from Pew and Barna and others who take the spiritual pulse of communities far and

wide, I find that many of the stated "intellectual reasons" for dismissing Christianity come from popularized (mistaken) notions about what Genesis 1–11 says. Time and again I hear this question, expressed or implied: "Why should I give serious attention to the message of a book that contradicts, right from the start, the established facts of science?"

The supposed contradictions have become "common knowledge" through the assertions of well-known personalities such as Michael Shermer, executive director of the Skeptics Society, and the cadre of "new atheists" led by Richard Dawkins, Daniel Dennett, and Sam Harris.

Shermer, for one, tells audiences that the Bible is wrong from the very first verse and goes on to present a litany of supposed inaccuracies.[4] Dawkins, Dennett, and Harris openly mock Genesis in their writings, debates, and countless media interviews. Because they are intelligent and articulate, not to mention emphatic, their words seem to carry substantial weight. Given the widespread appeal of these public figures *and* given people's ignorance of the Bible (not to mention of basic interpretive rules) many have been persuaded that the Bible holds no scientific credibility. This case-closed attitude has become increasingly widespread.

### Science-Scripture Models

Christians have developed a variety of responses to this dismissive attitude. These responses have evolved into a set of models used by creationists, as well as by evolutionists, whereby they interpret emerging data and address a wide spectrum of science-faith issues. The models fall into four distinct categories by their foundational assertions: (1) Science and Scripture are completely independent of one another; (2) Science and Scripture are in direct conflict with one another; (3) Science and Scripture can complement one another; and (4) Science and Scripture can be constructively integrated.

### 1. Separatist Models

The first set of models was eloquently described more than a decade ago by evolutionary biologist and paleontologist Stephen Jay Gould. In his article entitled "Nonoverlapping Magisteria" first published (1997) in the magazine *Natural History*[5] and later (1999, 2002) in the book *Rocks of Ages*,[6] Gould proposes "a blessedly simple and entirely conventional resolution to…the supposed conflict between science and religion." The proposed solution: recognize that science (based on tangible reality) and religion (based on sacred stories) define two different and completely independent domains of teaching, questions, and research. Since, according to Gould, the two domains do not overlap, there can be no conflict between the two.

Gould avoids any overlap by limiting the focus of science to the empirical realm—the collection of facts about the universe through experiments and observations and the development of theories that explain why the universe works as it does. Gould also limits the domain of religion to addressing questions of ultimate meaning and morality. To put it another way, science addresses the *what* and the *how* of phenomena while religion tackles the *why*.

Gould acknowledged that his proposal was not original, noting that the Roman Catholic Church had already adopted such a position, at least since Pope Pius XII's 1950 encyclical, *Humani Generis*. In 1984 the National Academy of Sciences, USA stated in its official publication called Science and Creationism, "Religion and science are separate and mutually exclusive realms of human thought whose presentation in the same context leads to misunderstandings of both scientific theory and religious belief."[7] Since the time of Gould's writings, most scientists holding membership in the National Academy of Sciences USA and many within the American Institute of Biological Sciences have embraced this approach to creation-evolution and other science-religion conflicts.

## 2. Conflict Models

Many Christians as well as antitheistic scientists flatly reject this separatist model. Understandably, Christians bristle at the assertion that science *alone* deals with facts and reality. Meanwhile Richard Dawkins and other antitheists seek to highlight the connection. Writing for *Free Inquiry*, Dawkins commented, "It is completely unrealistic to claim, as Gould and many others do, that religion keeps itself away from science's turf, restricting itself to morals and values. A universe with a supernatural presence would be a fundamentally and qualitatively different kind of universe from one without. The difference is, inescapably, a scientific difference. Religions make existence claims, and this means scientific claims."[8]

Dawkins, therefore, advocates a conflict model. If science and religion, such as Christianity, make contradictory claims about the state of the natural world, they cannot both be right. Thus, he sees no basis for peace. The two perspectives are inexorably locked in a war with only one possible outcome, in his view: science will emerge as the victor and religion, the vanquished.

Even before Dawkins articulated his battle-to-the-finish model, young-earth creationist organizations had trumpeted the call to arms, urging Christians to join them in a life-and-death (spiritually speaking) confrontation. The main difference between the two groups lies in their anticipation of who will emerge as the victor and who, the vanquished.

### 3. Complementary Models

Another response to the separatist model has been popularized by geneticist Francis Collins, director of the National Institutes of Health and founder of BioLogos. While Collins agrees with Gould that spirituality and moral ethics belong to a realm largely inaccessible to scientific investigation, he insists that science, religion, and other spheres do overlap, at least partially. However, he avoids conflict by maintaining the overlap is slight.

An example of the overlap may be seen in the biblical claim that the universe has a beginning, an origin of matter, energy, space, and time, brought about by a causal Agent from beyond space and time—a claim that agrees with the findings of mainstream science.[9] Another example of overlap is seen in the shared conviction that simple, small-bodied life on Earth precedes complex, large-bodied life.

Complementary models accept the overlap of science and Scripture on facts/truths accepted without question by both mainstream scientists and mainstream theologians—understandings unlikely to be altered by future research or ongoing study. Thus, complementarians work hard to limit the encroachment of one domain upon the other's territory. Given their view that science has nothing to say about spirituality or morality and ethics, they tend to discount research findings on these topics, including those published by cognitive psychologists and social neuroscientists.

Likewise, complementarians work hard to limit scientific inferences from what the Bible says about natural history. Some say those texts that address specific features of Earth's, life's, and humanity's origin and development must be interpreted within their cultural and historical context as nothing more than polemics against Near- and Middle-Eastern myths surrounding the writer's contemporaries.[10] Others say the "text does not offer scientific explanations"[11] and that "no passage offers a scientific perspective that was not common to the Old World science of antiquity."[12] (More on this later.) Some have suggested that the Holy Spirit willingly accepted into the texts certain misconceptions held by their human authors about the natural realm.[13]

The complementary model attracts a large number of adherents from all segments of the Christian community and beyond. Many if not most members of the American Scientific Affiliation would likely identify themselves as complementarians.

### 4. Constructive Integration Models

The fourth and least well known among the four categories of science-Scripture perspectives is the constructive integration model, also referred to (more or less accurately) as concordism. This view is articulated in a sixteenth-century Protestant doctrinal standard document, the Belgic Confession, Article 2, which states that both the words of the Bible and the record of nature provide trustworthy and reliable revelation from God, giving testimony to God's attributes and handiwork. During the Reformation, this approach to science and the Bible was predominant in Protestant theology and shared by some Roman Catholic clerics, as well.

Constructive integrationists see more than a slight overlap between science and biblical theology. Proponents of this perspective point out that the scientific method and the scientific revolution trace back to the Reformation period and to Reformation theology, in particular.[14] This observation says something about the motivation for research and wealth of scientifically reliable content found in Scripture. By some counts roughly 1,400 Bible verses describe natural phenomena and natural history, all of which can be tested in light of ongoing discoveries.[15] Meanwhile, science has made huge strides recently in exploring what was once considered the private preserve of theologians, such as the uniqueness of the human mind.

Based on the consistency of the message emanating from these two sources, constructive integrationists take a strong view of Scripture and a strong view of the record of nature. They see both domains as content-rich, addressing a wide range of similar issues and coming closer together through time. For them, the concept of divine inspiration is large enough to encompass the notion that each book of the Bible communicates relevant truth to and for all generations of humanity, not just the writer's contemporaries. As Peter comments in his first letter to the church, "It was revealed to them [the prophets] that they were not serving themselves but you."[16] Peter explains that Old Testament prophets (and even angels) longed to understand more fully what the Holy Spirit inspired them to record.[17] These writers contented themselves in knowing that a more complete understanding of their God-breathed words was meant for future generations.

Given that the Bible is divinely supervised and preserved revelation, it seems plausible that its ordinary words communicate extraordinary truths so rich in meaning that their message unfolds from one generation to the next. One brief passage may reveal truth in layers, with different levels of meaning and yet never self-contradictory as history unfolds and knowledge advances. Such communication exceeds the capability of mere humans. But the work of the Holy Spirit can explain the content layering of biblical texts such as the prophecies of Isaiah about his son-to-be[18] and the long-awaited son—and Son.[19] The search for different levels of meaning and layers of truth, of course, can be taken too far. One can fall victim to reading into the text what the text does not imply.

Constructive integration advocates freely acknowledge that conflicts can and do arise between theology and science. After all, theology is not the same as the words of the Bible. It is the human effort to interpret the Bible's words. Neither is science equivalent to the record of nature. It is the human attempt to interpret nature, past and present. Because human knowledge must always be incomplete and to some degree biased, both theologians and scientists sometimes arrive at incorrect conclusions about Scripture and nature, despite God's rendering these records perfectly reliable and trustworthy.

Therefore, constructive integrationists embrace the endeavor to ferret out faulty human interpretations. They welcome apparent conflicts between theology and science as opportunities to build a more detailed, more comprehensive, and more consistent understanding of what's true. In the case of the creation-evolution controversy, this group considers apparent contradictions as opportunities to test competing scenarios. If the number and severity of such clashes within a particular scenario shrink as theological and scientific research progresses, confidence in that scenario's accuracy grows. If the number and severity increase with advancing research, the scenario warrants alteration or elimination.

The goal of constructive integration is to show that the more we learn about the Bible and nature's record, the more compelling a case we can present not only for God's existence but also for His identity. Constructive integrationists also seek to clearly show that the words of Scripture and facts of nature come to us from the same divine Source, and together they present a trustworthy picture of God's attributes, including His special care for humanity. Toward this end, constructive integrationists seek to develop a worldview consistent with all sixty-six books of the Bible and all disciplines of science. In other words, they pursue a fully integrated understanding of God's two "books," Scripture and nature.

Building a robust model encompassing everything Scripture reveals and everything nature's record reveals about Earth's and life's origin and development, for example, is no easy task. Yet the Great Commission[20] demands it of us if we are to make disciples among those men and women at the highest levels of learning and research, not to mention the huge segment of society they influence.

## Concerns About "Concordism"
In the sixteenth, seventeenth, and early eighteenth centuries, the Western world's widespread conviction that the Bible and nature speak concordantly and harmoniously gradually eroded, and turf wars developed between theologians and scientists. When simplistic interpretations were challenged or overturned by

stunning discoveries and new theories based on them, a devastating schism grew. The split widened in the latter decades of the eighteenth century with the emergence of "higher criticism," a theological capitulation to the notion that Scriptural truth and scientific truth are irreconcilably at odds (see chapter 20) and that biblical inspiration must be redefined if not wholly abandoned.

By the end of the nineteenth century, most theologians had become convinced that scientific advance required abandonment of a concordant view, especially with respect to Earth's and life's history. Old Testament scholar and Assyriologist Friedrich Delitzsch wrote in his book *Babel and Bible*,

> All attempts to harmonize our biblical story of the creation of the world with the results of natural science have been useless and must always be so.[21]

In this climate, both the separatist and conflict approaches to biblical and scientific data gained strength and notoriety. And yet, however sharply and vigorously the various factions on one side of the divide disagreed with those on the other, all seemed to agree emphatically on the defeatest conclusion expressed by Delitzsch.

**Addressing Reasons for Resistance**
In my effort to identify, understand, and deal with what seems an unnecessary and even counterproductive commitment to keeping God's two books apart, I have identified some additional forces working to sustain separatism. Overall, I would describe what's going on as an extension of the "turf war" that erupted a few centuries ago. Specialists in science continue to vie with specialists in biblical/theological scholarship for ownership of "truth."

*1. Database Differences*
The biblical canon, the collection of 66 books comprising inspired Scripture, has been complete since the first century (though not formally adopted until the fourth century) AD. In the sciences, the database never stops growing and in some cases doubles within a decade or less. Because scientists' aim is to break new ground and replace old understandings with new ones, science claims exclusive rights to tell the unfolding story of what really happened.

Meanwhile, theology faculty and graduate students face the same "publish-or-perish" pressure as do faculty and researchers in the sciences. This intense pressure to break new ground by proposing new perspectives and insights leads to some excellent but also some questionable scholarship. Theologians and Bible scholars have rightfully argued that due to ongoing biblical scholarship former understandings of a particular text, such as one or more of the early chapters of Genesis, may need revision. However, the extreme stance is to argue that the Bible writers simply incorporated the (erroneous) beliefs about the natural realm of their time and culture as they followed the conventions of a particular genre, and we're wrong to look for meanings pertinent to the physical world that would be applicable for modern-day readers of the text.[22] The true "spiritual message," according to this interpretative approach, must be separated out from the mistaken notions about the physical world.

On the opposite side are those Bible interpreters, often referred to as *hard* concordists, who claim to see intricate scientific detail in the biblical text. This form of concordism no more represents constructive integration than wooden literalism represents biblical inerrancy. Constructive integration rejects attempts, for example, to draw a detailed description of special and general relativity or an exposition of the origin and structure of fundamental particles from Genesis 1. Such assertions seem more closely akin to claims of hidden codes embedded in the sequence of Hebrew letters in certain books of the Old Testament than to reasonable integration.

### 2. The Isolation of Specialization
The word "university" denotes an institution dedicated to uniting (and integrating) knowledge from all scholarly disciplines. Today, however, extreme specialization has propelled us into new frontiers of knowledge where scholars remain largely isolated from one another. Nowhere is this silo effect greater than what we see in the divide between scientists and theologians. The two groups appear to possess little if any awareness of, or interest in, the others' studies much less a desire for their studies to overlap. Some scientists openly regard religion as "emotional nonsense."[23] They react to attempts at integration as a "throwback to a prescientific model of reality."[24] Michael Ruse, well-known zoologist and philosopher of science, emphatically asserts this view.[25]

So does the National Academy of Sciences here in the US, which published this statement:

> Religion and science are separate and mutually exclusive realms of human thought whose presentation in the same context leads to misunderstanding of both scientific theory and religious belief.[26]

For their part, some clergy (since the trial of Galileo) seem to share this perspective. They tend to see theology as the "queen" not just "*of* the sciences" but preferably "*over* the sciences." In their view, theology is a realm of study that sits above all the sciences. Theologians address transcendent Truth (with a capital "t") and not the "changing truths" of science. A familiar refrain says: "The intention of the Bible is to teach us how to go to heaven, not how the heavens go."[27]

### 3. Beyond Intellectual Resistance

For obvious reasons, intellectual questions about Genesis are understandable, even expected. If they are genuine, the person who raises them will show a willingness to listen and explore possible answers. However, not everyone who raises questions really wants an answer. Some seem more interested in arguing. Some just walk away. Why?

How a person interprets the first eleven chapters of Genesis may be determined by how that person responds to some other part of the Bible. For example, if a person has been badly hurt or mistreated by someone bearing the "Christian" label and/or using the Bible as a weapon, his or her objectivity is seriously undermined. The same may be said of a person who, for any number of personal, experiential reasons, objects to biblical teachings (whether rightly or wrongly interpreted) based on moral issues.

Other reactions come from misunderstanding the biblical definition of faith. The prevailing view that God requires "blind" faith turns many away. Even some Christians fail to understand that facts are the crucial foundation for biblical faith. The misapplied mandate to "live by faith, not by sight"[28] frequently causes problems. Perhaps a deeper resistance, more difficult to express, is that connecting faith to scientific findings somehow subordinates the Bible to human endeavors or places Scripture at risk of contradiction as new discoveries overturn previously accepted interpretations.

Herein lies a paradox. People who seem most concerned with defending biblical inerrancy may be the most resistant to any information derived outside the Bible that might help illuminate what the Bible means. Logically, taking Scripture seriously means being passionately concerned about interpreting it correctly and thus welcoming any evidence that exposes erroneous understandings of Scripture.[29] Unfortunately, many zealous Bible believers confuse their favored *interpretations* of the Bible with the Word of God itself.

### Removing the Mistrust

Clearly, many hindrances stand in the way of any study or discussion of the scientific and spiritual content of Genesis 1–11. By identifying some of the obstacles at the outset, I hope to help readers acknowledge them and make the choice to suspend them, at least for as much time as it takes to read the pages that follow. For in these chapters I present what I have found in the latest scientific research to eliminate significant obstacles and cross the divide in a way that stimulates and enlivens studies of both Scripture and nature.

Let's continue the journey by opening the book!

# 3

# CREATION OF THE COSMOS

"In the beginning God created the heavens and the earth" (Genesis 1:1). With this simple yet profound declaration, the biblical account of God's plan for humanity begins. Thousands of pages of commentary have been devoted to this one statement alone.[1] Its explosive impact bursts upon the reader like the creative blast physicists have come to call the "big bang."

The assertion of a *beginning* immediately catches our attention. For centuries the philosophical pendulum has swung back and forth on the questions of the eternality of matter, energy, space, and time. Immanuel Kant was neither the first nor the last but perhaps the most convincing to propose an infinitely-old-universe model.[2] His concept donned scientific garb as the "steady state" model.[3] Later still, scientists revived the Hindu doctrine of a universe that oscillates forever through cycles of birth, death, and rebirth.[4] However, the Bible says in unequivocal terms that the "heavens and the earth" *began*, that they exist for finite time only,[5] and that God exists and acts inside, outside, and beyond the universe's space-and-time boundaries.[6] He alone is everywhere present and always existing.

## The First Act
The Hebrew verb for "created" is *bārā'*. In its basic form (used here) this verb appears in the Bible with only one subject: God. Its usage suggests the kind of creating that only God, and no one else, can do. Old Testament and Semitic languages scholar Thomas E. McComiskey comments: "This distinctive use of the word is especially appropriate to the concept of creation by divine fiat."[7] He adds that this verb choice "denotes the concept of 'initiating something new'"[8] and that "since the primary emphasis of the word is on the newness of the created object, the word lends itself well to the concept of creation *ex nihilo* [out of nothing]."[9]

Creation out of nothing can mean different things in different contexts (see sidebar, "Nine Kinds of Nothing," page 27). So we turn to the creation statement in Hebrews 11:3 for clarification of the intended meaning: "The universe was formed at God's command, so that what is seen was not made out of what was visible." Astronomers can see or detect matter, energy, space, and time (or their effects) throughout the cosmos. Thus, according to Hebrews 11:3 (among other Bible passages[10]) God operated outside, beyond, or transcendent to matter, energy, space, and time, when He created our universe of matter, energy, space, and time.

The verb *bārā'* appears just twice more in Genesis 1 (see Appendix B), in contrast to the frequently used verbs *'āśâ* (make, fashion, execute, manufacture),[11] *hāyâ* (be, happen, come about),[12] *dāshā'* (sprout, bring forth, or flourish),[13] *nātan* (set, put, place, give, or appoint),[14] *rā'â* (be seen, reveal, cause to be seen, or be shown),[15] and *yāṣā'* (go out from, come out from, bring forth, produce, or spring forth).[16] These two other uses of *bārā'* (verses 21 and 27) would also seem to imply that God brought into existence something new, something that did not previously exist (see chapter 6).

## The Heavens and the Earth

Hebrew differs significantly from English in many respects, including its vocabulary size. While English words number in the hundreds of thousands (depending on how one counts them), biblical Hebrew is comprised of a few thousand words.[17] To understand the meaning of *shāmayim* and *'ereṣ* ("heavens" and "earth") requires more than knowing the definition of each individual term.

*'Ereṣ* has six different meanings: the soil; the territory or land possessed by an individual, family, tribe, or nation; a city state; the territories of all peoples and nations; the underworld; or all the land and water, as well as the foundations that support them (what we now know as the planet Earth).[18] *Shāmayim*, a plural form (hence, "heavens"), has three meanings: the part of Earth's atmosphere where rain clouds form, that is, the troposphere; the abode of the stars and galaxies; and the spirit realm from which God rules.[19] New Testament writers and ancient and modern rabbis sometimes used the ordinals "first," "second," and "third" to identify which of these "heavens" they meant.[20]

According to Old Testament scholar Bruce Waltke, the phrase *hashamayim we ha'ereṣ* ("heavens" plural combined with "earth" singular) carries a distinct meaning, as would a compound noun in English. For example, when we put together "under" and "statement" or "dragon" and "fly" to form a compound noun, these words take on a specific and distinct definition. Similarly, the Hebrew expression *hashamayim we ha'ereṣ* refers uniquely to the totality of the physical universe, all its matter, energy, space, and time.[21] Biblical Hebrew includes no single word for the now familiar concept of a universe. Michael Shermer is mistaken in presuming that Genesis 1:1 refers to the universe and to planet Earth separately.

## A Unique Doctrine Validated

According to Genesis 1:1, the entire universe came into existence, entirely new, a finite time ago, by the creative act of God. This statement reverberates throughout the pages of Scripture.[22] No other "holy book" makes such a claim on its own. The concept appears elsewhere only in those books that borrow from the Bible, such as the Qur'an and the Mormon writings.

### Nine Kinds of Nothing

Scientists, philosophers, and theologians use different definitions of *nothing* depending on the context. Nothing can mean the complete absence of:

1.  matter;
2.  matter and energy;
3.  matter, energy, and the three large cosmic space dimensions (length, width, and height);
4.  matter, energy, and all the cosmic space dimensions (including the six extremely tiny space dimensions implied by particle creation models);
5.  matter, energy, and all the cosmic space and time dimensions;
6.  matter, energy, cosmic space and time dimensions, and created nonphysical entities;
7.  matter, energy, cosmic space and time dimensions, created nonphysical entities, and other dimensions of space and time;
8.  matter, energy, cosmic space and time dimensions, created nonphysical entities, and other dimensions or realms—spatial, temporal, or otherwise; or
9.  anything and everything real, created and uncreated.

Because God is an eternal Being, without beginning or ending, only the first eight kinds of nothing in the list above are possible. As for the universe, it came from nothing as in definitions 5, 6, or 7, above.

By contrast, those sacred books with no clear connection to the Bible claim that a god, gods, or forces created the cosmos *within* space and time, which, they say, have always existed. The Bible stands apart in declaring that space and time are not eternal but, rather, suddenly came into being by an act of God, a Being completely independent from—that is, transcendent to or outside of—space, time, matter, and energy.

The importance of this unique doctrine cannot be overstated. It sets biblical revelation apart from all other so-called revelatory writings. In light of what science has discovered, it provides potent evidence for the supernatural accuracy of Genesis.

Modern scientific support for the Genesis 1:1 creation event first arose from observations of the recession velocities of galaxies, which indicated a cosmic beginning. Rigorous verification first came via a theorem published by Stephen Hawking and Roger Penrose in 1970.[23] Their work on the space-time theorem established that a universe containing mass and in which general relativity reliably describes the motions of astronomical bodies *must* be traceable back to a beginning of space and time, implying it was brought into existence by a causal Agent who transcends space and time.

Over a ten-year span following the development of this theorem, researchers Arvind Borde, Alan Guth, and Alexander Vilenkin published five extensions arising from it. These extensions culminated in a theoretical "proof" showing that any *reasonable* cosmological model, that is, any model in which the universe expands (on average) throughout its history (the only conceivable cosmological models that will permit the existence of physical life) requires an actual beginning of space and time, implying the cosmos was initiated by a causal Agent operating beyond space and time.[24]

**Turning Point**

Something happens between verses 1 and 2 that powerfully impacts the reader's comprehension of the story to follow. Here, the frame of reference for the creation account shifts from the entire cosmos (the heavenly objects that make up the universe) explicitly to the surface of Earth. Perhaps because it comes so abruptly, this transition is easily missed, even by distinguished Bible scholars. I am persuaded that my immersion in science prepared me to see it. In fact, I was struck with amazement that this ancient document would be structured much like a modern research report.

The same steps scientists use to analyze and interpret natural phenomena appear on the Bible's first page. At the time I was unaware, as many people still are, that the step-by-step process we now know as the scientific method owes its formation to individuals familiar with the Bible. They recognized a pattern in biblical texts that describe a sequence of events (see sidebar, "Biblical Testing Method/Scientific Method," on page 30 and appendix A). The Genesis account, for example, clearly identifies the frame of reference (or viewpoint) from which the sequence of events is described, including a statement of the initial conditions, the chronology, the final conditions, and some conclusions about what transpired. Within the Bible itself we see instructions to consider contextual elements essential for developing correct interpretations.[25] We also see warnings against the dangers of overlooking them.[26]

### From the Heavens to Earth's Surface

These words depict the shift of perspective in Genesis 1:2:

> Now the earth was formless and empty, darkness was over the surface of the deep, and the Spirit of God was hovering over the waters.

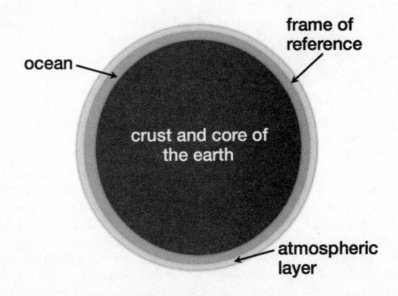

### Figure 3: Frame of Reference for Genesis 1:3–31
The events of the six creation days are described from the vantage point of Earth's primordial (water-covered) surface, underneath the cloud layer, as Genesis 1:2 indicates, and its early inhabitability for life.
Credit: Reasons to Believe

## Biblical Testing Method/Scientific Method

Although the wording and number of steps delineated may vary slightly from one introductory science text to another, the basic components of the scientific method include these seven:

1. Identify the frame(s) of reference or point(s) of view.
2. Determine the initial conditions.
3. Perform an experiment or observe the phenomenon, noting what takes place when, where, and in what order.
4. Note the final conditions.
5. Form a hypothesis about the how and the why of the phenomenon.
6. Test the hypothesis with further experiments or observations.
7. Revise the hypothesis accordingly.

These steps apply just as strategically to biblical interpretation as to nature studies. In the biblical context, step 3 calls for noting all the explanatory and descriptive details, and step 6 calls for testing the initial understanding (hypothesis) with parallel and/or relevant biblical passages. This approach may not guarantee objectivity and accuracy, but it certainly helps minimize the effects of oversight, personal bias, and presuppositions. Nevertheless, all students of science and Scripture must recognize that our knowledge and our comprehension of that knowledge remain limited. So, our interpretations always fall short of perfection, and we must be willing to adjust and fine-tune them as research continues. Conclusions must remain open to ongoing testing and refinement as we repeatedly apply the biblical testing method.

The advance of science over the past few centuries may be attributed, in large measure, to rigorous and repeated application of this step-by-step method. It keeps us moving closer and closer to a correct understanding of the natural realm. If and when students of Scripture apply this systematic approach just as rigorously to biblical interpretation, it moves us closer to "rightly dividing the word of truth." It promotes unity rather than conflict in establishing sound doctrine. In the case of the Genesis creation and flood accounts, applying the scientific method—derived primarily from these very portions of Scripture—offers our best hope for developing a consistent interpretation, one free of both internal and external contradiction.

The observer's vantage point is clearly identified as "the surface of the deep...
over the waters." Yet the vast majority of Genesis commentaries mistakenly pro-
ceed as if it were still high in the heavens, somewhere in the starry realm above
Earth. This one oversight seems to account for more misunderstanding, more
attacks on the credibility of Genesis, than all other interpretive errors combined.
The problem glares from the page at anyone slightly aware of how nature works.
If the storyteller's viewpoint lies in the heavens above, the unfolding sequence
of creative events contradicts the scientific record. It violates much of well-established Earth (and life) history. For example, it would place the production of
plants *before* the formation of the Sun, Moon, and stars.

**Initial Conditions**
In addition to clarifying the point of view, the Genesis 1 creation account also
identifies four of Earth's major features at the outset of the narrative. One of
these conditions is darkness. As the creation days begin, the darkness is pervasive.
A look ahead to the third creation day reveals that water initially covered Earth's
entire surface (Psalm 104:6):

> You [God] covered it [the earth] with the deep as with a garment; the waters
> stood above the mountains.

The book of Job makes reference to both the darkness and the water. Job 38:9
says that the Earth's surface was dark because of opaque enshrouding clouds.
God says in reference to "the sea" that covered Earth's surface, "I made the clouds
its garment and wrapped it in thick darkness."

According to the Genesis account, no continents initially rose above the
water, and the whole of Earth's watery surface remained in darkness. No light
reached through Earth's primordial atmosphere.

Next the passage mentions two more conditions, *tōhû wābōhû*, translated
variously as "formless and empty," "without form and void," and "unformed and
unfilled." Given that the creation account focuses on God's preparing Earth for
life and filling it with life, the reference to "unformed" for life and "empty" of life
makes sense. As Old Testament scholar David Tsumura explains, *tōhû wābōhû* is
not a description of chaos, but instead refers to Earth as "an unproductive and
uninhabited place."[27]

Context holds the key to interpreting *tōhû wābōhû* (see sidebar, "What about
the Gap Theory?" on page 33). The story builds step by step toward the climactic
moment when God created humanity. Thus, each creative act highlighted bears

significance in relation to God's preparations and provisions for humans' arrival and sustenance.

## Completed Acts

In analyzing the structure and grammar of Genesis 1:1 and 1:2 Hebrew linguists have determined that those texts proclaim that the creation of the universe and the formation of Earth must predate the events described in the six creation days by an unspecified but finite duration of time. Consequently, whichever one of the four usages (see sidebar, "How Long Are the Creation Days?" on page 35) one might choose for the Hebrew noun *yôm* (translated "day") to delineate the duration of the six creation days, Genesis 1 allows for both the universe and Earth to be as old as astronomers' and physicists' measurements have determined.

In his book, *Genesis 1–4: A Linguistic, Literary, and Theological Commentary*, C. John Collins writes, "The verb *created* in Genesis 1:1 is in the perfect, and the normal use of the perfect at the very beginning of a pericope [an excerpt from a text] is to denote an event that took place before the storyline gets under way."[28] He adds, "A number [of narrative pericopes] do begin with a verb in the perfect, and they do so in order to describe an event that precedes the main storyline."[29]

Rodney Whitefield in his book, *Reading Genesis One: Comparing Biblical Hebrew with English Translation*, and his booklet summary, *Genesis One and the Age of the Earth*, explains that in biblical Hebrew verbs by themselves do not specify the duration of actions. Nor do they determine the time ordering of actions. Instead, the ordering of past actions is established most straightforwardly by word order.[30]

Whitefield points out that most frequently in biblical Hebrew narrative the verb appears first followed by the subject of the verb. This is the case for the verbs that appear in all but three of the thirty-one verses that comprise Genesis 1. Exceptions, however, are found in Genesis 1:1 and 1:2. In describing the creation of the universe and the status of Earth, Genesis 1:1 and the first clause in Genesis 1:2, respectively, place the verb in the second rather than the first position. Placing the verb as the second word of a sentence or clause is one way, Whitefield explains, that biblical Hebrew establishes that a particular action has already been completed.[31] Thus, Genesis 1:1 declares that the universe has a beginning and that its creation is a completed event. Genesis 1:2 proclaims that Earth had existed in a formless and empty state. That is, the universe and Earth already are in place before the events of the six creation days.

The phrase "and God said" that (starting in Genesis 1:3) leads off the eight creative commands in the account of the six creation days confirms the

## What about the Gap Theory?

A century ago, when geologists were first discovering the long geological time spans, some biblical scholars put forth the gap theory, which interprets the *tōhû wābōhû* of verse 2 as implying a significant time gap in the account of creation.[32] They take the Hebrew verb *hāyâ* (translated "was") to mean "became." In other words, they suggest that Earth did not *begin* formless and empty but rather *became* formless and empty.

One rationale for this translation arises from the observation that *tōhû wābōhû* tends to carry a negative or pejorative connotation elsewhere in the Bible. A second rationale comes from the desire to reconcile the voluminous scientific evidence for Earth's antiquity with the popular twentieth century teaching that the Genesis days represent six consecutive 24-hour periods. (See chapter 8 for a detailed discussion of the Hebrew word translated "day" and its multiple *literal* meanings.)

What's called the "gap theory" proposes that the beautiful world God created "in the beginning" suffered ruination (most often attributed to the actions of Satan and his fellow rebellious angels) and that the six-day creation account in Genesis 1 describes its restoration. According to this theory, astronomers, geophysicists, and paleontologists are measuring the ancient, ruined creation, whereas the Bible addresses God's recent repair of creation.

This theory, popularized by a C. I. Scofield study Bible published at the beginning of the twentieth century,[33] still holds sway among some Bible interpreters.[34] However, it falters on several significant points, both biblical and scientific. Perhaps most significantly, the Hebrew conjunction *waw* in Genesis 1:2 is not connected with the verb *hāyâ* in a manner that would mean "became." Genesis 2:7 (man became a living being) has the *waw*-consecutive with *hāyâ* such that the definition "became" is implied. However, in Genesis 1:2 *hāyâ* is in the perfect form without an immediately preceding *waw*. This construct eliminates the possibility of translating *hāyâ* as "became" rather than "was."

For a more thorough, in-depth discussion of the gap theory and its flaws, see *The Christian View of Science and Scripture* by theologian and philosopher of science Bernard Ramm.[35]

conclusion of Collins and Whitefield. In each case, the eight such occurrences of "and God said…" starts a sequential narrative that follows up on what transpired before. Therefore, just as the text implies that the events of creation day three, for example, occurred after the events of creation day two, so also the events of the first creation day must have taken place after the events described in Genesis 1:1 and 1:2.

The completed nature of the creation of the universe and the formation of the primordial Earth implies that an unspecified duration of time transpired between the creation of the universe and the formation of Earth. Likewise, an unspecified time period transpired between Earth's initial formation and the events of creation day one.

**Initial Conditions Confirmed**

It's worth noting that water is one of the most abundant molecules in the universe. So, the watery covering of primordial Earth is no surprise. What ongoing research has revealed, however, is that a remarkable, exactingly orchestrated event adjusted the quantity, states, and distribution of Earth's water and atmosphere in a manner uniquely suitable for land-dwelling creatures, including humans. More of that story appears in the account of the Moon's formation (see chapter 4, pages 39–41).

Through ongoing research into how planets form, scientists have been able to explain and confirm not only the dark and watery but also the "formless and empty" features of early Earth. Technological advances in the 1970s allowed astronomers to observe "disks" around young stellar objects. Thousands of these objects have been studied thus far, and each one is surrounded by an extensive disk of gas, dust, and debris.[36] Theoretical studies as well as observational evidence show how these disks eventually condense into planetary systems.[37] Indeed, such planetary systems are being discovered at a rapid rate. To date, astronomers have discovered more than 2,300 planets (or likely planets) and have measured the physical and orbital properties of more than 1,000.[38]

They've learned that planets as massive as Earth and as distant from their host star (their "sun") typically start with a thick, opaque (light-blocking) atmosphere. The smallest of the extrasolar (outside our solar system) planets for which astronomers have a measurement of the planet's atmospheric mass is 6.5 times more massive than Earth and has an atmosphere at least 4,000 times "heavier" than Earth's atmosphere today.[39] Venus, which measures 19 percent less massive than Earth (implying that its weaker gravity will be less able to accrete an atmosphere) and 28 percent closer to the Sun (implying that its greater planetary surface temperature will cause more of its atmosphere to dissipate to outer space), nevertheless possesses an atmosphere 91 times more massive than Earth's. Thus, astronomers estimate that Earth's primordial atmosphere was at least 200 times more massive than our current atmosphere. So light from the Sun (or stars and other heavenly objects) would have been unable to penetrate to the early Earth's surface.

No life-supporting landmasses would have existed on early Earth either. Initially all the land in Earth's rocky crust lay below the surface of the deep. Islands and continents arose gradually—think hundreds of millions of years—as a result of volcanism (volcanic activity) and plate tectonics (movement and collisions of large crustal sections). Volcanism and plate tectonics, driven primarily by heat from radioisotope decay in Earth's mantle, generated the wrinkling of Earth's surface. This wrinkling, which eventually pushed land upward above the ocean's surface, continues to this day, but at a much lower rate.[40]

## How Long Are the Creation Days?

In contrast to English the vocabulary size in biblical Hebrew is tiny. If one discounts the names of people and places, biblical Hebrew contains only about three thousand words.[41] Consequently, most nouns in biblical Hebrew possess multiple "literal definitions" or common usages.

The Hebrew noun, yôm, translated "day" in Genesis 1 is no exception. It has four distinct literal definitions:[42]

1. part of the daylight hours; for example, from noon to 3 PM
2. all of the daylight hours
3. a 24-hour period
4. a long but finite time period

While modern-day Hebrew has two words for an extended, finite-duration time period, in biblical Hebrew no other word besides yôm possesses the meaning of a long but finite period of time.[43] Therefore, if Moses wanted to communicate a creation history consisting of six eons, he would have no other option but to use the word yôm to describe those eras.

With many distinct literal definitions for so many of the Hebrew nouns, how does the reader determine which ones apply in a specific biblical text? The answer lies in the grammar, sentence structure, and context. These considerations for yôm as it applies to the Genesis 1 creation days are addressed in chapters 9 and 10.

Tectonic and volcanic activity superseded erosion (the wearing down processes) until landmasses rose up above the oceans to cover about 29 percent of Earth's surface. They still do exceed the erosion rate, but to a much lesser degree. (Note: Earth's rotation rate has decreased by a factor of three or more over the past four billion years as a result of tidal interactions among Earth, the Sun, and the Moon.)[44]

Observational data, including the study of Earth's oldest rocks, and theoretical modeling of planetary formation together verify the historical accuracy of early Earth's conditions described in Genesis 1:2. Water did, indeed, initially cover all of Earth's crust.[45] The "formless" and "empty" conditions of Earth—relative to life—would appropriately depict a roiling surface shrouded in darkness by an opaque atmosphere and an accompanying cloud of interplanetary debris. Without light on Earth's surface, photosynthesis could not occur. With large pieces of interplanetary debris crashing onto Earth's surface at that time, no surface life could have survived. We can easily understand why we find no evidence of life on Earth prior to 3.8 billion years ago.[46]

The description of these conditions dramatically—and compellingly—sets the stage for the chronology of divinely engineered transformation and creation events presented in Genesis 1:3–27, the "days" of creation.

# 4

# CREATION DAYS ONE AND TWO

Think of Genesis 1 as a highlight reel. Its "countdown" from 10 to 1 fits the pattern of showing one feat after another, each more spectacular than the previous, building anticipation for the most amazing performance of all. This brief list of divine interventions by no means tells every detail of the creation story, and its brevity draws complaints from many readers. However, according to the book of Job, God's creation works are beyond human fathoming, measuring, or counting.[1]

The particular events selected for inclusion in Genesis 1 reveal a theme: God's preparation of a habitat for humanity. Each day describes a major transformative event, an essential step closer to the final event of day six. The chosen highlights also reveal God's perspective on what's most important for all generations to know about our origins.

People may bemoan the lack of any specific mention of dinosaurs, for example, or of the various species of human-like bipedal primates (hominids). However intriguing these and many other story elements may be, they did not make the cut. Neither the dinosaurs nor the hominids had any direct connection with Adam and Eve and their progeny.[2] So their mention (or lack of mention) makes no significant difference to the story's development. What's more, the Bible was written to communicate throughout the ages. Only in relatively recent history have people come to know about dinosaurs, hominids, and other details such as atomic particles and RNA molecules.

The brevity of Genesis 1 expresses God's wisdom in another way, too. God wants people far removed from the events in time and place to be able to verify the story's veracity. He allows us the privilege—and the thrill—of filling in the details. Rather than bury us under a mountain of data that might distract us, He introduces His main themes and sets up the basic plot, the ultimate and irreversible triumph of good over evil so that human life can continue in unbroken fellowship with Him.

For those eager to know more of the details, God has provided not only the means to study His handiwork directly but also the opportunity to hear or read more about it in multiple portions of Scripture. Depictions of creation are sprinkled throughout the Bible's 66 books (see table 9). Those in Job and Psalms offer abundant amplification. In fact, many or most of the information gaps modern skeptics tend to complain about are filled in by the creation passages in Job. Given that Job's epic story predates Moses' writing of Genesis by a few centuries or more, the summary format and narrative highlights Moses selects makes all the more sense.[3]

### Before Day One: Setting the Stage for the First Life

In addition to establishing the point of view and initial conditions from which the creation account unfolds, Genesis 1:2 hints that God's work of creating life on Earth began very early, even before the first day's dramatic event. This verse tells us (in English) that "the Spirit of God was hovering over the waters." The Hebrew word translated as "hovering" is *rāḥap*.[4] It's a rare word, used only one other time in the Bible by the same human author (Moses). In Deuteronomy 32:11 passage, it refers to a female eagle stirring up her nest and "hovering" over her young. This connection with the image of the eagle's activity has led a number of Hebrew linguists to infer that the Spirit's "hovering" over the waters, as stated in Genesis 1:2, refers to God bringing about life in Earth's ocean—even before light shone through.[5]

It's interesting that when we turn to the record of nature the geologic record testifies that marine life, in the form of single-celled microorganisms, did indeed arise before all other life-forms. The oldest fossils found to date are unicellular, marine organisms in ancient sediments.[6] Isotope evidence indicates that marine life was present and abundant on Earth as early as 3.8 billion years ago.[7] Some of this very early life was anoxic photosynthetic (life engaging in photosynthesis that cannot operate in oxygen's presence). Some was even oxic photosynthetic (life engaging in photosynthesis in the presence of oxygen and producing oxygen as a byproduct).[8]

### Day One: Light Comes Through

Light's appearance takes center stage on the first creation day. The Hebrew verb used in the opening statement for the day, "Let there be light," is *hāyâ*. It means "to exist, to be, to happen, or to come to pass,"[9] in contrast with the verbs *bārā'*, 'āśâ, and yāṣar, meaning "create," "make," and "form," respectively. This word choice seems significant. God created physical light (electromagnetic radiation) "in the beginning" when he brought the cosmos into existence. The matter and energy of the cosmos included light.

Recalling Earth's initial condition of darkness and that the frame of reference for this passage is Earth's surface, we can comprehend what happened on day one: light penetrated Earth's dark shroud for the first time. Some of the debris that had previously kept light from coming through cleared away and Earth's atmosphere changed from opaque to translucent—not transparent (yet), but able to permit light's passage.

The clearing of debris astronomers can easily understand. Through time, gravity (or gravitational accretion) pulls much of the dust and weightier material from the disk around the star into the star (in this case, our Sun) and into the forming planets. The change in Earth's atmosphere, however, presents a conundrum. The rule of thumb in planetary formation is that the greater a planet's surface gravity and the greater a planet's distance from its star, the heavier and thicker its atmosphere. Yet Earth departs from that rule. Theoretically, Earth should possess an atmosphere more than twice as massive as that of Venus. Instead, it is 91 times less massive.

**Moon Miracle**
The solution to this mystery apparently lies within the story of Earth's moon. Most solar system moons formed from the same solar disk material that clumped together to form the planets. A few moons orbiting the outer planets are foreign bodies that were captured by their planets' gravity. Typically, moons are tiny compared to their planets. Earth's moon, however, is the exception. It is huge compared to its planet, and its planet is close to the Sun. Earth's moon is fifty times more massive (relative to its planet's mass) than any other solar system moon.

Lunar meteorites and lunar rocks gathered by Apollo astronauts tell us that the Moon's crust is chemically distinct from Earth's and is younger. Detailed analysis of lunar metals shows that the lunar magna ocean crystallized 4.527 ± 0.010 billion years ago.[10] Earth's formation dates back 4.5662 ± 0.0001 billion years.[11] In other words, Earth is about 40 million years older than the Moon. Its distinct chemical makeup and its younger age establish that the Moon and Earth did *not* form together.

Astronomers have also observed and measured the Moon's slow and steady spiraling away from Earth[12] and the slowing of Earth's rotation.[13] Their calculations suggest that the Moon was much closer to Earth several billion years ago. It appears that some kind of collision or near collision occurred at that time.

Extensive work in theoretical modeling yields just one collision scenario that fits all the observed Earth-Moon parameters and dynamics. According to that scenario, a body at least the size of Mars (nine times the Moon's mass and one-ninth Earth's mass), possibly twice that large, collided with Earth at an impact angle of about 45 degrees and at an impact velocity (relative to Earth's motion) as low as 4 kilometers per second or less. (Typical meteorite velocities relative to Earth = 50 kilometers per second.[14])

Such a collision would have blasted nearly all Earth's original atmosphere into outer space, while the cloud of debris arising from the collision would have orbited Earth and eventually coalesced to form our Moon. This is the story derived from a vast complex of data. It may be refined as more data become available, but it will be no less remarkable.

This moon-forming event produced a multitude of life-favoring changes to our planet, including these:

- delivered Earth from a life-suffocating atmosphere and yielded a replacement atmosphere thin enough and of the right chemical composition to permit the passage of light to Earth's surface and, eventually, prove suitable for the operation of lungs.
- increased the mass and density of Earth enough to retain (by gravity) a large quantity of water vapor (molecular weight, 18) for billions of years, but not so high as to retain life-threatening quantities of ammonia (molecular weight, 17) and methane (molecular weight, 16).
- elevated the iron content of Earth's crust enough to permit a huge abundance of ocean life (the quantity of iron, a critical nutrient, determines the abundance and diversity of marine algae, which form the base of the food chain for all ocean life), which in turn permits advanced land life.[15]
- played a significant role in salting Earth's crust, mantle, and core with a huge abundance of long-lived radioisotopes, the heat from which drives most of Earth's exceptionally high rates of tectonics and volcanism.[16] (Heavy elements from the body colliding with Earth were largely transferred to Earth whereas the light elements were either dissipated to the interplanetary medium or transferred to the cloud that eventually formed the Moon.)
- gradually slowed Earth's rotation rate so that a wide variety of lower life-forms could survive long enough to sustain the existence of advanced life-forms, which required still slower rotation rates.
- stabilized Earth's rotation axis tilt, protecting the planet from

life-extinguishing climatic extremes.[17]

Based on an abundance of circumstantial evidence, we can say that this amazing collision appears meticulously orchestrated to transform Earth from a "formless and empty" blob into a place where life can not only survive but also thrive. The number of details fine-tuned to favor life's possible existence manifested in this one event argues powerfully on its own for the existence and intervention of a divine Creator. Even if the universe contains as many as 100 billion trillion ($10^{23}$) planets, probabilities would argue against the existence of even one that by natural processes alone would end up with the just-right surface gravity, surface temperature, atmospheric composition, atmospheric pressure, crustal iron abundance, tectonics, volcanism, rotation rate, rotation rate decline, stable rotation axis and degree of tilt for the benefit of advanced life.[18] Those who want to see a miracle are looking at one whenever they gaze up at the Moon.

### Day, Night, and Life

With sunlight now penetrating Earth's atmosphere (and its surrounding debris cloud), the day-night cycle became detectable on Earth's surface. Light had existed and Earth had been rotating since its beginning, but "day" and "night" had now become distinctly discernible (Genesis 1:5). As long as Earth's surface remained permanently dark, no means was available for marking time. From day one onward, a fixed period of light would follow a fixed period of darkness.

Just as importantly for future life, the much-thinned atmosphere resulted in temperature modulations. Air and ground temperatures began to vary smoothly and continuously from daytime highs to nighttime lows. No longer were Earth's surface regions characterized by unrelenting cold or heat.

With Earth's surface now bathed in light, photosynthesis could take off. Photosynthetic life began to transform large quantities of water and carbon dioxide into food: sugars, starches, and fats. Such food could support a complex ecosystem.

This scenario finds corroboration in Psalm 104. The psalmist describes God's meticulous and relentless work in building up a great abundance and diversity of life on Earth in preparation for humanity.

### Day Two: Water Cycle Begins

No less significant for terrestrial life's survival than light is a stable, abundant water cycle. By the time significant landmasses would emerge (day three), Earth would require a cycle of condensation and precipitation—abundant, but not too abundant. A system whereby snow, ice, and liquid water freely cycle from one state to another, condensing on and evaporating from Earth's surface, would be ideal for life. Research now reveals that advanced life can thrive only if the precipitation averages between 20 and 60 liquid water inches per year, and only if snow and rain condense in the right ratio.

To meet the needs of an abundance and diversity of species, the rainfall must vary from one geographical region to another. The range must fall between the extremes of about 2 inches and 600 inches per year—not just for a few millennia, but for a few billion years.

A water cycle that meets such exacting requirements demands intricate balancing of multiple factors:
- the physical characteristics of the Sun and Earth;
- atmospheric composition, temperature, and pressure;
- wind velocities; and
- the changing values of all these atmospheric characteristics at various distances out from Earth's surface.

As precisely fine-tuned as these environmental factors must have been to transform Earth's atmosphere from opaque to translucent, they required even more precise regulation to permit a stable, life-sustaining water cycle.

## A Delicate Balancing Act

As stars go, our Sun burns its fuel at an unusually constant rate, especially since entering "middle age," its most stable burning phase. But that's not to say its luminosity hasn't changed over time. As with any other star, nuclear burning continues in the Sun's core, where hydrogen is fused into helium. (Think of the Sun as a gigantic hydrogen bomb.) The newly formed helium increases the Sun's core density, which causes the nuclear furnace to burn more intensely. As a result, the Sun shines more brightly as it ages. If this increasing core density were the only factor affecting solar luminosity, the Sun's light would be roughly 30 percent brighter today than it was at the time Earth's first life appeared.[19]

However, a second factor comes into play in the history of stellar burning. During a star's birthing phase, it accumulates mass (via gravity), but then during its early burning phase it loses mass (via flaring, hard radiation emission, and star quakes). In this stage our Sun lost as much as 20–30 percent of its mass.[20] Because a star's luminosity is proportional to the fourth power of its mass, even a small mass gain or loss produces a dramatic effect. Figure 4 shows the changing luminosity of the Sun throughout its history.

The Sun's luminosity profile—an early decrease followed by a steady increase—perfectly suits the gradual introduction of life-forms, layer upon layer, in a sequence from primitive to advanced. Each life-form manifests distinct metabolic reactions and impacts erosion rates in a particular way. These differing metabolic reactions and erosion rates serve to alter the quantities of various greenhouse gases in Earth's atmosphere[21] and, subsequently, Earth's surface temperature—all of which impacts Earth's water cycle.

Astronomers, geophysicists, and geochemists have learned that throughout its history Earth was highly susceptible to either catastrophic glaciation or vaporization. Such disasters were avoided only by the exquisitely fine-tuned timing of first life's arrival, the rate and timing of subsequent life forms' introduction, and the diversity of life-forms introduced. Unless the early Earth is quite warm, glaciation would have occurred because, even with volcanic outgassing of carbon dioxide, oceans would tend to freeze much more quickly than the carbon dioxide, an effective greenhouse gas, could accumulate in the atmosphere.[22] On the other side, vaporization will occur if an overabundance of greenhouse gas traps enough heat to vaporize Earth's oceans and ice.

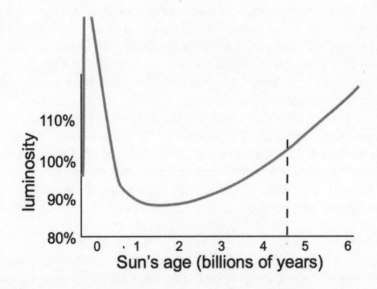

**Figure 4: The Sun's Luminosity during Earth's History**
When the Sun was young, it lost 20 percent or more of its mass, enough to cause more than a 100 percent loss of its luminosity (light emission). As it aged, its nuclear furnace converted more and more hydrogen into helium, causing the Sun's brightness to increase. The Sun's brightening continues to this day and will one day generate so much heat energy as to make Earth uninhabitable for all life.
Credit: Reasons to Believe

Unless certain kinds and abundances of gas-producing and gas-consuming life were introduced and others removed in synchrony with the Sun's changing luminosity, Earth's atmosphere would have destroyed life—by trapping either too little or too much heat. This synchronization is delicate, to say the least.[23] If the Sun's luminosity and Earth's biomass and biodiversity fall out of sync by even a slight amount, the result could have been either a runaway greenhouse (heating) effect or a runaway freeze, permanently eliminating all life on Earth. (See sidebar, "Runaway Climate Changes," page 45.)

Recent research has uncovered yet another delicate balancing act in maintenance of Earth's water cycle. Studies show that Earth's gravitational pull is not quite strong enough to hold onto all of Earth's atmospheric water indefinitely. However, an independent phenomenon largely unknown until the 1980s but verified in the late 1990s replaces the lost water (and carbon dioxide) in precisely the right quantity—a changing quantity, at that—to maintain the balance life requires. This phenomenon is an ongoing influx of water-rich extraterrestrial material. Comets of all sizes—regular, small, mini, and micro—which rain down on Earth's upper atmosphere, are the dominant contributors.[24]

Because the influx rate of cometary material cannot be directly influenced by the rates of tectonic, volcanic, and chemical activity or by the quantity and kinds of biological activity, the maintenance of a balance among all these processes seems all the more remarkable. More amazing yet, the maintenance of this balance must also compensate for

- an 80 percent decrease in energy released by the decay of radioactive isotopes (such as thorium-232, uranium-235, and uranium-238) resident in Earth's interior, energy that drives volcanic and plate tectonic activity,
- the impact of a 60–85 percent decrease in Earth's rotation rate, and
- a more than 90 percent decrease in the heat-producing tidal forces the moon exerts on Earth.

**The Dome Controversy**
In depicting the events of day two, the Genesis text says God made "the expanse" and separated the water under it from the water above it (verse 7). And God called the expanse "sky" (verse 8). The Hebrew words translated "expanse" and "sky" are *rāqîa'* and *shāmayim*. Both terms refer to the portion of Earth's atmosphere where clouds form and move.[25]

Some critics and skeptics of the Bible claim that the *rāqîa'* and *shāmayim* in verse 8 refer to the solid brass dome of ancient mythology. They cite Job 37:18 as support for their view: "Can you join him [God] in spreading out the skies, hard as a mirror of cast bronze?" However, it should be noted that the word "as" indicates the use of a figure of speech. The picture continues in Job 37:21: "Now no one can look at the sun, bright as it is in the skies after the wind has swept them clean." In ancient times, no humanly crafted surface reflected light more effectively than a polished bronze mirror. The simile in Job 37 simply compares the Sun's brightness on a clear day to the painfully bright reflection of light from such a mirror.[26]

## Runaway Climate Changes

A car parked in the sun provides a greenhouse effect example. Visible light from the Sun passes through the car's windows, is absorbed by the interior, and is reradiated at infrared wavelengths. But the windows, being less transparent at infrared wavelengths, trap the infrared radiation inside the car. Thus, heat accumulates inside the car. Carbon dioxide and water vapor in the atmosphere work like the car's windows, trapping heat.

Earth's early atmosphere contained more carbon dioxide and water vapor than our current atmosphere. Providentially, the first photosynthetic life extracted carbon dioxide and water and released oxygen. Hence, the increase in the Sun's luminosity was balanced at Earth's surface by the decrease in the greenhouse effect of Earth's atmosphere caused by plants' consumption of carbon dioxide and water.

However, if the Sun's luminosity were to increase even slightly more rapidly than it does, as it would if the Sun were slightly more massive, the extra warmth would evaporate water more efficiently. This extra water vapor would trap more heat. This extra heat would evaporate yet more water, which, in turn, would trap more heat. Eventually, all of Earth's ice and liquid water would be transformed into water vapor.

In the opposite scenario, if the Sun's luminosity were to increase a little more slowly, as would be the case if the Sun were very slightly less massive, runaway freezing would result. With a slower increase in heat, more snow and ice would form on Earth's surface. Since snow and ice reflect better than other surface materials, Earth would absorb less solar energy. Thus, the surface temperature would drop. In turn, more snow and ice would form, reflecting away even more heat. Eventually, all of Earth's water would turn to snow and ice.

The Hebrew verb 'āśâ (meaning "make," "manufacture," or "fabricate")[27] in the day two narrative, implies that God himself designed and built Earth's atmosphere with its intricately balanced water cycle. In view of the fine-tuning this construction required, the necessity of a purposeful, powerful Designer seems apparent, as does a historically accurate account of his work.

God's "separation" of the waters seems a clear and direct statement of his formation of the troposphere, the atmospheric layer just above the ocean where clouds form and humidity resides, as distinct from the stratosphere, mesosphere, and ionosphere rising above. Psalm 148, a psalm reflecting on the events of Genesis 1, distinguishes the "highest heavens" from the "waters above the skies" and declares that God "set them in place." The psalm begins and ends appropriately with this refrain: "Praise the LORD."

The stage is now set—with light available for photosynthesis, with water available in all its forms and in appropriate ratios, and with surface temperatures modulated within a limited range—for the next major development in the creation drama. The significance of light and water, heat and cold, would have been just as comprehensible to the ancient understandings as to readers today who have access to the scientific details. And so we continue to navigate.

# 5

# CREATION DAYS THREE AND FOUR

With light now penetrating the unbroken overcast with the buildup of appropriate atmospheric gases and the removal of other gases, and with a firmly established water cycle, the stage is perfectly set for the advent of land life. All Earth needs is a place to put it. That place is just what the Creator provided on day three.

Through most of recorded history Earth's dry land has been taken for granted. No one thought to question it as a permanent fixture of the planet. The Genesis 1 reference to early Earth as a water world raised questions and considerable skepticism—until scientists in the budding disciplines of geology and geophysics began to probe.

**Day Three: Dry Land**
"Let the water under the sky be gathered to one place, and let dry ground appear" (Genesis 1:9; see also Psalm 33:7). This simple statement matter-of-factly describes an enormously dramatic series of events. While solid ground already existed, it remained—until this time—under water. As research now confirms, however, plate tectonic activity began to transform the heavy basalts of the ocean floor into lighter rock called silicates. (Silicates are essentially hydrated basalts.) Because silicates are lighter than basalts, they float above the basalts. In due time, enough silicates built up to rise above sea level, and at that point dry land appeared.

Once landmasses rose above sea level, erosion began to wear them down, but erosion could not keep up. Earth's landmass buildup has continued to exceed the wearing down processes. When land emerged, it was here to stay.

As an introduction to this event, the Genesis text refers to the gathering of Earth's surface waters "to one place." Psalm 33:7 colorfully describes this breakthrough event: "He [God] gathers the waters of the sea into jars; he puts the deep into storehouses." Job 38:8–10 also speaks of the time when God "shut up the sea behind doors" and "fixed limits for it and set its doors and bars in place."

The "one place" mentioned in Genesis 1 simply differentiates the sea's place from the land's place. Related passages in Job 38 and Psalm 33 speak of multiple oceans. Psalm 104:8 says God sent the waters "down into the valleys" to the area "assigned for them."

Researchers of geology and geography have been working to piece together this same story. The physical evidence they have gathered tells us that over a period of 4.56 billion years, Earth's landmass grew from 0 percent to 29 percent of the planetary surface (see figure 5). Evidence also indicates there were times in Earth's history when virtually all the land came together to form one contiguous continent. Three of the supercontinents researchers have named include Columbia, dated at 1.9 billion years ago; Rodinia, some 0.9 billion years ago; and finally, Pangaea—the most widely known—at 0.25 billion years ago.[1] All this movement of land, together and apart, resulted from tectonic forces in Earth's crust.

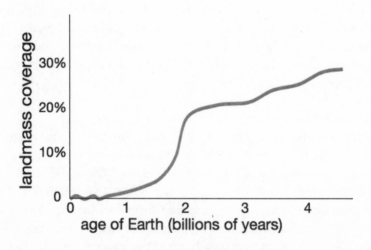

**Figure 5: Continental Landmass Growth as a Percentage of Earth's Surface**

For its first 750 million years Earth alternated between total and near total water coverage, with a few volcanic islands occasionally popping up above sea level. Then, with ongoing plate tectonic activity, Earth experienced a period of rapid growth in continental landmass. The current continental growth rate (mostly from tectonic activity) is only slightly greater than the shrinkage rate (caused by erosion).
Credit: Reasons to Believe

British geologists and geophysicists have learned (from osmium isotope measurements) that Earth's continental crust grew in stages, not in a gradual, linear way. It advanced through what researchers describe as a series of pulses.[2] Evidence indicates upper mantle "melt events" occurred 2.7, 1.9, and 1.2 billion years ago. Each of these events led to a surge in landmass growth, but the greatest surge by far came from the earliest of these events.

The Genesis 1 reference to the large burst of continental landmass growth places it at the beginning of creation day three, nearly halfway through the creation chronology. This timing harmonizes well with the latest geophysical research. As figure 5 shows, continental landmass growth was most aggressive when Earth was about two billion years old, somewhat less than half its current age of 4.5662 billion years.[3]

Thousands of years before scientists had any clue about either the origin or the timing of continental landmass growth, we see a depiction of the breakthrough event in Genesis 1. The ancient text accurately describes the geophysical history of Earth.

Psalm 104 implies that though the entire surface of Earth was once covered with water,[4] a time came when God sent this water to its assigned location and dry land was here to stay.[5] The psalmist proclaims, "You [God] set a boundary they [the waters] cannot cross; never again will they cover the earth."[6] (The implications in this passage concerning the Genesis flood event are addressed in later chapters.)

The text also implies that the land and water will remain in a relatively balanced state. Today we can explain why (see sidebar, "More of the Scientific Story," page 50).

**Plants on the Land**

The story of creation day three continues: "Let the land produce vegetation: seed-bearing plants and trees on the land that bear fruit with seed in it, according to their various kinds" (Genesis 1:11). Here we read that the newly formed dry land now brings forth something new: vegetation.

Skeptics often point to this verse as a supposed error in the biblical account of life's history, both in content and in chronology. Evidence for land plants, especially for advanced ones such as fruit trees, shows up late in the fossil record— *after* the fossils of animal life, a day five creation event.

A closer look at the text and at the emerging scientific evidence, however, eliminates the basis for such error claims. The word for vegetation in the original Hebrew text is *deshe'*. It means vegetation or green plant life and would apply generically to any photosynthetic land life.[7] Following the use of this generic term, Genesis 1:11 list three examples of the *deshe'*. Obviously, other examples of *deshe'* could exist as well.

The words for the three examples, translated "seed," "trees," and "fruit," have more specific meaning in English than in Hebrew. The Hebrew nouns used here: *zera'*, *'ēṣ*, and *p$^e$rî*, mean, respectively, "semen" or "the embryos of *any* plant species,"[8] "*any* large plant containing woody fiber,"[9] and "the food and/or embryos produced by *any* living thing."[10] *zera'* and *p$^e$rî* could refer to any plant species that has ever existed. The *'ēṣ* includes all large plants containing cellulose and could possibly refer to all larger-than-microscopic plants whose fibers provide a measure of stiffness. In light of this range of meanings, the description of creation day 3 is at least consistent with the discoveries of modern science. The earliest land plants fit the biblical description. Thus, the original text can be interpreted as a reference to some of the plant species scientists have identified as the earliest land vegetation.

### More of the Scientific Story

Plate tectonics and volcanism continue to this day, but the forces propelling them have significantly subsided. And yet we need not be concerned about a recurring water world. The ongoing "spin down" (slowing) of Earth's rotation and the diminishing tidal influence of the Moon (as it slowly drifts away from Earth) together work to reduce the effects of wind and water erosion. It's safe to say that erosion will never eradicate Earth's continents.

It's worth noting, also, that according to recent research, the proportion of Earth's surface area covered by land and oceans plays a crucial role in life's development. This ratio determines the amount of biodiversity and biocomplexity possible on the planet. According to theoretical and observational findings, the current ratio of 29 percent land surface to 71 percent water surface, in combination with the shapes, sizes, and positions of the continental landmasses today, permits the maximal diversity (not to mention complexity) of life.[11] This ratio, together with the positioning of the continents, works with lunar gravity to yield tides just strong enough to enrich the seashores and continental shelves with nutrients and to cleanse them of pollutants, but not so strong as to devastate them with erosion.

In the specific case of land plants, absence of evidence cannot be taken as proof of absence. Plants, after all, do not fossilize as easily as the bone and shell structures of animals. Nor are their structures as easily preserved. Indirect evidence of plants' early presence comes from our understanding of the oxygenation history of Earth's atmosphere. Because atmospheric oxygen comes from photosynthetic activity, scientists surmise that the aggressive oxygenation of Earth's atmosphere[12] that paved the way for the Cambrian explosion (~ 543 million years ago) could have been achieved only if vegetation had long been present on the continental landmasses.

Today more direct evidence supports the biblical statement that vegetation preceded the proliferation of animal life,[13] especially the proliferation identified as the Cambrian explosion. In fact, land plants likely existed for hundreds of millions of years before the Cambrian event. In 2009 two biologists reported in *Nature* the discovery of isotope evidence indicating that photosynthetic life was as abundant on continental landmasses for the 200 million years prior to the Cambrian explosion as it was for the 200 million years after.[14] More recently, a team of paleontologists uncovered extensive fossil evidence for nonmarine (i.e., non-ocean-dwelling) eukaryotic life-forms that date back as early as 1.2 billion years ago.[15]

The team said of their fossil findings, "They offer direct evidence of eukaryotes living in freshwater aquatic and subaerially exposed habitats during the Proterozoic era."[16]

Can all the structures this research team found be attributed to vegetation? Probably not. Some may be the remains of early animal life. In one sense, however, no proof of pre-Cambrian plant life is needed, based on the principle that wherever animal life flourishes, the vegetation it feeds upon must be available already.

## The Question of Plant Evolution

Genesis 1:11 says that God caused dry land to abound with vegetation, not that *all* forms of land vegetation appeared at this early date. The Hebrew verb used in this passage (*dāshā*) means "to bring forth" or "produce." Some interpreters take this verse to mean that plants arose through natural processes. An equally accurate reading of the text says that plants arose by supernatural intervention. Any combination of divine intervention and natural process would be an acceptable interpretation, from a linguistic point of view. In other words, this particular text makes no definitive statement about the extent to which God may or may not have allowed natural processes to produce plant life. The answer remains open to scientific determination.

Plants appear to possess a limited capacity for speciation (production of new species) through natural processes. Botanists have observed a few plants generate new "species."[17] However, in these cases the word "species" is defined loosely. Boundaries between plant species are much less distinct than boundaries between animal species. Human observers have yet to document development of a plant species remarkably different from a previously existing species. The rapid rate at which plant species go extinct, both today and during the fossil era,[18] would seem to suggest that supernatural, rather than strictly natural, work gave rise to major changes observed in the record of plant history.

**Day Four: Lights in the Sky**

For many millions of years after light first pierced the dark shroud surrounding Earth, the sky would have continued to resemble the heavy overcast of a stormy day. Certain atmospheric constituents, along with air temperature, pressure, and humidity, would have prevented any break in Earth's cloud cover. Volcanic activity also may have contributed to the perpetual overcast. Atmospheric carbon dioxide and water vapor levels were substantially higher than current levels, contributing to high humidity. At the same time, the oxygen level was much lower. Fossil evidence affirms such conditions.

Through time, however, changes in these and other environmental factors—such as stabilization of air temperature and pressure, plants' increasing consumption of carbon dioxide and water vapor and production of oxygen (see figure 6, page 58), as well as decreasing volcanic activity—would have brought about another major atmospheric transformation, this time from translucent to transparent. At least for some brief moments, probably only a few at first, the clouds would break, making the Sun, Moon, and stars visible to creatures on Earth's surface.

Plants had help in removing carbon dioxide and water vapor from Earth's atmosphere. Carbon dioxide easily reacts with atmospheric water to form carbonic acid. This carbonic acid quickly falls to the surface, where it reacts with crustal rocks (from creation day three onward) to form carbonates. If it were not for some mitigating factors, these carbonates would have leached enough carbon dioxide and water from the atmosphere to turn this planet into a permanently frozen, arid wasteland. This scenario does, in fact, describe what happened on Mars.

Earth escaped this carbonate doomsday because of its ideal plate tectonics and volcanism. Plate collisions drove surface carbonates deep underground. Pressure, heat, and chemical components deep in the crust broke down the carbonates into carbon dioxide, water, and minerals. Subsequently, volcanoes re-cycled most of these trapped residuals back up to the surface.

As chapters 3–4 explain, the driving force behind plate tectonics and volca-nism is heat release from slow-decaying radioisotopes in Earth's crust, mantle, and core.[19] The spectacular collision that resulted in the Moon's formation helps explain how Earth acquired some of its enormous abundance of long-lasting, heat-releasing radioisotopes. Strategically for life, this heat release diminishes through time, simultaneously slowing down the processes it drives. Today, Earth's tectonic activity and volcanism have dropped to one-fifth their original level.[20]

This drop favors life. Too many and hugely powerful earthquakes and vol-canic eruptions would be catastrophic to life. Too few, on the other hand, would render the planet too cold and dry for life.

Advanced species show the least tolerance for earthquakes and volcanoes; primitive species, the greatest tolerance. We can reasonably surmise that God created primitive life on Earth at the earliest opportune moment and created hu-mans near the last (and most) opportune moment. He designed the Sun, Earth, and Moon to maximize the proliferation and duration of life on Earth. In so do-ing, God endowed humans with abundant biological resources—e.g., several feet of topsoil, trillions of barrels of oil, trillions of tons of coal, quadrillions of cubic feet of natural gas, quadrillions of tons of limestone and marble, and millions of diverse species of life (see chapter 19).

One result of all these changes—and from all these forces working in bal-ance—appears in Genesis 1:14:

> Let there be lights in the expanse of the sky to separate the day from the
> night, and let them serve as signs to mark seasons and days and years.

On creation day four, the Sun, Moon, and stars became distinctly visible from Earth's surface for the first time.

Verse 14 also explains the significance of this new visibility. It allows these lights to "serve as signs to mark seasons and days and years." For whose specific benefit do they serve as signs? As zoologists now recognize, none of the life-forms that existed prior to the fourth creation day needs to know where the Sun, Moon, and stars are in the sky. This early life lacks complex biological clocks. However, all the life described on creation days five and six are sufficiently complex to re-quire awareness, at least on occasion, of the positions of the Sun, Moon, and/or stars. This awareness guides their instincts as to the best times to feed, reproduce, migrate, and/or hibernate.

Verse 16 tends to cause confusion for readers who fail to recognize it as a parenthetical note, or a brief review:

God made two great lights—the greater light to govern the day and the lesser light to govern the night. He also made the stars.

The Hebrew verb *'āśâ*, translated "made," appears in an appropriate form for past action. There are no verb tenses in Hebrew to parallel verb tenses in English. Rather, three Hebrew verb forms are used to denote action already completed, action not yet completed, and commands. (There are also participles, which are bridge forms, in that they can function either more like verbs or more like nouns.)[21] Verse 16 makes no specification as to when in the past the Sun, Moon, and stars were made. However, the wording of verses 17 and 18 does provide a hint:

God set them in the expanse of the sky to give light on the earth, to govern the day and the night, and to separate light from darkness.

The echo of wording from day one (verses 3–5) is significant. It suggests both when and *why* God created the heavenly lights. The mention of *shamayim wa'eres* (heavens and earth) in Genesis 1:1 places the existence of the Sun and stars before the first creation day; thus, the Sun was already in place to fulfill its role on the first creation day.

**An Atmospheric Miracle**
While the transformation of the atmosphere from translucent (light-diffusing) to transparent (light-transmitting) would seem to require intricate design and implementation, to accomplish this change without exposing land life to too little or too much ultraviolet radiation would demand even more. As the plants introduced on creation day three were consuming carbon dioxide through photosynthesis, they were also expelling oxygen. After a period of time ranging from thousands to millions of years, enough oxygen diffused into the upper stratosphere to permit, under precise conditions, formation of a thin and delicate ozone layer.

This stratospheric ozone layer offers essential protection for life. It absorbs ultraviolet radiation from the Sun that would otherwise damage and destroy advanced land life. Only recently have scientists recognized the significance and fragility of this ozone shield (from 6 to 15 miles above Earth). Some express fear that the nitrous oxides, fluorocarbons, and particulates expelled by human activity already may have damaged it, perhaps even threatened its temporary destruction. Recent measurements indicate a thinning of the stratospheric ozone layer.[22] Various studies show that more ultraviolet rays are coming through to damage our skin and our crops.[23]

On the other hand, researchers recognize that too thick a stratospheric ozone layer would present problems equally severe. If too little ultraviolet radiation reaches Earth's surface, plant growth is inhibited and the quantity of certain vitamins, especially vitamin D, will be insufficient for the needs of certain animal species. In other words, unless the stratospheric ozone layer is neither too thin nor too thick, Earth's biomass, biodiversity, and biovitality will be impaired.

## Divine Light Source?

Because the verb translated "made" in verse 16 provides no clear indication as to when God created the heavenly lights, some readers interpret the placement of this reference to these objects as an indication that they originated on the fourth creation day.[24] To explain how the plants (created on day three) survived without sunlight, these interpreters speculate that God initially sustained plants with the light of His glory, the same "Shekinah" radiance that glowed from Moses' face on Mount Sinai.[25]

Aside from its exegetical problems, this interpretation runs into a wall of scientific implausibility. First, the light needed for plant survival must exhibit the exact spectral response and effective temperature as the Sun's. Second, both the Sun's light and its gravity are essential to sustain plant life on Earth. The Sun's gravity holds Earth, the Moon, planets, asteroids, and comets in their positions and orbits, and these are essential to life's existence. The Sun's gravity also critically influences Earth's rotation period. Such gravity implies that the "divine light source" sustaining the third creation day plants must manifest both the identical mass and position, relative to Earth, of the Sun.

For all practical purposes, the hypothesized divine light source would be indistinguishable from the Sun itself, with all its characteristics—hardly a match with what radiates from Moses' face or from the New Testament event referred to as the transfiguration.[26] Genesis 1:1 eliminates the need for such speculations.

Ozone in the troposphere (the first six miles above Earth) also fulfills a strategic role for life. Tropospheric ozone (about 10 percent of the total) appears to be augmented, rather than depleted, by human activity, but this augmentation wields a deadly impact. Fossil-fuel burning and agricultural burning have so increased tropospheric ozone in regions over the north mid-latitudes and the continental tropics as to increase the incidence of respiratory failure in humans and other large animals, reduce crop yields, and wipe out certain ozone-sensitive plant species in these regions.[27] However, the presence of some ozone in the troposphere is essential. In the appropriate quantity, it helps cleanse the atmosphere of certain kinds of biochemical smog (mainly from trees) and industrial smog.[28] Ozone may be considered the troposphere's detergent.

Mesospheric ozone (about one percent of the total) deserves mention, as well. Ultraviolet absorption by ozone in this high atmospheric layer (from 15 to 50 miles above Earth) helps govern the chemistry and circulation of gases in that layer.[29] Mesospheric chemistry and gas circulation largely determine which gases are retained and which are lost by Earth's atmosphere, and these quantities are vitally important to life's long-term survival. Again, the ozone quantity must be carefully balanced between too much and too little.

The existence and integration of the rare, exacting conditions necessary for development of our delicate, life-essential set of ozone shields constitute a whole suite of miracles. (I use the word *miracle* here to mean something in the natural realm that manifests supernatural design and/or supernatural timing and placement.) For anyone interested in further study of the miraculous, it may be found in recent studies of interlayer ozone transport mechanisms, especially of their stability throughout hundreds of millions of years.[30]

Until this point in the creation narrative, the focus has remained primarily on God's intervention in Earth's physics, from far under the crust to far above it. As day four draws to a close, the story grows all the more captivating. From this point onward it tells of advanced living things, of creatures with whom we can personally relate, on one level or another.

# 6

# CREATION DAYS FIVE AND SIX

The stage is meticulously prepared now for another dramatic scene to unfold. Earth is at long last ready—with light, breathable air, and a stable water cycle for support; dry land and oceans for habitation; abundant and diverse plants for food; a visible Sun, Moon, and stars for guidance; and an ozone shield for protection—to welcome a new wonder: advanced animal life.

**Day Five: Sea Animals**

> Let the water teem with living creatures, and let birds fly above the earth across the expanse of the sky.

The Hebrew nouns for the different animals mentioned here in Genesis 1:20 are *shereṣ*, *nepesh*, and *'ôp*. *Shereṣ* refers to swarms of small or minute creatures.[1] This same word appears frequently in the Pentateuch (first five books of the Old Testament) with reference to smaller body-sized species that are neither birds nor mammals. Scientifically speaking, when used for land life, it usually includes amphibians, reptiles, and insects. When used for fresh- or saltwater creatures, it typically includes mollusks, crustaceans, fish, and amphibians.

This particular verse mentions only the water-dwelling *shereṣ*. It does not specify which kinds of *shereṣ* appeared in the water. But we now know that water-dwelling *shereṣ* are the most primitive creatures to require the visibility of the heavenly bodies for regulation of their biological clocks.

Clearly, many species of *shereṣ*, even whole phyla, receive no mention in this description of day five life-forms. However, this brevity seems an understandable feature of the text, as I've mentioned previously, given its focus on the most important preparations for the introduction of humankind.

**Explosive Speciation**

The fossil record testifies that for the first 85 percent of life's history on Earth there were no creatures we would refer to as animals. Then, suddenly, in shallow seas and on continental shelves, life-forms manifesting nearly every conceivable body plan appeared. In both the Avalon explosion (575 million years ago)[2] and the Cambrian explosion (543 million years ago)[3] swarms of diverse sea animals abruptly emerged. For the first time in Earth's history creatures sported append-ages, limbs, skeletons, and specialized organs. In fact, of the 182 mathematically possible skeletal designs conceivable for physical life, 146 show up in the fossil record of the Cambrian explosion event.[4]

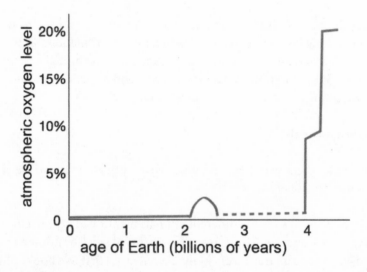

**Figure 6: Earth's Atmospheric Oxygenation History**
When radiation from uranium, thorium, and potassium-40 decay passes through pockets of water, it converts some of the water into oxygen. However, not until sometime after photosynthetic life emerged (750 million years after Earth's formation) does the quantity of oxygen in Earth's atmosphere rise to nearly 1 percent. Because of Earth's enormous oxygen "sinks," photosynthetic life must function for a few billion years to push the atmo-spheric oxygen level up to the point where complex animals with body sizes exceeding a centimeter long or wide can survive. The oxygen levels shown above were derived from the quantities and ratios of certain uranium and thorium oxides present in Earth's shale record (C. A. Partin et al., "Large-Scale Fluctuations in Precambrian Atmospheric and Oceanic Oxygen Levels from the Record of U in Shales," *Earth and Planetary Science Letters* 369 [May 2013]). This record is incomplete. There may have been some small rises and declines in oxygen levels between 1.9–0.6 billion years ago.
Credit: Reasons to Believe

Scientific research reveals at least three factors to explain why the Avalon and Cambrian events could not have occurred earlier. The most important: the lack of available oxygen. Only through billions of years of photosynthetic activity could Earth's atmosphere and oceans build up sufficient oxygen to support animal life (see figure 6).[5] The very moment oxygen reached appropriate levels, the Avalon and Cambrian explosions occurred. The lack of any appreciable gap between the time of oxygen's rise to minimum life-sustaining levels and the appearance of animals argues strongly for the involvement of a purposeful Creator. Mindless natural processes seem vastly inadequate to explain the Avalon and Cambrian events.

A second factor in the long delay of the Avalon and Cambrian events is the level of tectonic activity and erosion. These two processes must continue for a few billion years to generate the appropriate habitats (shallow seas and continental shelves) for swarms of small sea animals.

The Sun plays a third role in the timing. Its luminosity has changed since it first formed. After an early and extreme drop, its brightness began to increase. For the sake of sustaining more advanced life, it had to increase sufficiently (see figure 4) to prevent the possibility of a snowball event—a circumstance wherein (given the context of a dimmer Sun) some catastrophe, such as volcanic super-eruptions, a mass extinction event, or a galactic spiral arm crossing, generates a runaway freezing. Runaway freeze events have covered up to 90 percent of Earth's surface area in an icy blanket. One such snowball event is known to have occurred just prior to the Avalon and Cambrian explosions.

The challenge of these explosive appearances of new life-forms to macroevolutionary hypotheses has been acknowledged by several of the world's leading evolutionary biologists. Richard Dawkins in his book, *The Blind Watchmaker*, wrote:

For example the Cambrian strata of rocks, vintage about 600 million years, are the oldest ones in which we find most of the major invertebrate groups. And we find many of them already in an advanced state of evolution, the very first time they appear. It is as though they were just planted there, without any evolutionary history.[6]

Gregory Wray, in the journal *American Zoologist*, stated:

The Cambrian "explosion" of body plans is perhaps the single most striking feature of the metazoan fossil record. The rapidity with which phyla and classes appeared during the early Paleozoic, coupled with much lower rates of appearance for higher taxa since, poses an outstanding problem for macroevolution.[7]

Kevin Peterson, Michael Dietrich, and Mark McPeek, in the journal *BioEssays*, declared:

Thus, elucidating the materialistic basis of the Cambrian explosion has become more elusive, not less, the more we know about the event itself...[8]

## Day Five: "Soulish" Animals

Genesis 1:20–21 introduces animal species radically different from any previously mentioned. These creatures are identified by the Hebrew noun *nepesh*. Hebrew lexicons list a range of possible meanings, including these: "soulish" creature; person; mind; land creature with the breath of life; creature capable of expressing yearnings, emotions, passions, and will; a self-aware creature.[9] In the 754 times the word appears in the Old Testament, *nepesh* denotes any species characterized by what scientists would identify as a nurturing behavior toward progeny or mate or both. On this basis, all bird and mammal species would fit the meaning of *nepesh*. A few reptile species, such as alligators and crocodiles, which protect their hatchlings, may qualify, but only a few. With something more than nervous, digestive, respiratory, circulatory, and reproductive systems (as marvelous and intricate as those systems may be) these creatures manifest attributes of mind, will, and emotions—traits the ancient Hebrews (and others) would consider "soulish" attributes.

Anyone who has enjoyed much contact with birds and mammals realizes these creatures are uniquely endowed with the capacity to form relationships—with each other and with humans. They possess and express a certain level of understanding, choice, and feeling. Unlike other animals, *nepesh* creatures can be trained to perform tasks that are irrelevant to their survival. They respond to human authority and personality. They show delight, sadness, fear, anger, and more. They form emotional bonds with humans. Obviously, though, some *nepesh* are much more capable than others to bond with humans and to serve and please humans.

Here, for only the second time in Genesis 1 (verse 21), the verb *bārā'* is used. (See chapter 4 for a discussion of the meaning of *bārā'*.) In this passage both *bārā'* and another Hebrew verb, *'āśâ*, appear. Without reading more into this word choice than may be warranted, I see at least the suggestion that God manufactured ( *'āśâ*) some aspect of the *nepesh* from existing resources and, additionally, created something totally new, something that did not exist previously. I see *'āśâ* as applying to the making of the physical body, and *bārā'* as applying to creation of the soulish quality.

The soulishness evident in birds, mammals, and a few higher reptiles sets them apart from previous animal species, such as trilobites and sponges. These creatures also have greater needs, and God expects us to treat them with as much care, respect, and consideration as their well-being deserves.

Soulish creatures also differ from others in the way they can be impacted by human treatment. For example, a pet dog that has been treated appropriately and lovingly will typically be friendly and affectionate, while a dog abused by its owner will likely be mean and vicious or else cowering and anxious. By comparison, human affection or abuse bestowed upon a cockroach has no appreciable effect on the cockroach. Sadly, because the behavior of birds, mammals, and higher reptiles can be powerfully altered by human behavior, they alone, among all Earth's animals, are sometimes included with humans in God's judgment against profound human wickedness.

### Sea Mammals' Timing

Because Genesis 1 introduces sea mammals (of day five) before the land mammals (of day six), its accuracy has been called into question by some paleontologists. A close reading of the original Hebrew, however, removes the apparent problem. The fifth creation day narrative refers to sea mammals generically, while the sixth day account narrows in on three specialized kinds of land mammals, the kinds most crucial to humanity's needs. When other land mammals arrive on the scene the text does not say. Scientific research will need to fill in that information.

Although they do not predate the first land mammals, the first sea mammals have been found to date much earlier than paleontologists previously realized. Four extinct species of whales, for example—the *Pakicetus*, *Nalacetus*, *Ambulocetus*, and *Indocetus*—date back to the era between 52 and 48 million years ago.

Research on these whales contributes powerfully to the case for God's involvement in their origin and design. Phosphate isotopes in the teeth of their fossilized remains tell of a rapid transition from freshwater habitat to saltwater habitat. Geologists and anatomists from the United States and India discovered that *Pakicetus* and *Nalacetus* processed only freshwater. *Ambulocetus* relied on freshwater at least through its formative years, probably all its life, and *Indocetus* ingested saltwater only.[10]

In the span of just a few million years or less, whales' physiology changed radically. The transition from freshwater ingestion to saltwater ingestion requires radically different internal organs. The number and rapidity of "just right" mutations required to achieve such a transition defies limits set by molecular clocks (biomolecules for which mutation rates can be determined). Proponents of punctuated equilibria, one naturalistic alternative to gradualism (traditional Darwinism), suggest that dramatic genetic changes occurred in sudden jumps propelled by severe environmental stress. However, the period from 48 to 52 million years ago appears to have been remarkably tranquil, far less stressful than any such scenario would demand.

### Transitional Forms

For several decades now, creatures referred to as "transitional forms" have been thought to argue against a creation interpretation of the fossil record data and in favor of a naturalistic interpretation.[11] An apparent progression in the bone structure of mesonychids (prehistoric land-dwelling mammals),[12] ancient freshwater-drinking whales, ancient saltwater-drinking whales, and modern whales has persuaded biologists that modern whales developed from land-dwelling animals. However, further research on the structure of ancient whale ankles shows that the ankles of all whale species are so distinct from those of mesonychids (and of artiodactyla, the only other suggested ancestor of whales) as to seriously call into question the descent of modern whales from land-dwelling mammals.[13]

Ironically, this "best example" of naturalistic evolution may turn out to be among the best evidences in favor of creation. No animal is less likely to evolve substantially than a whale. No animal has a higher probability for rapid extinction than a whale. Many factors severely limit whales' capacity for change and, at the same time, threaten their extinction. One of the more important factors is adult body mass (see sidebar, "Size Matters"). Other factors include these:

1. relatively small population levels
2. long generation period (time between birth and the ability to give birth)
3. low numbers of progeny per adult
4. high complexity of morphology and biochemistry
5. specialized food requirements
6. relatively advanced cultural and social structures
7. high metabolic rates
8. relatively small habitat size (for some species)
9. relatively low ecological diversity

A fundamental problem biologists observe (for well understood biochemical reasons) is that deleterious mutations vastly outnumber beneficial mutations.

## Size Matters

The extinction risk for mammalian species rises dramatically with increasing body mass (as an average per adult within the species). Likewise, according to paleontologists and molecular biologists, speciation rates appear to correlate inversely with body mass.[14] The greater the one, the lesser the other.

One team of biologists found that the extinction risk in smaller species is driven primarily by environmental factors, while in larger species it is driven by a combination of environmental factors and intrinsic traits.[15] This team's research demonstrated that factors driving extinction "increase sharply above a threshold body mass around 3 kilograms."[16]

Additional studies corroborate the conclusion that body size significantly impacts a species' survivability. One showed that mammals with an average adult mass of 369.5 kilograms accumulate "slightly deleterious mutations in mitochondrial protein-coding genes" at a higher rate than do mammals with an average adult mass of 275 grams.[17] Another study, this one specifically on primate species, showed that the greater the females' body mass, the greater the extinction risk.[18]

Two physicists tested a quantitative model for terrestrial mammal evolution for which the extinction probability increased logarithmically with average adult body mass. Their findings matched the fossil record data for mammal species' extinctions between 95 and 50 million years ago.[19]

An abundance of research confirms that large-bodied terrestrial mammals become extinct at a rate far more rapid than the most optimistic estimates of natural-process speciation rates.[20] Field biologists report not one example of a new mammal's emergence during the human era while in that same period Earth has lost half of the mammal species—some four thousand—present at the time the first modern humans appeared on the scene. Although many of these four thousand extinctions resulted from human mismanagement or abuse, others disappeared independent of human involvement.

The fossil history of large-bodied mammals fits well with the biblical claim that a Creator intervened, in the prehuman era, to create new life-forms, and then ceased to do so since the advent of humanity. Based on this evidence, it seems less likely than ever that humanity could be related to the great apes or to the various hominid species through common descent.

Estimates range anywhere from a deleterious-to-beneficial ratio of 10,000 to 1 up to 10,000,000 to 1. These numbers mean that only species with enormous populations, short generation times, and small body sizes would be able to survive long enough to advance through beneficial mutations. The onslaught of deleterious mutations coupled with environmental stresses—such as Earth's declining rotation rate, the Sun's increasing luminosity, changes in the chemical composition of the atmosphere, supernova eruptions, asteroid and comet collisions, solar flaring events, and climate cycles, among others—would drive most life-forms to extinction.

Biologists directly observe significant evolutionary advance *only* for those species exceeding a quadrillion individuals with body sizes less than one centimeter and generation times less than three months. To be specific, significant evolutionary advance is confirmed by direct field observations for some virus and bacteria species. It is debatable for ant and termite species. But that's it.

It seems safe to say that whales lack even the remotest possibility for significant evolutionary advance. Moreover, the evidence implies that deleterious mutations and environmental stresses would tend to drive any given whale species to extinction relatively rapidly.

The same conclusion applies to horses. The internal and external factors limiting whales' potential for natural-process advance also severely restrict horses' capacity to evolve. While research documents the extinction of several horse and whale species during human history, none records a measurable change *within* a horse or whale species, much less the appearance of a distinctly new one.

Genesis presents us with this scenario: God created the first sea mammals on the fifth creation day. And, as the fossil record shows, these creatures have persisted on Earth from that time until now, though not without interruption. Multiple extinction events have occurred, implying that they remain because God repeatedly replaced extinct species with new ones (see chapter 9 for further discussion on this topic). In most cases the new species differed somewhat from the previous ones, and this fits with the necessities of Earth's changing dynamics (rotation rate and tidal forces), geology, and biology. Step by step over the millennia, God filled Earth with appropriate life-forms in preparation for His ultimate creation—the human race.

Psalm 104 seems to support this history of ongoing extinction and speciation. In verses 27–28 the psalmist declares that all of Earth's creatures depend on God for their needs. Verse 29 refers to those instances when Earth's creatures die off. But then, according to verse 30, God recreates and renews the face of the earth.

The many "transitional" forms of whales (and horses) would seem to suggest that God performed more than just a few creative acts here and there, letting natural processes fill in the balance. Rather, it appears God was involved and active in creating multiple whale species—the first, the last, and those in between. Today, as we learn more about the complexities of balancing greenhouse gases to compensate for increasing solar luminosity and its potential effects on Earth's ecosystem, researchers are beginning to recognize how the precise timing and proliferation of whale species throughout the past 50 million years has contributed to maintaining a delicate balance.[21]

### About the Missing Dinosaurs

Even individuals who feel no particular fondness for reptiles describe an almost irresistible fascination with dinosaurs. The enormous-bodied (and a few smaller) dinosaur species appear to have dominated Earth's landscape and seascape from 250 million to 65 million years ago.[22] Their creation and duration on Earth most likely occurred on the fifth creation day.

Because of dinosaurs' sheer enormity and longevity, some people have difficulty imagining why the biblical creation story would make no mention of them. The Bible offers no explicit explanation, and yet we can draw some reasonable inferences. One comes from consideration of the account's theme and the other from consideration of its historical context.

The story of Genesis 1, as mentioned previously, serves primarily to identify the transcendent Creator to whom all humans owe our existence and worship. His attributes, including infinite power and love, shine forth from the step-by-step unfolding of His purposeful preparations for us. From a historical perspective, only a few people ever to read this story—people living mostly in Western cultures since the nineteenth century—would possess any awareness of or interest in dinosaurs. So, given that the Bible is a book for all generations, dinosaurs simply would not make the cut in the creation highlight reel.

### Dinosaurs in the Bible?

Some Christians assert that the Bible *does* speak of dinosaurs. They claim the "behemoth" and "leviathan" of Job 40 and 41 must be references to *Triceratops*, *Tyrannosaurus rex*, or some other dinosaur species. This reading, they say, is *the* "literal" meaning of the passage because the descriptive words used for these creatures are too fearsome to associate with any other.

This interpretation seems to overlook the heavy use of figurative language in Job 40 and 41, colorful imagery clearly marked by repeated use of "like" and "as."

No real creature ever breathed fire or had bones of iron and brass, for example. These similes give the passage its emotional impact, not its literal message.

A close look at the Hebrew text offers additional clues. The Hebrew word for "behemoth" appears in Genesis 1 in its singular form, $b^e\bar{h}\bar{e}m\hat{a}$, as part of the description of certain land mammals created on the sixth creation day. Given that dinosaurs were reptiles, not mammals, "behemoth" would seem to apply to some creature other than a dinosaur.

From an extrabiblical perspective, commentators often point to two species living in the human era that strike terror and cause mayhem resembling what's depicted in Job 40 and 41: one is the hippopotamus and the other, the crocodile. In some parts of Africa, these two species account for more human deaths per year than all other large animals combined.

In its wider context, which includes Job 39 and 42, the passage conveys a message about the *nepesh* animals as a critical part of God's provision for the human race. Each kind was created for a purpose, and each has something to teach us. The behemoth and leviathan convey a pointed lesson: While humans have managed to tame or subdue virtually every kind of soulish animal—including even the behemoth and leviathan in rare cases—only God can tame the pride of a human heart. That task is far more difficult.

### Day Six: Specialized Land Mammals

The account of God's work on the sixth and final creation day begins with the mention of three specific kinds of land mammals: "livestock, creatures that move along the ground, and wild animals." The specificity of this list suggests that it is not referring to land mammals generically. A closer look suggests it focuses, rather, on three categories of land mammals strategically important for the support of humans.

To infer that these three types of creatures bear some special relationship to humans seems reasonable, given their placement in the text. The three Hebrew nouns used for these creatures have multiple meanings, some general and some specific, but the context is best served by the narrower usage. The Hebrew words $b^e\bar{h}\bar{e}m\hat{a}$ and $hayy\hat{a}$ in this context seem best understood as a reference to two groups of long-legged land quadrupeds: those that can be easily tamed or domesticated for agricultural purposes and those that are difficult to tame but have potential to become excellent pets and helpers for humans. The Hebrew word *remeś* most likely refers to short-legged land mammals such as rodents and hares.[23]

The obvious question, 'Why these?' again finds an answer in the context. If a person were to identify which animals have played the most significant role through the ages, from earliest times to this day, in the care and comfort of human beings, these would be the top three. In brief, agricultural animals (mainly herbivores) made possible and still sustain civilization. Wild animals (carnivores) maintain the vitality of the herbivores. Studies show that without these predators, herbivores in the wild cannot thrive.

Wild animals humans have tamed, such as canine and feline species, have been valued since ancient times for their service (initially as the village cleanup crew, later with other tasks) and their capacity to give and receive affection, not to mention their entertainment value. Such creatures bless us with companionship and with some significant life lessons, as well.

The third group, sometimes erroneously identified as insects (due to wording of the King James Version) played a vital role in humanity's spread across a wide range of climate zones. The rodents' and hares' luxuriant fur helped humans survive through cycles of extremely cold weather, keeping us warm until technology provided other options. Today rodents play a vital role in medical research, a substantial benefit to our quality of life. Even the armadillo deserves mention, for this creature is allowing humans to develop better cures for leprosy.

With the planet now fully endowed with everything necessary to human thriving, the stage is set for both an end and a beginning. Conditions are now perfect—not for eternal life, yet—for fulfillment of God's ultimate purposes in creating the world. The story has reached a dramatic climax, a turning point on which all of cosmic history hinges. God turns His attention to shaping the first human—and then, at the just-right moment, to creating man's mate.

# 7

# THE FINAL ACT (FOR NOW)

**A**new and surprising expression appears in Genesis 1:26. Up to this point in the narrative, each creative act is introduced with a divine directive aimed *outward*—at light, water, land, or whatever needs fine-tuning in the stepwise buildup toward the entrance of humankind. Here, by contrast, we see a unique instance of divine self-reference: "Let us..."

### Day Six: A Reflection of God's Identity
The plural pronoun raises questions: Does its usage in this context merely exemplify the majestic "we" invoked by royalty, when the monarch speaks on behalf of the body politic? Jewish scholars argue for this interpretation, but this linguistic convention reflects awareness of the plurality behind it. What plurality does the Creator represent?

> Let *us* make mankind in *our* image, in *our* likeness (verse 26, emphasis added).

Then in the same breath, so to speak, the text reverts to the singular pronoun forms:

> So God created mankind in *his* own image, in the image of God *he* created them; male and female *he* created them (verse 27, emphasis added).

Here Scripture gives a brief but significant glimpse into a foundational doctrine that unfolds throughout the Old and New Testament canon. The *Trinity*—God's singular essence manifested in three persons, Father, Son, and Holy Spirit—is a word devised to convey this picture. God's triunity remains mysterious and cognitively challenging because it exceeds human capacity to visualize, and yet the transcendent nature of the Being who creates time and space, matter and energy, renders it a wholly plausible reality.

The three persons that make up the Godhead explain the origin of love in the creation. Love, by definition, is the expression of compassion and affection by a person toward another person. Therefore, if God were one and only one person, He could not possess love. But, because the triune God did possess and express love before He created anything, He could create love.

The singular essence of the triune God explains the unity, consistency, and harmony of creation. The record of nature reveals just one creative plan and just one integrated, compatible set of purposes and destinies for creation.

### 'ādām: A Reflection of God's Image

In the account of God's involvement in fashioning 'ādām (the word used for "mankind" in this passage),[1] we see the third and final usage in Genesis 1 of bārā' (see sidebar, "Three Origins of Life"). And, just as in the case of the nepesh creation, a second verb, 'āśâ, is also used. This word choice suggests something about 'ādām was completely novel, and something about him was not.

The not part is still miraculous. God manufactured Adam's body from "the dust of the ground."[2] However, the dust was not brand new. It predated Adam.

The novel part of Adam was his spirit. No earthly creature before him possessed a spirit. The spiritual dimension of this one creature set him above and apart from all previously existing physical and soulish creatures.

Only God's final work of the creation bears not only the imprint but also "the image" of God. This distinction applies to no other earthly creature.

Image does not imply identity. Only Jesus of Nazareth is the "exact representation" or "exact likeness"[3] of God in human flesh.[4] The human species bears His image in that like Jesus, we are physical, soulish, and spiritual beings.

That humans are body, soul, and spirit does not imply that humans are made up of three separate parts. The New Testament defines the human entity as an essential dichotomy between flesh and spirit (for example, Matthew 26:41 and John 6:63) wherein the soul operates somewhat like an interface between the material body and the nonmaterial spirit. This interface-like property of the human soul is well described in Romans 7–8 where Paul relates how his mind agrees with God's law, which is imparted into the spirit of every human being, but finds his mind sometimes powerless to subdue the sinful desires inherent in his body. While the soul and spirit of a human are functionally distinct, they are not substantively distinct. While the Bible does acknowledge the possibility of a human existing apart from his or her physical body, it appears to eliminate the possibility

### *Three* Origins of Life

Until recently the origin-of-life question discussed among scientists has focused exclusively on the emergence of physical life. However, a series of research studies and publications in neuroscience and cognitive psychology have compelled a broadening of the debate. As Genesis 1 foreshadowed thousands of years ago, that discussion includes two additional origination events.

The beginning of physical life appears to coincide with the earliest part of the Genesis narrative, as God's Spirit "brooded" over the waters. Sometime during creation day five (with the second use of *bārā'*) God introduces a new kind of life—life that is both physical and soulish. Then, toward the end of creation day six (with the third use of *bārā'*) comes yet another new life-form—the one and only species that combines physical, soulish, and spiritual characteristics, human beings.

Origin-of-life researchers now know that life originated on Earth within a geologic instant of time without the benefit of prebiotic building block molecules.[5] No prebiotic soup and little or no time eliminate the possibility of a naturalistic origin of life on Earth. As for life arriving from outer space, the more we learn about biochemistry, about life's complexities, and about the environment of the early Earth and extraterrestrial sites, the more we see the necessity of divine intervention to initiate life.[6]

Likewise, research shows that birds and mammals possess attributes of cognition nonexistent to *any* degree in bacteria, plants, insects, or amphibians.[7] Within the confines of naturalism, no mechanism can explain how these attributes emerged. Likewise, experiments suggest that the "human mind," including capacities identified as spiritual, manifests attributes nonexistent to *any* degree in any bird or other mammalian species.[8] Given the observational data and the fundamental principle of cause and effect—effects cannot be greater than their causes—the necessity of supernatural intervention seems inescapable. And that's the story Genesis 1 tells.

of a soulless human or a spiritless human.

The spirit capacity God "breathed" into *'ādām* made this new life-form profoundly different. Throughout the rest of Genesis and all of Scripture, as well as throughout human cultural history, we see that difference, as it's expressed in these uniquely human qualities:

1. consciousness of a self

2. concerns about death and about life after death
3. a propensity to worship and desire to communicate with a higher being
4. an innate awareness of right and wrong, or conscience
5. language capability that includes complex symbol cognition and expression
6. capacity for abstract thought, including a drive to discover truth and absolutes

These traits find expression (or effortful repression) in every human being, regardless of time and place and intellectual level. Even infants and people with severe mental or emotional impairment may express them to a limited extent. These qualities define what it means to be human, and any creature who lacks them cannot be considered 'ādām. In other words, the term "spiritless" human represents a contradiction.

One noticeable outgrowth of humanity's spiritual qualities is the development of culture and the ongoing advancement of technology and civilization. While many animal species use tools, form communities, and even divide certain roles and responsibilities with the community, the community life that developed among humans represents a whole new level of complexity, diversity, and growth. Human culture bursts upon the scene.

## Tracing Human History
Anthropologists describe evidence for six cultural "big bang" events, each of which reflects the difference spirit expression made. While the bipedal primate species that preceded *Homo sapiens sapiens* (anatomically modern humans) used only primitive tools and exhibited no advancement in tool technology during their lengthy sojourn on Earth,[9] the arrival of humans brought a huge and rapid leap in tool technology—axes, awls, needles, hammers, barbed fishhooks, shovels, harpoons, and more.[10] The arrival of humans also launched the first clothing[11] and jewelry industries.[12] Dates for these cultural big bangs all cluster around 40,000 to 45,000 years ago.

These explosive cultural developments were accompanied by the first appearance of sophisticated art and music, as well as the first worship and religious practices.[13] A large gallery of advanced art is displayed in the Chauvet cave in France that dates back 36,000 years.[14] Sculpted figurines found in German caves date at least 35,000 years in age.[15]

In several cave sites along the South African coast, archaeologists have discovered engraved ostrich eggs dating back 60,000 years ago[16] and jewelry beads and heat-treated microlith blades dating between 70,000 and 80,000 years ago.[17] While all these dates were achieved through luminescence techniques, which typically provide upper limits only, in one case the research team determined a thermoluminescence date for the artifacts and an optically stimulated luminescence date for an overlying dune.[18]

The accumulation of enough artifacts to leave discoverable traces requires certain minimum population levels and technological development. To reach such levels requires time. So these archaeological markers suggest a much earlier advent of humanity.

Establishing a time frame from the biblical text also represents a challenge. The genealogies in Genesis 5 and 11 provide some indication of how recently humans appeared. However, they offer only a rough measure, in part because of the varying usage of the Hebrew words for father and son, '*āb* and *bēn*. '*āb* can also refer to grandfather, great-grandfather, great-great-grandfather, and so on.[19] It can also mean forefather or ancestor.[20] Similarly, *bēn* may mean son, grandson, great-grandson, great-great-grandson, and so on or a member of a group.[21]

For example, in the book of Daniel we see that Belshazzar's mother refers to Nebuchadnezzar as Belshazzar's father when, in fact, two kings came between them and they were not biologically related.[22] Such flexibility in the usage of '*āb* and *bēn* can explain the apparent discrepancies between parallel genealogies (see, for example, 1 Chronicles 3, Matthew 1, and Luke 3). Even the apparently detailed genealogy in Genesis 11 omits at least one name. The parallel record in Luke 3 includes the name Cainan, which Genesis 11 does not.[23]

The existence of gaps in the Genesis genealogies should not be construed as flaws. The gaps mean we must treat the lists as abbreviations. The words translated into English—and into our Western way of thinking—may say this: "When X had lived Y years, he became the father of Z." The same passage in Hebrew— and read from a Middle Eastern perspective—could say this: "When X had lived Y years, he became the father of a family line that included (or culminated) in Z."

The challenge in deriving a biblical date for the creation of Adam and Eve is to ascertain the relative completeness of the Hebrew genealogies. Comparative analysis of overlapping genealogies throughout the Bible yields a wide range of possibilities, anywhere from about 10 to 90 percent completeness. Using genealogical data alone, the date for the creation of Adam and Eve would seem roughly between about ten thousand and a hundred thousand years ago. An attempted calibration of the Genesis 11 genealogy suggests a date of approximately 60,000 years ago (see sidebar, "Biblical Date for Adam's Creation" on page 75), but with admittedly substantial error bars.

## DNA Dates for Adam and Eve

Though far from definitive, DNA analysis now provides some insight on the timing of humanity's origin. Two portions of human genetic material do not tend to recombine (mix up) in reproduction: (1) mitochondrial DNA (that is, DNA that resides in specialized structures called *mitochondria* that exist outside the cell's nucleus); and (2) a large segment of the Y-chromosome. Though both men and women carry mitochondrial DNA, all of us inherit nearly all our mitochondrial DNA from our mothers only. Only men carry the Y-chromosome segment. That is, males receive a large portion of the Y-chromosome from their fathers only.

Molecular anthropologists take advantage of the features of mitochondrial and Y-chromosome DNA to construct molecular clocks for humanity's origin. They measure the differences among presently existing human populations for these genetic segments and then determine natural mutations rates for the segments by comparing the DNA of humans who are presently alive with the DNA of human remains of known ages. The date for the first human male and the first human female then is equal to number of genetic differences divided by mutation rate.

Mitochondrial DNA analysis of individuals across a wide range of ethnicities has indicated that the human species can be traced back to a female living 108,000 years ago according to one study[24] and 250,000–300,000 years ago according to another study.[25] For both these results the research teams presumed constant but different rates of mutation. However, much evidence establishes that human mutation rates are far from constant. One attempt to roughly calibrate the changing mutation rates determined that the first woman (mitochondrial Eve) lived 157,000 ± 40,000 years ago.[26]

All this research, however, failed to take into account that 10–20 percent of the human population inherits two sets of mitochondrial DNA from their mothers (a phenomenon called heteroplasmy) and nearly one percent inherits three sets (triplasmy). If the analysis were to take into account heteroplasmy and triplasmy, it could yield a date for the first woman as recently as 50,000 or 60,000 years ago.[27]

Meanwhile, a sampling of Y-chromosome DNA across a wide range of ethnicities shows that humans trace back to a male individual who lived, according to four different studies employing four different constant rates of mutation, 51,000 ± 9,000 years ago,[28] 108,000 ±7,000 years ago,[29] 142,000 ± 16,000 years ago,[30] and 409,000 ± 172,000 years ago[31] respectively. Like the mitochondrial DNA mutation rate, the Y-chromosome mutation rate most likely varies in a difficult-to-establish manner. Thus, the Y-chromosome date for the first man

(Y-chromosomal Adam) remains at this point a ballpark figure (probably in the middle of those estimates, or about 100,000 years ago) only.

As new technologies and new cultural discoveries emerge, the timing of humanity's origin will likely become more precisely known. Even now, as crude as the date estimates may be—based on the scientific and biblical information currently available—these estimates appear to converge. In this respect, the biblical account of creation retains its credibility in the light of advancing research. It's no surprise that the scientific literature uses the names Adam and Eve to describe the earliest humans and the Garden-of-Eden hypothesis to describe their latest models of humanity's origin.

### A Possible Purpose for the Hominids

The discovery of multiple "hominids" (human-like species) through the years since evolutionary theory was introduced raised serious questions about the reliability of the Genesis 1 story. The physical resemblance between humans and the great apes had already raised speculation about a line of descent when discovery of skeletal remains more closely resembling human morphology hit the news. As the argument for common descent gained momentum, so did doubts about the literal accuracy of the biblical account.

### Biblical Date for Adam's Creation

The Genesis 11 genealogy includes 11 names: Noah, Shem, Arphaxad, Shelah, Eber, Peleg, Reu, Serug, Nahor, Terah, and Abram. Biblical and extra-biblical historical records indicate that Abram (who became Abraham) lived about 4,000 years ago. Genesis 10:25 says that "the world was divided" in the days of Peleg. In the Genesis 11 context of humanity's migration beyond the Middle East, this dividing may well refer to the breakup of the great land bridges—physical connectors that joined Siberia to Alaska, Britain to France, Korea to Japan, Queen Charlotte Islands to mainland British Columbia, for example—near the close of the last ice age.

Carbon-14 dating indicates that sea levels rose to make both the Bering and Hecate Straits impassable at about 11,000 years ago.[32] If Peleg lived at the time those bridges broke apart some 11,000 years ago and Abram, about 4,000 years ago, *and* if the patriarch's lifespans recorded in Genesis 11 are proportional to the passage of time, then Noah would have been alive roughly 40,000 years ago and Adam and Eve anywhere from 60,000 to 100,000 years ago.

A major issue in the creation v. evolution controversy came from the lack of biblical mention or explanation of these creatures that looked so much like human beings and seemed to possess greater intelligence than other primate species. As I've mentioned before, the omission makes sense given that this story was written for readers throughout the ages, most of whom have no knowledge of these bipedal creatures. It makes even more sense if no significant link existed between these creatures and modern humans.

Yet a question lingers: Why would God create these hominids? What possible purpose would these creatures serve? One reasonable, though still speculative, answer emerges from a study of animal extinction records.

Genesis makes clear that God gave humans the responsibility to care for Earth's animals as part of managing Earth's resources for the benefit of all life.[33] Fulfillment of that assignment would demand total adherence to their Maker's wisdom. But they tossed away that possibility when they chose their own wisdom over God's and declared their autonomy. The consequences of that choice is a brokenness that haunts us still today. It wreaks havoc on all levels of our existence, including our management of the animals.[34]

Because God endowed various creatures with special capacities to relate with us, human sin turned their affinity into an enormous risk, the risk of abuse. This problem of human sin escalated drastically after the flood of Noah's era, when humans transitioned from a vegetarian diet to one that also included meat.[35] In response to this formidable risk, God brought "the fear and dread of [humanity]…upon all the beasts of the earth and all the birds of the air."[36]

Knowing far in advance, however, what damage the predatory behavior of sinful humans would do, the Creator would have made advance preparation.[37] Human-resembling hunters may well have fulfilled a preparatory role. The statistics on animal extinction suggest such a possibility.

Humanity's mismanagement of animal life can be documented in what happened to bird and mammal species present on Earth since the time Adam and Eve arrived. Of the 21,000 extant bird species, only about 9,000 remain today, and of the approximately 8,000 land mammal species, just 4,000 remain.[38]

An assessment of where and when this devastation occurred indicates that the scenario would have been far worse if not for God's introduction of a succession of carnivorous or omnivorous hominid species, each successive one more adept at hunting for food. Gradually birds and mammals learned to keep their distance from bipedal creatures carrying weapons—a lesson quickly relearned when Noah's descendants began to hunt. This scenario may have contributed to the transition described in Genesis 9:2, when soulish animals changed from welcoming human contact to fearing human contact.

The findings of large-bodied mammal extinction research lend support to this hypothesis about the hominids' impact (see table 7).[39] In Australia, where fossil evidence suggests no hominid species resided prior to humans, only 1 out of 16 large-bodied mammal genera survived the arrival of humans. By contrast, in sub-Saharan Africa where the full panoply of hominid species fossils have been discovered, only 2 out of 44 large-bodied mammal genera went extinct upon modern humans' arrival. Apparently, increasing exposure to the predatory skills of successive hominid species allowed birds and mammals to prepare for the future shock of a super predator.

**Table 7: Late Pleistocene Extinction Rate of Large (Adult Body Weight Averaging 40 kg/88 lbs) Mammals**

| Continent/Region | Extinction Rate |
|---|---|
| Australia | 94% |
| South America | 79% |
| North America | 73% |
| Europe | 30% |
| Sub-Saharan Africa | 5% |

As a side note, table 7 also provides evidence for the beneficial impact of day five and day six animals on development of human civilization. In those continental regions that lacked bipedal primate species previous to humans and where most of the large-bodied mammal species were wiped out shortly after the arrival of humans (Australia, South America, and North America) humans there advanced little, if any, beyond a stone-age existence. Not until the arrival of both people and large-bodied mammals from Europe and Asia in the sixteenth century was this limitation overcome.

**Humanity's Assignment**
Genesis 1:28 records God's commands to the first humans to fill Earth and to "rule over" the planet and all it contains. In other words, as mentioned above, humans bear responsibility—under God's direction—to manage Earth's resources, both living and nonliving. God clearly expects humanity to exercise wise, ecologically judicious management of our habitat. In chapters 37–39 of the book of

Job, a revelation that may predate Genesis 1 by as much as a few centuries, God provides an essential instruction manual, one that's applicable to this day.

Instructions are one thing. Obeying them is another. The Scriptures from Genesis 3 to Revelation tell the story of humanity's failure to follow God's instructions in submission to His authority. How grateful we can be that these same Scriptures also bring the good news, the gospel, the proclamation of God's personal offer to suffer the consequences of our sin and to provide for all who'll receive it a new heart, a spiritual rebirth into a life of following and serving the Creator of all things.

## A Final Reflection on the Creation Story

For many secularists and even some Christians, the scenario of God's creation and then later replacement of hominid species, not to mention countless species of whales, horses, and bipedal primates, by other species seems counter to the expected character and attributes of the biblical God. To their thinking, an all-powerful, all-loving Creator would create life as it now exists in the first place. Progressive creation appears to them the trial-and-error efforts of a bumbling, wasteful, or cruel Creator. Biologist (and theist) Kenneth Miller comments, in his critique of the intelligent design perspective:

> The designer is never satisfied—or perhaps can never get it quite right. ...
> Our designer doesn't just design: he does it again and again—and his designs don't last.[40]

The question must be raised, however, about what is meant by "quite right." Right for what or whom? If by that word we mean "perfect" in the way we anticipate heaven to be, the explanation becomes clear. We're like students who want to pass their courses without passing the final exam.

The Bible reveals evil existed before Adam and Eve rebelled in Eden. It was initiated by Satan's rebellion and drew in other spiritual beings as well, who remain forever in that state of rebellion. We can infer from Romans 8, Revelation 20–22, and other Bible passages that God created the universe with the specific features it possesses in preparation for the perfect creation yet to come—the new heavens and new earth. God made this cosmos as a way, through Him, to enter a realm where free will is fully intact but freer than we can now imagine because the fall and its consequences have been dealt with once and for all.[41] Whether or not evil existed before the creation of the universe is irrelevant because its coming was known to God.

He made a universe in which gravity, electromagnetism, thermodynamics, expanding dimensions of space and a finite dimension of time all play a part in the ultimate plan to conquer evil with His perfect goodness.[42] In order for these physical laws and dimensions to fulfill their purpose, certain necessary features of Earth and Earth's life must be subject to change, through time, all in a carefully orchestrated progression that aligns multiple narrow time windows allowing for the existence, survival, and thriving of human life.[43]

For example, the abundant limestone, marble, ozone, oxygen, water, topsoil, coal, oil, gas, salt, phosphate, gypsum, and concentrated insoluble metal ore deposits on which human civilization depends require countless generations of life and death long before our arrival on the planet (see chapter 17). What's more, because Earth's environment changes with respect to time, different species are suited to different conditions and many play a vital role propelling life-beneficial changes for future species, ultimately including humanity. Only the most primitive and minute forms of life, such as bacteria, could survive the radiation emanating from the youthful Sun's intense flaring and from the decay of radioactive isotopes in the early Earth's crust.

More advanced life requires a more delicately balanced set of conditions. What we see in the fossil record is that as conditions changed, God replaced former species with the ones best suited for the new conditions. Sometimes these new ones were closely similar; sometimes, not.

Research reveals that plants and animals play the primary role in removing greenhouse gases (such as carbon dioxide and water vapor) from Earth's atmosphere as the Sun grows brighter, so that Earth's atmosphere traps less and less heat. By this means, Earth's surface temperature is maintained at a survivable level for life.

The intricate complexities of sustaining abundant life on Earth for 3.8 billion years cannot be overstated. In addition to surviving radiation changes, life survived the changing size and distribution of Earth's continents, changing tidal forces exerted by the Moon, and the changing rotation rate of Earth.[44] Given life's observed vulnerability to extinction, what accounts for its endurance—and its astonishing progression toward greater complexity?

Psalm 104 offers this insight:

How many are your works, O Lord! In wisdom you made them all; the earth is full of your creatures…living things both large and small….These all look to you to give them their food at the proper time. When you give it to them, they gather it up; when you open your hand, they are satisfied with good things. When you hide your face, they are terrified; when you take away their breath, they die and return to the dust. When you send your Spirit, they are created, and you renew the face of the earth.[45]

The creation scenario set forth in this passage seems perfectly consistent with the character and attributes of the biblical God, the transcendent Creator. Yet, questions and doubts remain. How can we know that the stories and songs and histories of ancient days really are the inspired, inerrant, authoritative Word of God? Even some highly educated theologians view them as a compilation of writings from various times, places, and peoples. The next chapter in our navigation through the story of creation examines this question of source.

# 8

# SOURCE CONTROVERSY

**G**enesis 1 succinctly and eloquently tells the story of who we are and how we came to be—and it matches the scientific account of Earth's origin and development and of life's origin and development. The ancient text correctly identifies Earth's initial conditions. It describes the sequential steps, in a scientifically accurate chronological order, by which Earth became ready for human habitation. Then it declares the uniqueness of humankind, male and female, made by God in His image.

This flawless overview of an enormous body of natural history comes to us in just one page, a few dozen sentences. Moses, the apparent writer, recorded this narrative more than 34 centuries ago.[1] By means which can only be described as miraculous, the story he presented aligns with the still-accumulating evidence from multiple scientific disciplines.

### Identifying the Source
Current opinion among many scholars places this Genesis story (circa fifteenth century BC) in the larger body of creation mythology collected from various ethnicities around the world. In fact, because it may not be the oldest *written* account of creation, many scholars assume it represents a "borrowed" and embellished version of an earlier creation myth, perhaps the first. This earlier document, the Enuma elish, is the Akkadian story recovered from the library of Ashurbanipal (circa 640 BC) in Nineveh. Most scholars believe the Enuma elish was written in the Bronze Age near the time of Hammurabi (eighteenth to sixteenth centuries BC).[2]

Among the world's creation myths, the Enuma elish and the nearly identical Atrahasis Epic of the Sumerians bear the greatest resemblance to the biblical story.[3] They describe creation as a sequence of discrete events beginning from a watery chaos. First comes light, then the creation of land, the appointment of various celestial bodies for signs, seasons, and days, and the creation of beasts and creeping things.

In the light of modern science and in comparison with other nonbiblical creation stories, the Enuma elish and the Atrahasis Epic stand out. These other creation myths, as intriguing as they are, may best be described as testimonies to the wondrous imaginative capacities of the human mind.[4]

The Enuma elish and its Sumerian counterpart certainly seem more connected with reality. However, they also depart from it on several matters, including these:

1. They place the creation of man before the creation of the animals, large and small.
2. They speak of a saltwater ocean and a freshwater ocean as one (that is, in contact with each other) prior to the creation of land.
3. They say the material comprising celestial bodies, land, and human bodies comes from the corpses and blood of gods killed in combat with one another.[5]

A singularly powerful impression emerges from a study of these and other creation stories from around the world. It seems that all humans everywhere crave an explanation of our origin and destiny. The belief that our life has meaning in some greater context than its limited span is pervasive.

The first humans, whom the Bible identifies as Adam and Eve, enjoyed close fellowship with their Maker, until they chose to "do their own thing." It makes sense that before the fall they talked with Him about their beginnings as a way to understand their significance and their place in the world. That story would have been passed from parents to progeny for many generations. Finally, to protect and preserve its accuracy, God delivered it to Moses in what Exodus declares as a direct discourse.[6] If the story in its oral form became increasingly distorted with time and distance from its source, we would expect the people nearest to its source in space and time, such as the Akkadians and Sumerians, to retain versions closest to the original.

### Genesis Account Features
While Abraham (2100 BC), the patriarch of Moses and the Israelites, shared the same geography with Hammurabi, he predated him by two or three centuries. Therefore, it seems safe to say that the original creation story, an oral account given long before the written, seems more likely identifiable by its distinctive characteristics than by the date of the earliest extant manuscript.

Hebrew did not become a written language until the fifteenth century BC. So the Hebrew people could not have produced an earlier *written* account of creation than the Enuma elish. Also, based on textual evidence it appears that the content of the book of Job may predate that of Genesis by as many as five centuries.[7] Except for its introduction and epilogue, the entire text of Job is structured in a way that lends itself to memorization. Thus, its message could have been faithfully preserved without the benefit of written language. By its timing, Job's soaring account refutes the claim that the Enuma elish is the oldest detailed depiction of creation.

As all other creation stories stand side by side with Genesis 1, striking differences become obvious. Rather than groping its way through a primeval mist and wandering down dark corridors where demigods engage in typically human behavior (or misbehavior), the biblical account outlines physical events in an ordered, matter-of-fact sequence. My motive is not to disparage the sacred texts of other faiths, but I would encourage those interested to read those books for themselves.[8]

The gods of other creation stories bear little resemblance (if any) to the God of the Genesis account. The biblical Creator exists discretely apart from His creation. He possesses unlimited power and goodness. He is a personal being, not just a force or an abstraction. He is the deity who controls all nature, who is in no way confined or limited by nature, though He is also personally present throughout it. He is not some deified part of nature or even the deification of nature itself. He manifests none of the moral weaknesses of humanity. Though evil exists both in the physical realm and in the spiritual realm, the evil is not *in* God, as pantheistic and monistic myths assert.

The creating accomplished by the God of the Bible fundamentally differs from any creating of which humans are capable. This God creates material and spiritual substance out of nothing (see sidebar, "Nine Kinds of Nothing," page 27). No other account yet uncovered even vaguely suggests that the Creator brought into existence all matter, energy, space, and time.

Another aspect of the biblical creation account distinguishes it from others: it bears no hint of political motive. The Enuma elish unabashedly advances the cause of Babylonian supremacy over Mesopotamia.[9] Similar racist, elitist, or economic agendas can be detected in other creation myths. Some seem blatant, others subtle. The biblical Adam, however, is simply "man"; Eve, "the mother of all humans"; and their dwelling place, "a garden in the East."

The most important feature of the Genesis 1 creation story lies in its clear, simple, and straightforward presentation of crucial, life-relevant data, which we can now verify. What's more, it demonstrates what scientists call *predictive* success. It conveys details only recently known and understood to be factual.

Genesis 1 correctly identifies four initial conditions of the planet in the era before life appeared. It accurately describes ten major transitional events (creation events) and places all ten in the correct chronological order. None of the nonbiblical creation accounts comes close to this level of accuracy. The Enuma elish comes closest, and for reasons we can understand, but it strays far into the fictional realm.[10]

As if in anticipation of modern skepticism, Genesis lies open to testing against advancing knowledge of science and history. Although widely publicized misinterpretations of Genesis 1 clash with accepted fact (see chapters 20–22), no problems remain when biblical (and scientific) rules of interpretation are applied. This openness to testing—testing for validity, testing for human limitations and biases—commands attention. The Genesis creation account cannot be dismissed as irrelevant or inconsequential. If the certainty of its "supernatural" truthfulness can be sustained, then we must indeed face its spiritual implications.

# 9

# MESSAGE OF DAY SEVEN

**A** chapter about rest may seem about as exciting as watching grass grow. But it's not time to start yawning. While the creation story may have come to an end, another story has yet to unfold. And this final day, day seven (Genesis 2:2–3), provides a pregnant pause.

Make no mistake about this: the word *rest* in the context of the creation account does *not* imply that God grew weary. The Hebrew word for God's "rest" here, is *šabbāt*. Some Bible translations include a footnote to explain that it means God "ceased." Anyone who studies music will recognize this meaning as it also applies to the English "rest." When musicians come to the "rest" symbol in their musical score, they refrain from sounding their instrument for as long as the symbol indicates. This pause has no connection with weariness.

**Seventh Day Wisdom**

Like any good story within a story, the creation account needs a wrap-up and a transition, best of all one that connects on a personal level with the reader. That's exactly what we find in Genesis 2:2–3. This statement makes the point that the created order is now complete. Nothing more is needed for the physical support of human existence. It's all here, and it's enough.

Now the writer seizes the moment to drive home a lesson: Remember that God is the one who established, by example, the pattern of one work-free day (of 24 hours) in seven for humans[1] and a work-free "day" (of one year) in seven for tilled land.[2]

Even in this detail, modern research affirms the wisdom of Scripture. God knew what would be best, from a biological standpoint, for people and their cultivated land.

For humans, the wisdom of the seventh day was demonstrated by social experiments in revolutionary France and Soviet Russia. In their attempt to de-Christianize society and to increase productivity, French Republicans and Soviet Russians altered the calendar. The French Republican calendar in effect from 1793–1805 divided each month into three weeks of ten days each, and citizens were expected to work for nine consecutive days, with rest on the tenth day. The Soviet calendar in effect from 1929–1940 experimented with five- and six-day work weeks, with rotating rest days in each of the work weeks. These social experiments were abandoned when it became clear that they diminished rather than enhanced productivity.

For agricultural land, allowing the land to lie fallow for one year out of seven proved optimal for controlling pests such as nematodes (worms). Before the widespread use of pesticides, the only way to prevent catastrophic pest epidemics was to starve the pests periodically by resting the land. One rest year out of seven years appears to maximize agricultural productivity.

God has no biological limitations. His work days and rest day could be arbitrarily long or short in duration.

### Seventh Day Cessation

In terms of creation activity, the scientific record affirms the continuance of the seventh day—the cessation of aggressive speciation. According to the fossil record, new life-forms proliferated through the millions of years before modern humans arrived on the scene. Though frequent extinctions occurred, the introduction rate for new species matched or outstripped the extinction rate. Then it abruptly halted.

Throughout human history, the extinction rate has increased significantly—some environmentalists would say frighteningly—to some extent because of human activity.[3] Removing the human factor still leaves an extinction rate of at least one species per year. The introduction rate, however, immediately plummeted to a virtual zero when the human era began. According to environmentalist pioneers Paul and Anne Ehrlich, "It has been more than a century since Charles Darwin started biologists thinking about speciation, and the production of a new animal species in nature has yet to be documented."[4]

A few zoologists and many or most botanists, nevertheless, do argue for ongoing speciation. The basis for this argument is wide disagreement among biologists as to what qualifies as a speciation event. This speciation problem has spawned over a dozen different definitions for the term *species* in the scientific literature.[5]

Field botanists have noted real-time development of some distinguishable differentiation among plants.[6] Whether all of these new plants deserve distinct "species" labels remains a debatable question. Many scientists see most of the new plants merely as new breeds, or strains, of the old, rather than as new species. Whatever the case, no one denies the glaring, even frightening, imbalance between extinction and speciation. As noted in chapter 6 (pages 62–65) this imbalance is especially stark for large-bodied advanced animals. By anyone's terms, no new mammal species has appeared during the human era. Meanwhile, half of all mammal species present at the time of our origin have gone extinct.

Physical conditions on Earth before Adam and Eve, during the era of species proliferation, compared to now, are essentially the same. Research indicates that natural evolutionary processes, or the observable microevolution (in viruses and bacteria, for example), occurs at roughly the same rate today as it did before humans appeared. Science offers no explanation, as yet, for the catastrophic drop in the generation of new species, genera, families, and orders. The Bible, however, does offer one. The difference comes from the change in God's level of creative activity. Before Adam and Eve, it was high. After Adam and Eve, it ceased.

Long-term evolution experiments confirm the difference between the human and prehuman eras. In one such experiment a team of evolutionary biologists at Michigan State University noted that dozens of repeated structural outcomes appear among plants and animals that have no discernible evolutionary connection. An example would be the structure of the eyes and tongue of the sand lance (a fish) and the chameleon (a reptile). In both cases their eyes move independently, the cornea rather than the lens is used to focus on objects, skin coverings for their eyes camouflage them from prey and predators, and their long tongues are spring-loaded for snagging prey.

The Michigan State research team developed an experiment with twelve different E. coli bacteria populations to determine whether highly controlled breeding conditions could force a repeated microevolutionary outcome.[7] The answer, after twenty years and over 40,000 generations of the E. coli reproduction, was no.[8] This finding calls into question the means by which hundreds of documented examples of repeated outcomes appear among unrelated species.

This long-term experiment on E. coli still continues. At 45,000 generations, researchers had observed the equivalent of about a million years of human evolution. Under highly artificial laboratory conditions designed to force a particular morphological alteration, just one of the twelve E. coli populations underwent a microevolutionary change.

Other long-term evolution experiments performed on bacteria, yeast, fungi, and fruit flies confirm how limited natural processes seem to be in their capacity to generate significant changes in existing life-forms.[9] The biblical account of divine intervention in the development of life seems a thoroughly plausible explanation for the proliferation of substantial change in the past and the lack of it in the present era. For six days God created. On the seventh day God ceased from His physical creation activity.

**Day Seven Duration**
In Genesis 1, each of the six creation days (except the seventh) is marked off with the same refrain: "There was evening, and there was morning." Many readers recognize this marker as the basis for the Jewish belief that a day begins at sundown. It seems likely this unusual structure—evening first, followed by morning—emerges from the story itself. On creation day one, God brought light out of the darkness. The movement goes from darkness to light.

Until day seven, that progression continues. We see God's work of transforming the world from darkness, as a symbol of chaos, toward light, as a symbol of order until that day. But, by the seventh day the transformation God intended is complete, and that day remains open-ended.

This picture of an ongoing seventh day receives mention in other portions of Scripture. Psalm 95:7–11, John 5:16–18, and Hebrews 4:1–11 (each by a different writer) indicate that the seventh day began, from an earthly perspective, after the creation of Adam and Eve and extends through the present era to a future time. Revelation 21 tells us that the seventh day will eventually end for us, when God's purposes for this cosmos have been fulfilled and God unveils an entirely new heaven and earth for us, a new creation with new physical laws, appropriate, as always, to the fulfillment of His divine purposes and plans for life beyond cosmic time.[10]

If the seventh "day" continues, as Scripture indicates, it may reveal a significant clue for interpreting the word yôm, or "day," for each of the six creation days. It would seem to be a time span much longer than 24 hours. Interpretation of this word became a controversial issue in the last few hundred years, as the Bible was translated into English and widely distributed. Many Bible readers were, and still are, unaware of the differences between Hebrew and English, and inaccurate conclusions have resulted.

In English the word day enjoys flexible usage. We refer to the day of the dinosaurs and the day of the Romans, and no one misunderstands our meaning. We recognize this usage as appropriate. We also recognize other definitions for day: a 24-hour period, from midnight to midnight, and either some of or all of the daylight hours (roughly 12, but varying from one latitude and season to another).

English offers us many more word choices if we want to denote a longer time pe-riod—*epoch, era, eon,* and *age,* among others.

Hebrew, however, with its small vocabulary (more than a thousand times smaller than English), has more flexibility. Most words, especially the nouns, have multiple meanings that can all be considered literal. The word *yôm* possesses four distinct literal definitions: a portion of the daylight hours, all of the daylight hours, a 24-hour period, or a long but finite time period.[11] In biblical Hebrew, as opposed to modern Hebrew, no other word besides *yôm* carries the meaning of a long but finite time period.[12]

Because the Bible contains dozens of lengthy texts on various themes relevant to creation (see table 9, "Relevant Biblical Creation Texts"), it provides a means for testing and amplifying interpretations of the Genesis 1 account. An integrative analysis of all these passages leads to the conclusion that *yôm* refers to a long, but finite, time period. This understanding of "day" yields a consistent reading of all the Bible's creation texts. It eliminates any internal contradictions. To interpret the Bible literally is not enough; one must also interpret it with internal (as well as external) consistency.

The wording in the King James Version of the Bible reads, "And the evening and the morning were the first day" (and "the second" and "the third," and so on). It is a graceful wording, but it represents some license on the part of the transla-tors. It appeared acceptable, given that the Hebrew text, precisely rendered, says "evening was and morning was" followed by *yôm* and a number. The translators' choice of sentence structure convinced many English readers that the literal in-terpretation of "day" must be the 24-hour interpretation.[13] Thus, they viewed the creation chronology as a series of events packed into six consecutive 24-hour days.

Later, when geologists, physicists, and astronomers advanced compel-ling evidence for the antiquity of Earth and the cosmos,[14] battle lines formed. From many a pulpit, churchgoers heard they must choose between the "sure Word of God" and the "uncertain findings of science," between the "pure motives of godly Bible scholars" and the "questionable motives of godless scientists." All of this rancor arose from a rather simple misunderstanding.

Few other issues have generated as much animosity among Christians and between Christians and secularists as does this doctrine of a recent, 144-hour creation week. The idea that the beginning of the universe, Earth, and life on Earth dates back only a few thousand years dismisses—at best—all the sciences and infuriates scientists. Some, who might be open to considering the good news of redemption in Christ, never give the biblical message a chance because of its seeming nonsense about creation. What's more, the supposed Bible-based attacks on science and scientists nudge those who respect both to cling all the more tenaciously to naturalistic evolutionary theory for fear of giving way, or even seeming to give way, to a demonstrably false notion.

**Removing the Barrier**
As long as people confuse the *doctrine* of creation with the *date* of creation, the barrier will be difficult to budge. The early church fathers understood the distinction, but many twenty-first-century fundamentalists and evangelicals struggle with it.

## Table 9: Relevant Biblical Creation Texts

| reference | creation theme |
|---|---|
| Genesis 1 | Creation chronology: a physical perspective |
| Genesis 2 | Creation chronology: a spiritual perspective |
| Genesis 3–5 | Human sin and its damage |
| Genesis 6–9 | God's damage control |
| Genesis 10–11 | Global dispersion of humanity |
| Job 9 | The Creator's transcendent power |
| Job 34–38 | Physical creation's intricacy and complexity |
| Job 39–42 | Soulish creation's intricacy and complexity |
| Psalm 8 | Creation's appeal to humility |
| Psalm 19 | Creation's declarative message |
| Psalm 33 | God's sovereignty over nature |
| Psalm 65 | The Creator's authority and optimal provision |
| Psalm 104 | An elaboration of physical creation events |
| Psalm 139 | Affirmation of God's involvement in each human life |
| Psalms 147–148 | The Creator's power, wisdom, and care in nature |
| Proverbs 8 | The Creator's existence before creation |
| Ecclesiastes 1–3 | The constancy of physical laws |
| Ecclesiastes 8–12 | The limits of human control of nature |
| Isaiah 40–51 | The origin and development of the universe |
| Romans 1–8 | God's purposes in creation |
| 1 Corinthians 15 | Life after life |
| 2 Corinthians 4 | The Creator's glory in and beyond creation |
| Hebrews 1 | Cosmic creation's temporality; the role of angels |
| Hebrews 4 | God's ongoing rest |
| 2 Peter 3 | Creation's end |
| Revelation 20–22 | The new creation |

Ante-Nicene scholars (those prior to AD 325) devoted some two thousand pages of commentary to the "hexameron," the portion of Genesis 1 describing the six creation days. No other section of Scripture received more of their attention. Yet in all their pages of commentary, only about two address the meaning of "day" or the time frame for creation.[15] Their comments on the subject remained tentative, with some favoring the day-age (typically a thousand-year period) interpretation—and their studies preceded the influence of science. Not one explicitly endorsed the 24-hour-day interpretation.[16] But all believed that God was intimately involved in the creative process, and that this creation doctrine—the *Who* and the *how* of creation but not the *when*—makes a difference in how we respond to God and His Word.

The inclusion of day seven in the creation story, with its clue to the meaning of "day" as an extended time period, has become a treasured gift from the One who inspired the Word—if we recognize and accept its implications. However, the pressure to resist what it tells us about long days springs from a powerful source, a highly emotional reaction to the idea that death of any kind must have been part of a "very good" creation prior to humanity's act of rebellion against God.

## "It Was Very Good"

The statement "it was good" appears six times in Genesis 1. In the concluding remarks in verse 31 God evaluates the sum of all His creation work as "very good."

Many Christian leaders, including a number of prominent creationists, interpret all these declarations of the goodness of God's creation as proof that no disease, parasites, or carnivores could have existed before Adam and Eve's sin against God in the Garden of Eden. They go so far as to conclude that no death or suffering of any kind occurred previous to that rebellious act.[17]

These leaders overlook three critical points. First, Adam was not the first fallen created being. That distinction belongs to Satan. The Bible is silent on how long before Adam's rebellion Satan's mutiny occurred.

Second, God possesses total foreknowledge. Before He created the universe He knew when, where, and how Adam's rebellion would occur. Consequently, He possesses the capacity to design the universe, Earth, and Earth's life ideally in advance of the future advent of human sin.

Third, while the present creation is "good" and "very good," it will some day be replaced by a far superior creation—the new creation described in Revelation 21–22. In the new creation there will be no death, decay, suffering, grief, evil, sin, disabilities, disease, or restrained free wills. The present creation is very good in that it is the best possible creation for God to redeem those humans who so desire freedom from their slavery to sin. To put it another way, it is the perfect creation for God to eradicate evil and suffering and enhance the free will capacity of redeemed humans to experience and express love.

## Unequal or Overlapping Days?

In discussion of the creation days as long time periods, a question often arises about whether the days must be of equal duration. The text provides no clear answer to that question. The definitions of *yôm*, *'ereb*, or *bōqer* in the grammatical structure of Genesis 1 and the literary context do not require that the days be of equal length. To suggest that they are not consecutive seems out of keeping with the structure and purpose of the passage, but any given day may be longer or shorter than another without doing violence to the syntax. The scientific record of Earth's history seems to say the creation days grew progressively shorter from one to six.

As to whether the creation days might overlap, the syntax suggests they do not. On each creation day God initiates a specific transformative event. On that basis, Genesis 1 indicates no sea mammals or birds were created until day five. However, God's *initial* creation of bird and sea mammal species on day five would not mean He created no more of these creatures on day six.

Renewals and replacements of various species are important for two reasons: First, the Sun continues to grow brighter with time (see figure 4, page 43). So to compensate for the brightening Sun, God must replace life-forms that are less efficient in removing greenhouse gases from the atmosphere with those that are more efficient in doing so.[18] Second, bird and mammalian species are prone to rapid extinction due to their sensitivity to environmental conditions and their specialized food requirements. To keep the planet full of birds and mammals, the Creator apparently continued making new kinds of birds and mammals as conditions changed. They certainly were plentiful when humans first came on the scene.

Romans 8:18–23 declares that the law of decay (a.k.a the second law of thermodynamics, law of entropy, or Murphy's Law) that permeates the entire universe must remain in effect until the fullness of the number of human beings who are destined to receive God's redemptive gift and the eternal salvation that accompanies it has been attained. In another book I explain how the physics of decay operates as a tool in God's hand to restrain the expression of evil.[19] Because the law of decay plays a role in constraining evil, one can conclude that decay is the result of the fall. God (in His foreknowledge) knew that the fall of Satan and later that of Adam would occur. In advance of those events He would have designed the universe with the best possible physics to restrain the evil resulting from those falls. (The Bible is silent on the timing of Satan's fall. His rebellion may have occurred before the cosmic creation event.)

The law of decay brings heat and light from the Sun. The law of decay makes possible photosynthesis and all the food photosynthesis provides. It allows us to digest our food. It allowed Adam, before and after his fall, to perform work. The law of decay brings about many more good things, but it also produces inevitable pain, suffering, and death.

Those who believe animal death prior to Adam's sin implies a cruel God need to consider again what God was willing to suffer for our sake. Nothing was more costly and painful for Him than allowing His Son to die for all our sins. Jesus' death was the ultimate expression of God's love. These same individuals also need to ponder anew the pervasive New Testament message that the only way to truly live is to die (Philippians 1:21). They also need to consider that Romans 5:12 declares that "sin entered the world through one man, and death through sin, and in this way death came to all people." By saying "all people" rather than "all life" and by specifying "death through sin" Paul here clarifies that Adam's fall did *not* inaugurate animal death.

How can physical death be entirely bad when it is the only means by which we can gain true life? Far worse than physical death is the death we experience in our slavery to sin. As Paul explains in his first letter to the Corinthians, "The sting of death is sin. ...But thanks be to God! He gives us the victory through our Lord Jesus Christ."[20]

# 10

# SPIRITUAL PERSPECTIVE ON CREATION: GENESIS 2

**G**enesis 2 seems to tell a different creation story. It starts with a reference to the beginning, when God shaped the earth and the heavens, but from there onward, the point of view refocuses just as radically as it does between the first and second verses of chapter 1. Once again, that shift of perspective makes all the difference.

While Genesis 1 focuses almost entirely on the physical creation—*what* God made or made happen and in *what order*, Genesis 2 begins to elaborate on the *why*, or *purpose*, of creation. The Genesis 1 storyteller describes the unfolding scene of the six creation days from a vantage point somewhere just above Earth's surface, but below the clouds, as God prepared a suitable habitat for humanity. Genesis 2 zooms in on a small portion of Earth's surface (Eden) and what occurred from the vantage point of one human being (the first human) in that locale, walking and awakening to the sights and sounds all around.

**Shift of Purpose**
Genesis 2 elaborates on who we humans are in relation to God and to the rest of creation, including each other. It describes the extent of our authority and responsibility. Given the strong emphasis on chronology in Genesis 1, a reader may have difficulty adjusting to the nonsequential arrangement of physical details in Genesis 2. Its summary parenthetical reference back to the chronological account performs a literary function, bringing some cohesiveness to the two passages.

In other words, Genesis 1 presents the major physical creation events in a time-ordered sequence. It includes a parenthetical, highly abridged summary of humanity's responsibilities but moves on to wrapping up the chronological account of the physical creation. In Genesis 2 God introduces the first humans to their setting, first to the misty land itself, then to the plants, then to the higher animals and, finally, to each other. That is, God sequentially lays out humanity's authority over and responsibility to manage different components of His earthly creation but offers only a highly condensed, nonsequential summary of His physical creation activity. No contradiction can be inferred legitimately from differences between these two versions of the creation story.

**Setting the Garden Scene**

Starting with verse 5, the account contrasts the early condition of Earth with the richness and beauty held in store in the garden God specially planted for Adam and Eve (see sidebar, "Eden: Global or Local?"). The words are arranged for sensory impact, not for time sequence. The text simply reminds us of a time and place devoid of "shrubs," "plants," "rain," and "man" (Genesis 2:5). It does not imply that shrubs predate plants or that plants predate rain.

The description of streams that "came up from the earth and watered the whole surface of the ground" (Genesis 2:6) most likely refers to freshwater springs in the area surrounding the storyteller's position, not to the entire planetary surface. The distinction between "rain" (verse 5) and "streams" (verse 6) has sometimes been misconstrued as indicating that rain had not yet fallen anywhere on Earth until the time of the flood. However, the Hebrew word for rain is *māṭār*, and it refers to any kind of liquid precipitation.[1] The Hebrew word for "streams" is *'ēd*. It has been translated as "mist," "vapor," or "flood," as well as "stream."[2] Mist, of course, would be encompassed by the word *māṭār*. The two words, *māṭār* and *'ēd*, may be synonymous here. Both imply that the rainbow God showed Noah after the great flood (see chapters 13–19) was not a reference to the first time rainbows appeared on Earth.

In Genesis 2 we're reminded that Earth at one time had no water cycle (before creation day two), and we're told that Eden's environs, just prior to God's planting of the garden, was watered by streams and perhaps mist. If Eden were situated somewhere in the mid- to southern portion of the Mesopotamian plain or in the Persian Gulf Oasis (now the Persian Gulf), this description would be an appropriate depiction of geographical and meteorological conditions.

The continuity of clouds and rain from Genesis 1 through Genesis 10 (and beyond) is confirmed by Job 36:27–30, 37:13, 38:25–30; Psalm 104:3–6, 148:4–8; and Proverbs 8:28. These poetic reflections on Genesis 1 clarify that the "water above" (a reference to the second creation day) included clouds, rain, and other forms of water precipitation.

Geological evidence shows that rain began falling on Earth long before the human era.[3] Certain sedimentary deposits preserve the splash patterns of ancient raindrops, large and small, just as clearly as other sedimentary deposits show us the pattern of ancient waves lapping ocean beaches and lakeshores. The Bible and the geological record agree that raindrops of all sizes have fallen on the earth throughout human history and for millions of years before.

### Eden's Location

Genesis 2:8 says God planted a garden "in the east."[4] Given that Moses (the likely writer) considered Canaan or possibly Sinai, as the center of his compass, we can reasonably assume Eden was located somewhere east of today's Israel or east of Sinai.

The text also tells us that four rivers met together in Eden: the Pishon, Gihon, Tigris, and Euphrates.[5] The Tigris and Euphrates have been identified throughout human history as the two primary rivers flowing through Mesopotamia. The Genesis text states that the Pishon flowed out from Havilah, "where there is gold," and the Gihon flowed out from "the entire land of Cush."[6]

---

### Eden: Global or Local?

Some people picture Eden as a paradise that encompassed Earth's entire land area.[7] Several textual clues, however, indicate that Eden was limited to just one geographical locale. Genesis 2 informs us that at different times Adam lived both outside and inside the garden of Eden. This same chapter tells us God planted the garden "in the east." Later, in Genesis 4, we read that God banished Cain to the land of Nod, "east of Eden."

Given that Eden is a localized piece of geography, Adam's perspective on life and the world would have been somewhat different from Eve's before the time they disobeyed God's instruction about the tree. Eve knew from firsthand experience only about Eden. Adam, who was placed into Eden, experienced the difference between the wild creation outside and a divinely manicured garden.

---

The details here point in the direction of the Hejaz, a mountainous region in the west central part of Saudi Arabia. This 6,000-foot range contains the only known source of workable gold in the region. The land of Cush has long been identified with Ethiopia and the Horn of Africa. Given that the Bab el Mandeb strait and much of the Red Sea were dry near the end of the last ice age (some

50,000–15,000 years ago), Cush would have included the mountains in Arabia's southwestern corner. Both the Hejaz mountains and the mountains in the southwest corner of the Arabian Peninsula were well watered as recently as 5,500 years ago.

Satellite imagery reveals the dry beds of two major rivers that once flowed from west-central and southwestern Arabia into the Persian Gulf region (see figure 10.1). Ice and snow atop mountains in those parts of Arabia would have fed both rivers. Today, only the Tigris and the Euphrates still flow continuously. However, toward the close of the last ice age all four rivers were mighty watercourses.

**Figure 10.1: Satellite Image of the Arabian Peninsula**
In a high-resolution version of this image available at http://upload.wikimedia.org/wiki-pedia/commons/8/86/Arabian_Peninsula_dust_SeaWiFS-2.jpg the Euphrates and Tigris Rivers in Mesopotamia are clearly visible, as are two dry riverbeds coming out of the mountains of west-central and southwestern Arabia and descending into the Persian Gulf. Credit: SeaWIFS Project/NASA/Goddard Space Flight Center, and ORBIMAGE

If most of the Persian Gulf were dry at that time, as researchers believe it was, all four rivers would have come together in a place that is now under the southeastern part of the Persian Gulf. This place seems the most likely location for Eden (see figure 10.2).

Recent archaeological discoveries lend support to a Persian Gulf location for Eden. University of Birmingham archaeologist Jeffrey Rose reported on the discovery of more than sixty new archaeological sites, all dating back more than 7,500 years, along the Persian Gulf's current shoreline.[8] Rose describes them in some detail: "These settlements boast well-built, permanent stone houses, long-distance trade networks, elaborately decorated pottery, domesticated animals, and even evidence for one of the oldest boats in the world."[9]

Rose reasons that during the latter part of the last ice age a thriving civilization existed in what is now the Persian Gulf. As sea levels rose and water rushed in through the Strait of Hormuz to begin filling up the Persian Gulf, people would have exited the Gulf Oasis and formed settlements along the rising shoreline.

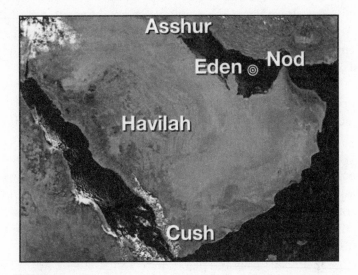

**Figure 10.2: Probable Location of the Garden of Eden**
According to Genesis 2, the Tigris and Euphrates flow through Asshur, the Pishon flows through Havilah, and the Gihon, from Cush. The one location where all four rivers could come together is under the southeastern part of what is now the Persian Gulf, noted above as Eden.
Credit: SeaWIFS Project/NASA/Goddard Space Flight Center, and ORBIMAGE

Hans-Peter Uerpmann, an archaeologist at Eberhard Karls University, Tübingen, recently uncovered remains of the most ancient human settlements yet found: three villages at the base of Jebel Faya[10]—a limestone mountain rising a thousand feet above current sea level in the United Arab Emirates. A research team led by Uerpmann published uncalibrated, optically stimulated luminescent dates of 31,000–43,000 years ago for the most recent of the three settlements and

82,000–143,000 years ago for the most ancient.[11] Although the lack of calibration means the dates could be off by a factor of two or three (approximately several tens of thousands of years), these finds still rank as the oldest known village remains.

In his paper Rose points out that during the late Pleistocene era (150,000 to 12,000 years ago) reduced sea levels periodically exposed what's called the "Gulf Oasis." The Persian Gulf receded far enough to expose a landmass as large as, or larger than, Great Britain. Rose reports this landmass was well-watered by four rivers fed at the time by snow and ice melt: the Tigris, Euphrates, Karun, and Wadi Al-Bāṭin. Freshwater springs fed by subterranean aquifers beneath the Arabian subcontinent also watered the region. Such an abundant, well-distributed freshwater supply and the region's warm weather could have supported a lush agricultural enterprise. This description of the Gulf Oasis fits well with the Genesis 2 portrayal of Eden.

### Adam's Introduction to the Creation
Genesis 1 declares that God created the first man and first woman during creation day six. Genesis 2, as noted below, describes a lengthy series of events between the creation of Adam and the creation of Eve. Therefore, just as the seventh day must be much longer than twenty-four hours, so also the sixth day must be.

Genesis 1 introduces three "layers" of God's creative work, each distinguished by the use of the verb *bārā'*: first, the physical creation; second, the soulish creation; and third, the spiritual creation. In Genesis 2 we see that God introduced Adam to His creation in exactly this order.

Adam first met Eden's soils and plants. In tending to them, Adam must have begun to learn how to manage Earth's physical resources. At the same time he experienced the joy that comes from working a magnificent garden. As enjoyable as gardening may have been for him, however, God had something more wonderful for Adam.

Next God introduced to Adam all the *nepesh* animals—birds, mammals, and higher reptiles—in Eden. Adam discovered the wonders of God's soulish creation while giving a descriptive name to each of these creatures. In this process Adam experienced relationships he had not known with the plants. These creatures could communicate with him and with each other. Their intriguing behavior reflected their capacities for reason, choice, and feeling. Such qualities revealed how the creatures could serve and please him, each one in its unique way.

These creatures harbored no fear or distrust of Adam (Genesis 9:2). So, as much as we enjoy animals today, whether viewing them in the wild or caring for them as pets, Adam must have enjoyed them even more. During this time, Adam began to learn about the needs of the various animals and to realize the awesome responsibility, as well as the privilege and joy, of providing for their needs. But, as delightful as these new relationships must have been, God had something still more wonderful in store.

Finally, the time came for Adam to sense his need of an equal companion, someone to share life with at a level above what the animals possibly could. At this point, God introduced Adam to Eve—a physical, soulish, and spiritual creature as he. Adam's exclamation upon awakening to see Eve, *happa'am*, means "at last now."[12] Here was a creature he could relate to at all levels, one who could explore with him the height, depth, and breadth of human capacities—body, soul, and spirit!

This step-by-step introduction communicates to us, as it did to Adam and Eve, God's desire that humanity appreciate and enjoy everything he created, from the stars in the sky to the starfish in the sea, from the moon above to the dirt below, from the tiniest flower to the fellow-creature who looks, acts, thinks, and feels as we do. He wanted Adam and Eve to understand the full extent of their mutual enjoyment as well as their responsibility and authority in caring for the creation. After all, they had the capability, under God's guidance, to extend the conditions of Eden throughout Earth's land area.

**Filling the Earth**

In Genesis 1:28 we first learn of God's command to Adam and Eve:

> Be fruitful and increase in number; fill the earth and subdue it. Rule over the fish of the sea and the birds of the air and over every living creature that moves on the ground.

God assigned them as caretakers of all Earth's resources. To carry out their responsibilities, they would need helpers, and they would need to spread out. They and their progeny would need to search out the geographic distribution of the various kinds of life; determine the size, habitat, characteristics, and needs of these species; and learn the ways each species enhances the well-being of others, including humans. They also would need to ascertain the kinds and quantities of physical resources required for life and discern how these resources could best be managed for the benefit of all life. No wonder God commanded them to be fruitful and multiply. This job was big!

But was it too big? Though the numbers that follow may seem incredible, they can be checked on any pocket calculator (see chapter 12). If Adam and Eve and their progeny had reproduced at the rate of just one child every four years during the years of their long life-span-equivalent to the childbearing years of today's average life span, they could have produced as many as 17 billion offspring and still have had many years to enjoy them before their 900th anniversary. Clearly, they did not complete their assignment (for reasons to be discussed later).

**Vegetarian Diet**
In Genesis 1:29 we first learn of the dietary guidelines God gave Adam and Eve. Given their capacity to live hundreds of years, they needed guidance in how to maintain their vitality:

> I give you every seed-bearing plant on the face of the whole earth and every tree that has fruit with seed in it. They will be yours for food.

Some interpreters consider this statement merely an indication that all food resources derive from plants. However, Genesis 9:3 suggests that it was, indeed, a specific instruction about what not to eat:

> Everything that lives and moves will be food for you. Just as I gave you the green plants, I *now* give you everything [both plants and animals] (emphasis added).

Vegetarianism suits the potential longevity of the first humans. Animal tissue contains between ten and ten thousand times the concentration of heavy metals that plant material contains. This difference, as enormous as it may seem, poses an insignificant health risk for people living about 120 years or less (the limit God imposed after the flood).[13] However, the difference is by no means trivial for people living nearly a thousand years.

Recent research establishes two more benefits of a vegetarian diet. Caloric restriction (reducing the calories consumed on a day-to-day basis) has been shown to extend average and maximum life spans of many species, including mammals, by 20 to 40 percent.[14] Similarly, minimizing intake of oxidants and maximizing intake of antioxidants increases the mean life span of some species by as much as 40 percent.[15] Typically, meats are rich in oxidants whereas certain vegetables are rich in antioxidants, and, caloric binging usually is rarer because it is more difficult on a vegetarian diet than on a meat diet. A well-designed vegetarian diet, therefore, could have significantly enhanced longevity by preventing caloric overload and reducing oxidative stress.

In Genesis 1:30, God had also set the diet for birds and mammals:

> And to all the beasts of the earth and all the birds of the air and all the crea-
> tures that move on the ground—everything that has the breath of life in
> it—I give every green plant for food.

He did not alter this instruction when He widened human dietary limits
(Genesis 9:2–3). So it seems fair to assume that this guideline represents clues for
the sake of management rather than restriction.

The distinction between God's gift to people, "every seed-bearing plant…
and every tree that has fruit with seed in it," and his gift to animals, "every green
plant," may carry some significance. Both animals and humans ingest some non-
green plants—mushrooms, for example—but green plants serve as the foundation of the food chain. Perhaps to assist Adam and Eve in their management of
the planet's resources, God helped them understand that all the life entrusted to
their care—whether herbivores, detritivores (decomposers), parasites, or carnivores—depends ultimately on green plants for survival.

**Animals Came When?**
The narrative structure of Genesis 2:19 has been used to support claims of a contradiction between Genesis 1 and 2. Some readers have interpreted the verse as if
it implies God created animals *after* creating Adam.

> Now the LORD God had formed out of the ground all the beasts of the field
> and all the birds of the air. He brought them to the man…

Such a reading of Genesis 2 represents what can only be called a "manufactured" problem. Whether it results from poor scholarship or a skeptical agenda
is unclear. However, I recently learned that this purported internal contradiction
is routinely "exposed" in European schools and universities. Is it any wonder the
Bible holds so little credibility among people educated in these nations?

As mentioned in chapter 5, verb tenses do not exist in biblical Hebrew. Biblical Hebrew employs three verb forms, one for completed action, another for
action not yet completed, and another for commands. The verb form used in
Genesis 2:19 is the one for completed action. It simply indicates the beasts and
the birds were created sometime in the past. This text says nothing about when
such creatures were created relative to the time of Adam's creation. There was no

need. The sequence had already been established in Genesis 1.

## Naming of the Animals

The next question has to do with Adam's task in naming all the animals and birds. Does *all* mean every one of Earth's 5.8 million terrestrial animal species?[16] Part of the answer to this question comes from a look back at the words used for "living creatures" and at the list of animals created on days five and six.

> He brought [the animals] to the man to see what he would name them; and whatever the man called each living creature, that was its name. So the man gave names to all the livestock, the birds of the air and all the beasts of the field (Genesis 2:19b–20a).

The Hebrew word for "animals" and "living creatures" in this passage is, as in Genesis 1:24, *nepesh*, a reference to soulish creatures, a narrower group. A second narrowing of Adam's task becomes evident in the specific mention of livestock and beasts of the field, two of the three kinds of mammals specified on day six. We see an expansion, too—with the addition of birds from day five.

To date, ecologists have tallied some 9,500 bird species and 4,500 mammal species currently present on Earth, and they anticipate discovery of several hundred more, especially birds, in future field studies.[17] Fossil evidence indicates birds and mammals suffered very high extinction rates at the hands of early humans. So a reasonable estimate would suggest double the number of species existed at the time of humanity's advent.[18] If we subtract the ground-hugging mammals (rodents) and sea mammals (about 40 percent of all mammal species), then about 20,000 bird species and 5,500 relatively long-legged land mammal species inhabited Earth when Adam came on the scene. If we also consider that bird and mammal species' habitats then were much larger than now, as fossils also indicate, we can reasonably conclude that approximately 4,500 bird and mammal species inhabited Eden's environs.

If Adam were to examine one or more pairs of each species, or kind, as Genesis words it[19] (see sidebar, "What Is a Kind?" on page 106), for 30 to 60 minutes to ascertain its physical characteristics and relational capabilities before assigning an appropriate name (an Old Testament custom), he would need about a year to complete his task—that's if he were to devote about 40 hours a week to the job. Given that he had additional responsibilities for gardening and harvesting, he might have needed more time.

A year or two may seem long to us, and perhaps it felt even longer to Adam, although he had plenty of work to occupy his time. In view of his total life ex-pectancy, however, a year or two amounted to a drop in the bucket—not enough time to age, noticeably, but sufficient time to appreciate his need of a partner. As Genesis 2:18–20 says, despite the rewarding relationships Adam experienced with the many different kinds of *nepesh* animals, he felt his aloneness. The passage of a year or two—and observing the animals with their mates—would explain why.

Those who view the creation days as 24-hour periods face a challenge in explaining how all the activities of the latter portion of day six, including Adam's naming of the animals and awareness of his loneliness, could have taken place so rapidly. Some suggest that before falling into sin Adam's mental capabilities were vastly greater, enabling him to examine and name animals at hyperspeed.[20] However, we find no hint of this possibility, or of its many implications, within the text. Nor do we see evidence that an extraordinarily high IQ would offer an enormous speed advantage in the examination and naming of animals.[21]

### Eve from Adam's Side

A popular translation of Genesis 2:20–21 concludes that God made Eve from one of Adam's rib bones. I take a slightly different view. A careful reading of the text reveals a somewhat different scenario, paraphrased here: First, God put Adam into a deep sleep, such as the "sleep" induced by anesthesia. While Adam slept, God removed a *sela*, a portion, or what might be referred to as a biopsy[22]—we don't know how big or how small or what kind of tissue it was—from Adam's side and used that tissue in crafting Eve.

Nothing in the text indicates that God made Eve totally and only from the tissue sample taken from Adam. And yet it does imply that the portion taken from Adam served a significant and substantial role in God's creation of Eve.

Genetics reveals how God could have used this biopsy from Adam. It most likely included a complete DNA blueprint of Adam's morphology. Making certain modifications here and there, the blueprint for Eve would have been sufficient-ly similar and sufficiently dissimilar to generate the desired and essential result, woman. The New Testament sheds light on why God may have chosen to create Eve using Adam's tissue:

> In the LORD, however, woman is not independent of man, nor is man inde-pendent of woman. For as woman came from man, so also man is born of woman. (1 Corinthians 11:11–12a)

God created men and women as interdependent beings. In His full awareness

## What Is a Kind?

In Genesis 1 the created animals are said to reproduce after their own kind. The Hebrew word translated as "kind" is *mîn*. The usage of *mîn* in Genesis 1, Leviticus, and Deuteronomy implies that creatures belonging to a *mîn* faithfully reproduce characteristics of that *mîn* from one generation to the generations that follow.[23]

From a scientific perspective, how broad a range of animals fits within a single *mîn* has been the subject of much debate. Theistic evolutionists and evolutionary creationists argue that the word's definition is broad enough to accommodate their theories of how living organisms are descended from one or a few common ancestors. Young-earth creationists claim a breadth adequate to explain how a few thousand animal pairs on Noah's ark could differentiate rapidly to account for all land-dwelling species on Earth today.[24]

Such broad definitions of *mîn* seem contradicted by the repeated references in Genesis 1 to the created animals' reproducing after their own kind. It also appears contradicted by usages of the word and an alternate form of the word, *kil'ayim*, in Leviticus and Deuteronomy. (*mîn* always occurs in the singular form while *kil'ayim* has just one definition, "two kinds.")[25] For example, Leviticus 19:19 commands: "Do not mate different kinds [*kil'ayim*] of animals." This text acknowledges that different *mîn* can be similar enough to mate and produce offspring. Since such mating is not possible for species that are members of different families or orders, and rarely for members of different genera, a narrow definition of *mîn* is implied.

Leviticus 11:22 lists as separate *mîn* the locust, katydid, cricket, and grasshopper. Deuteronomy 14:12–18 catalogs the eagle, falcon, hawk, red kite, black kite, vulture, and black vulture as separate mîn. In both Leviticus 11:15–17 and Deuteronomy 14:15–17 the horned owl, screech owl, little owl, great owl, and white owl are all referred to as distinct mîn. Thus, at least for *nepesh* life-forms, the Torah (the first five books of the Bible) seems to rule out broad definitions for mîn. Rather, the word appears to accommodate a range of animal differentiation no greater than that of the English word *species*. For insects, the differentiation appears no greater than the usage of the term *genus*.

of how men and women would later struggle over gender roles, God chose a means for creating the human race, male and female, that would make clear to all cultures and generations their equal but distinct identity.

## Adam's Ally

Both women and men take offense at Eve's familiar designation, Adam's "helper" (or, as the King James Version says, "help meet"). Again, the English word choice, with its "underling" connotation, creates a needless controversy. The Hebrew word translated "helper" ('ezer) in Genesis 2:18, 20, is a term used elsewhere in the Old Testament (see 2 Chronicles 28:16 and Psalm 121:1–2) for an ally, one that's essential for victory or for the completion of an assigned task.[26]

As Genesis 1 reveals, the role God assigned to humanity exceeds the limits of an individual. And Genesis 3 is about to reveal that humanity faces a daunting foe, a literal "enemy force," both within and without. By himself, Adam lacked the resources to face the challenges ahead. He needed an ally—the right kind of ally.

In war, allies contribute a variety of assets necessary for victory, and whatever they bring, they become equally valuable and valued partners. Together, Adam and Eve, men and women, can conquer obstacles and achieve great accomplishments. Divided and embattled, they fail.

## Adam and Eve in Paradise

According to some translators, such as those for the Septuagint, Eden means "delight." What Adam and Eve enjoyed in Eden—a garden designed and planted by God Himself—defines the word paradise, the word consistently chosen for Eden by Jewish scholars who first translated the Old Testament into Greek. Its fruit trees both "pleased the eye" and yielded "good food." Its perfect watering system kept it verdant and gorgeous.

Eden offered more than an idyllic haven for plants, animals, and humans. It contained other riches as well: "gold, aromatic resin, and onyx" (Genesis 2:12). This list gives us only a sampling of the available riches, not a complete inventory. Yet it illustrates the point that everything prized by humankind could be found in abundance in Eden.

What's more, in Eden our first parents had access to "the tree of life." According to what we learn in Genesis 3, this tree, if they had partaken of it, would have allowed them to live forever physically, apparently free from the effects of aging and injury.[27] (The text does not indicate to what degree Adam and Eve, before sinning, experienced aging or potential injury.)

Adam and Eve enjoyed perfect peace and harmony with the birds and mammals, which approached them without fear, hesitation, or any desire to harm. Better yet, the man and woman enjoyed harmony and fearlessness with each other. Better still, they enjoyed harmony and fellowship with God Himself. Their Creator was near, available, and perfectly loving, and they knew it. If they wanted guidance, direction, or answers to questions of any kind, they could ask and receive.

Genesis 2 ends with the profound statement that Eden was free from shame. Because of shame, none of us today really knows what perfect love and harmony feels, looks, or sounds like. When we submit to Jesus Christ's authority, receiving His pardon for sin and spiritual regeneration, we begin to experience the love, acceptance, and inward transformation that help erase our shame. But we live in a sinful world. We experience the effects of evil—our own and others'—and still struggle (and fail) to resist temptation. Our thoughts and motives are tainted. In Eden, before sin, Adam and Eve experienced life differently. They never felt embarrassed or insignificant.

What a life! Eden seems the picture of perfection, and yet it lacked one thing. That one thing is what makes love real; that one thing gives meaning to worship, friendship, virtue, and more. That one thing will make paradise just that, paradise. That one thing is choice. Adam and Eve had yet to exercise it, and until they did, the picture would not—and could not—be complete.

God's ultimate plan for humanity[28] exceeds even the untold splendor of Eden. After all, Eden existed in an earthly realm constrained by the laws of physics, limited by cosmic matter, energy, and space, and a single time dimension. All these limits God established in advance, knowing what Adam and Eve would choose. Someday these constraints will be lifted, but that's a topic for later.

For now, the story moves on toward the moment of primal conflict on which all of human history hinges, the confrontation with temptation and with the greatest of all tempters.

# 11

# HOW FAR THE FALL? GENESIS 3

According to the ancient book of Job, angels (Lucifer among them) witnessed the creation days.[1] This same Lucifer, the most majestic and powerful of the angels God created, in one cataclysmic moment swelled with pride and asserted himself as God's equal, drawing a third of the heavenly host into rebellion with him.[2]

This act of defiance and self-exaltation tore a clear divide between good and evil. It demonstrated the reality—and cost—of choice. Whether it occurred before or during God's creation of Earth the Bible never says, but we know it predated Eden.

We know also that God, the Creator, could have kept Lucifer (a.k.a. Satan) away from Eden and away from Earth. And, under God's guidance, Adam and Eve and their descendants might have begun to spread Eden's beauty and bounty throughout the world. But with humans, as with angels, the risk of rebellion would have lingered as an ever-present possibility.

But, God had a plan.

## Adam and Eve's Expulsion from Eden

Genesis 3 tells us God set up a simple test. He explained to Adam and Eve that they could eat the fruit of all the fruit-laden trees in the garden—except one. His mandate came with a warning of dire consequences: a violation of His divine authority in this matter would result in death.[3]

Whether Adam understood the meaning of "death" from his observation of the world outside the garden, or whether he grasped its deeper meaning (such as what Lucifer experienced), we cannot know. However, the text offers no indication that he asked for clarification, and we see no expression of surprise when Adam and Eve found themselves still alive and breathing after having eaten the forbidden fruit.

Reflecting the fearless harmony of Eden's creatures, Eve showed no alarm when a serpent approached her and spoke. We can surmise from later contextual clues that the serpent served as an instrument in Satan's hand. His communication reflected Satan's mind, and his voice surely emerged from a supernatural source. (Later, in Moses' time, Balaam's donkey similarly was used by a supernatural being.[4])

The text portrays with remarkable matter-of-factness the profound change that occurred as first Eve, then Adam, ate from the forbidden tree. Suddenly they became aware of their nakedness. A sense of vulnerability and shame sent them running for cover, to hide from each other and from God. Fear has interfered with all our relationships ever since. What a loss! We see the first humans hiding from responsibility as well. The first instance of blaming holds a mirror before our faces.

Some critics seem outraged that an act so small could possibly carry such horrendous consequences as banishment from Eden and the curses God spelled out. These critics miss the point. They fail to recognize the dreadful dangers and destructive chaos invoked by the creatures' autonomy from the Creator. The history of the world's oppression, strife, greed, and injustice all traces back to the moment when Adam and Eve stood in our place, doubted God's character and motives, and chose to trust their own.

As soon as Adam and Eve experienced the loss of an open, free, and trusting relationship with God and with each other, God took action to ensure that they and their progeny would *not* be trapped forever in this broken condition, a condition described in Scripture as spiritual death. God barred their access to the tree of life.[5] God prepared—in fact, had already prepared—a way out, a way through, this tragic dilemma. Death of the humans' physical body would become a part of His strategy for deliverance.[6] By this plan, God would deliver humanity from the far worse consequence of *eternal* spiritual death.

Because of sin, humans were no longer morally and spiritually fit to live in the presence of God. Now the tree of life became a danger to humanity, as did the once easy life in the Garden. God knew that Adam and Eve needed the extra work and pain afforded by life outside Eden to restrain their exertion of self-centeredness and many other "fruits" of autonomy. Nevertheless, God's plan would mercifully allow them to play a part in His plan for redeeming a large fraction of humanity from this dreadful condition.

**Did the Fall Change Physics?**

Anyone can point to certain conditions in the world that seem too bad for a good God to have created or planned. Some people presume that the natural tendency toward decay (the second law of thermodynamics) and carnivorous animal behavior, for example, must be attributable to human sin, not to God's design. So if God is in charge, these things resulted from the fall.

Skeptics wonder why an all-loving, all-powerful God would have created a system that includes waste, disorder, disease, and pain. They argue that either God is not there or God does not care. Atheist physicist Victor Stenger has commented, "Does God really need so much pain and suffering to achieve his ends?" He concludes, "This is a possible God but a hideous one."[7]

A careful reading of Genesis 3 offers a helpful perspective on these issues. First, the text does *not* say Eve's sin created the experience of pain. Rather, it says Eve's pain in childbearing, physical and otherwise, would be greatly increased (verse 16). Second, the text does *not* say that Adam now worked for the first time. Rather, it says that because of Adam's sin, his work would be harder and less efficient than before. The problems and distractions brought on by sin would hinder his management efforts (compare Genesis 2:15 and 3:17–19). All humanity would now suffer a greatly increased level of pain, work, and wasted time.

God told Adam, "Cursed is the ground because of you."[8] The universe and its physics had not changed, as some suggest. In Jeremiah we read that the laws of heaven and earth are "fixed."[9] In Ecclesiastes, Solomon affirms the constancy of the physical laws.[10] In Genesis 1–3 we note that the Sun and stars are shining both before and after Adam and Eve had succumbed to Satan's temptation. Stellar burning is extremely sensitive to even the tiniest changes in the laws of physics. The change occurred in Adam, and because of the change in Adam, the ground and all the life that depended on it—and on humans' care—would suffer.

Driven from the garden, Adam and Eve found themselves in an untamed world with *all* its natural characteristics. An untended wilderness, they discovered, could be far more difficult to manage than anything they had previously known. But they *had* known work.

Adam would have had no tending to do at all in the days before sin if thermodynamic laws were not already in effect. Physical work of any kind—even eating and digesting food—involves the second law of thermodynamics.[11] This law describes how food is converted to work energy, or into movement of any kind. Adam and Eve surely ate and moved, talked and walked, before the fall (see Genesis 2:16; 3:2–6).

Before humans or any plants and animals were created, God made the stars and the Sun (see Genesis 1:1–16). These heavenly bodies elegantly manifest the second law of thermodynamics, which also can be described as a general flow of heat from hot bodies to cold bodies. Stars radiate heat very efficiently. They rank among the most entropic (heat-radiating) entities in the universe. Thus, Genesis implicitly affirms the operation of the second thermodynamic law before the first humans sinned.

The apostle Paul describes how this particular physical law affects the entire creation:

> For the creation was subjected to frustration, not by its own choice, but by the will of the one who subjected it, in hope that the creation itself will be liberated from its bondage to decay and brought into the glorious freedom of the children of God. We know that the whole creation has been groaning as in the pains of childbirth right up to the present time.[12]

This passage refers to "the whole creation," "right up to the present time." General relativity, one of the best-established principles in all physics,[13] makes clear that the entire creation includes all matter and energy *and* all the space-time dimensions along which matter and energy are distributed.[14] In fact, matter and energy are inseparable from the space-time dimensions. Thus, Paul's words can be interpreted to mean that the second thermodynamic law has been in effect since the creation of the universe and throughout the whole of the universe.

Cosmological research establishes that unless the universe were both extremely entropic and homogeneous (meaning that entropy must be roughly the same everywhere in the cosmos) throughout all of its existence, physical life would not be possible. The cosmic entropy level stands as but one of over a hundred features of the universe discovered so far that must be exquisitely fine-tuned for life's chemical components even to exist.[15] If the second law of thermodynamics had not been in effect from the first moment of creation until now, the cosmos would be devoid of stars, planets, and moons.[16] A cosmos without stars, planets, and moons is a cosmos without physical life.

Given that the second thermodynamic law is essential for life's existence, for eating, for mobility, and for many other enjoyable activities, there is no reason to judge the law bad. Thermodynamic laws were included when God declared His creation "very good."[17]

We must not confuse God's *very good* creation, however, with His *ultimate* creation, or more accurately, with His ultimate goal for humanity. In the new creation described in Revelation 21–22, there will be no thermodynamic laws—no decay, no frustration, no groaning, no grieving.[18] The thermodynamic laws are good, in spite of "decay," "frustration," and "groaning," because they are part of God's strategy for preparing humans (who choose so) to enjoy the rewards of everlasting life in the new creation.[19]

### Did the Fall Initiate Death and Predation?

Just as some Christians insist Adam's sin inaugurated changes in the physical laws, likewise some are convinced that none of Earth's creatures died before Adam's rebellion in Eden.[20] The Bible passage they cite to support this interpretation is a portion of Romans 5:12. It reads: "Just as sin entered the world through one man, and death through sin."

The entirety of Romans 5:12 reads, "Therefore, just as sin entered the world through one man, and death through sin, and in this way death came to all people, because all sinned" (NIV 2011). This verse addresses death through sin, not death in general. Of all the kinds of life God created on Earth only one kind, namely the human race, is capable of sinning. Therefore, Romans 5:12 tells us when human death began, not when the death of plants and animals began. This conclusion is confirmed in the verse's ending: "Death came to all people [not all life], because all [life capable of sin] sinned."

Another biblical passage, 1 Corinthians 15:20–22, also clarifies that the death Adam's sin introduced was limited to humans. This text speaks of the resurrection of humans ("in Christ") whose death was sealed "in Adam." Nowhere does the Bible claim that plants and animals did not die before Adam sinned. Furthermore, Adam was not the first rebellious creature. That credit goes to Satan and the Bible is silent on the date of Satan's first act of rebellion against God.

As for predation, this aspect of nature is described in several biblical texts. For example, in Psalm 104 God takes credit for providing prey for the lions.[21] In Job 38 God declares that He satisfies the hunger of lions and ravens by giving them their prey.[22]

Genesis 1:24–25 identifies two different kinds of long-legged land mammals, those that are easily domesticated and those that are wild, or more difficult to tame. As we know them today, the first group is herbivorous and the second, carnivorous. While herbivores serve our agricultural needs well, we tend to choose our pets from among the carnivores. To put it another way, it appears God designed herbivore mammals primarily to serve us and the carnivore mammals primarily to bring us pleasure.

The digestive systems of these creatures make a crucial difference in our relationship possibilities. The carnivores, such as dogs and cats, spend only a brief portion of their day eating. They have sufficient control over their elimination that they can be housebroken. Eating and digesting food does not interfere with their playful activity. They can run, jump, and play games with us, and do our bidding if we invest some effort in training them. Compared with herbivores, which spend many hours a day in the eating-digesting process, carnivores typically are more active, agile, and engaging.

We humans are able to maintain a moderate activity level on a fruit-and-vegetable diet only because we can process vegetable matter into high-calorie, highly nutritive, low-fiber forms. The only option for large, active mammals in the wild is to eat herbivores, the one significant natural source of "processed" vegetable matter.

Research shows that herbivores actually depend on carnivores. Carnivorous activity maximizes herbivore population levels and quality of life. One set of studies demonstrated, for example, that feeding squid to sperm whales and krill to baleen whales made for larger, healthier populations of squid and krill.[23] The whales' fecal matter fertilizes the oceans' photic zones, thereby raising the population of phytoplankton, which in turn feed the zooplankton and fish on which krill and squid feed. Game wardens also verify that a lack of carnivorous predatory activity leads to the spread of disease, starvation, and genetic decline among herbivore herds.

God made herbivores difficult for carnivores to hunt, some by their size, some by their speed, and some by their camouflage or other defense mechanisms. We humans are the only predators able to kill the best individuals within a species. Other carnivorous animals go after the weakest, sickest, least aware, and most genetically damaged individuals. In this way they protect and enhance the quality of herbivore species.

### The Death Benefit

Among humans, death is a different matter. The earthly body dies, but the spirit does not. For us, physical death is paradoxically grievous and good.

Although we are born with Adam's propensity to go our own way, God makes available to each person the power, through faith, to choose a life of service to Him rather than of service to self. A man named Paul, who exercised that faith, considered even his very hard life worthwhile and his impending death, "gain."[24] He could see death as his release into a new and expanded realm of ongoing personal life in God's presence.

Physical death is beneficial in another way, too. It limits the amount of harm those who reject God's offer can do to themselves and to others. Sin becomes a growing malignancy, if allowed to grow unchecked. The story of Adam and Eve's sons paints a horrific picture of what it can do—and of physical death as essential for the preservation of life.

# 12

## CAIN'S STORY: GENESIS 4

Genesis begins with God's bringing light and order and life out of darkness and chaos. The beauty of creation grows more and more wondrous as the story progresses and reaches a peak in chapter 3, where the element of conflict enters. Once Adam and Eve fall prey to temptation, the story takes a turn toward a new kind of darkness, chaos, and ugliness.

Murder, with all its awful consequences, is the theme of chapter 4. Adam and Eve took life into their own hands, but their firstborn also took death. In a fit of jealously, Cain killed his younger brother, Abel, and a downward spiral ensued.

### Was God Surprised?

Many skeptics point to Genesis 4 as "proof" that the biblical God must *not* be almighty and all-knowing. Some cite the questions God posed to Cain (verses 6, 7, 9, 10) as evidence that God was either ignorant of Cain's intentions and actions or lacked the power to stop Cain.

A thoughtful consideration of the context leads to a different conclusion. Anyone who has worked with people recognizes these questions as God's appeal to Cain's conscience and his acceptance of responsibility. One of the best ways to correct and restore someone of any age caught in bad behavior is to ask questions.

When Cain refused to say why he was angry, God revealed that He already knew (verse 7). Later, when Cain refused to answer the question of his brother's whereabouts, God revealed that He already knew (verse 10). God's purpose in asking had nothing to do with His lack of information.

The account of God's interaction with Cain prior to the murder provides essential insight to God's character as well as to human nature. God acknowledged Cain's anger and its deeper root, the pain of rejection. After reassuring Cain he would be accepted and on what basis, God warned Cain of the dangers of refusing to do what he knew to be right. If not resisted and subdued, temptation gains power and sin gains power in a person's life. God's warning about sin led to Cain's moment of decision. He could have humbled himself, asked for God's help, and received it, but he did not. God allowed Cain to make that choice.

Yes, God could have prevented Cain's crime, but God in His sovereignty chose to allow Cain's free will to take its course. Ultimately, neither love nor character growth can happen among humans unless God permits the exercise of free will. In this case, Abel's life was cut short, a grievous loss to be sure, but Abel's eternal destiny was secure. The significance of early humanity's grasp of the warning Cain ignored about temptation's power and sin's grip was so great as to cost a man's life.

### Impact of Cain's Sin

Although some people may have taken hold of God's lesson, many did not. Cain's murder led to an apparent epidemic of murder. Four times God spoke to Cain, initially to warn Cain against carrying out his evil plan and later to elicit a confession of responsibility (Genesis 4:6–15). Four times Cain rejected God's appeal. At the time of his banishment, Cain expressed fear that he would be killed by anyone who found him. By the time a descendant named Lamech came along a few generations later, murder apparently had become something to brag about (Genesis 4:23–24).

Genesis 4 hints that wanton murder prevented human population from taking off. Cain's sin must have grown out of control. Estimated numbers, even if trimmed to a conservative extreme, indicate that murder must have become the leading cause of death in the days before the flood of Noah's time. Perhaps as many as nine out of ten or more apparently died at the hands of their fellow humans. (See potential population statistics in table 12, page 121.)

The earliest commentaries on Genesis 4–6 support this scenario. The Jewish scholar Josephus, writing in the first century AD offers this description:

> Nay, even while Adam was alive, it came to pass that the posterity of Cain became exceedingly wicked, every one successively dying one after another more wicked than the former. They were intolerable in war, and vehement in robberies; and if anyone were slow to murder people, yet was he bold in his profligate behavior, in acting unjustly and doing injuries for gain.[1]

If this depiction has merit, it would explain the extreme language used in Genesis 6 to describe the evil into which preflood people had fallen (see chapter

18). Because God-fearing people, such as Abel, were more likely to be murdered than those armed and ready to express malice, we can understand why Noah's contemporaries manifested such chilling irreverence and why so few righteous people remained. It explains God's decision to use a flood and an ark for rescue. Humanity lay in danger of self-extermination. It explains further the strong language God used with Noah in Genesis 9:6, commanding Noah's descendants to exercise whatever means were necessary, up to the death penalty, to restrain the sin of murder.

The Genesis 4 narrative indicates the development of rampant murder took several generations to unfold. Thus, the population numbers introduced (page 121) to suggest where Cain found marriage candidates and the citizens to fill a city would still hold.

### Cain's Wife and City
At first glance, Genesis seems to report that Adam and Eve had just three sons: Cain, Abel, and Seth. This reading has led to questions and doubts among readers and skeptics for centuries. For the human race to continue, Cain and his brother Seth would have to find wives, but how could they, if they were the only people on the planet?

The apologetics problem grows more complicated. After murdering Abel, Cain was banished to an eastward land called Nod.[2] (Seth was born after Cain's departure.[3]) There, Cain not only found marriageable women but also enough people, by the time his son Enoch was born, to build and populate a city. The question ringing in readers' minds, the question asked of Christian apologists more often than almost any other, is this: where did Cain's wife and all these other people come from?

The answer to these questions requires looking ahead a few verses. Adam, and perhaps Eve as well, lived a very long time. The text tells us Adam lived 930 years, 800 of them after Seth's birth, and had "other sons and daughters"—too many to list by name, apparently. The genealogy of Genesis 5 indicates that every descendant of Adam down to Lamech had "other sons and daughters" whose names are not included in this record. Some of the offspring chosen for inclusion were born when their fathers were 65, some after their fathers turned 500. This record gives a rough indication as to the extent of the ancients' childbearing years.

Considering the long life spans recorded in Genesis 5 (see chapter 13), and estimating that couples remained reproductive for approximately two-thirds of their life spans, the possibility of a veritable population explosion becomes evident. Without effective birth control options, the first pair alone would likely have given birth to at least 150 children. Their children would have begun producing families while Adam and Eve continued to add more sons and daughters of their own. The same would be the case with their grandchildren, great-grandchildren, great-great-grandchildren, and so on.

The potential population growth during Adam's life span appears in table 12. If Cain waited to marry until he was about 60 or 70 years old, he would have had several women to choose from, providing some migrated eastward to Nod with other family members. If he waited another 200 years to build a city, he could have had at least a few thousand people to help him, again assuming some migration occurred. Cain may have had sisters or nieces from whom to choose a wife even before his banishment and before Seth's birth. The text does not say.

The lack of archaeological evidence from the era prior to the flood indicates that the preflood population never grew anywhere nearly as large as table 12 shows was possible. Infant mortality may have been one factor suppressing growth, but this problem alone seems vastly inadequate to explain the lack of a population explosion.

### The "Incest" Question

The implication of brother-sister marriage in Genesis 4 and beyond seems disturbing, if not morally repugnant, to modern readers, especially in the West with its laws forbidding incest. In this case, once again, historical context is a key to understanding. Not until God established a set of moral and civil laws for the emerging nation of Israel did He rule out marriage between siblings (Leviticus 18:6–18). The timing of this command makes perfect sense from a biological perspective. Genetic defects as a result of intrafamily marriage develop slowly. They would present no risk until after the first several dozen generations.

On that basis no law of conscience or society forbade marriage between brothers and sisters or other close relatives—except parents and children (see Genesis 19:30–38)—in the early centuries of human history. Even at the time of Abraham, the practice of marrying siblings continued as an acceptable practice.[4]

### Cain's Mark

Genesis 4 says God placed a mark on Cain to warn others against avenging Abel's blood. The mark's necessity indicates that the population had grown, or would soon grow, large enough that Cain ran two risks: first, the risk of being recognized and killed as an act of vigilante justice; and second, the risk of being unrecognized and randomly murdered.

The text says nothing about what kind of mark Cain received and makes no suggestion of its being passed on to his progeny. This chapter provides no basis whatsoever for identifying a race or ethnic group as bearers of Cain's mark, as some sectarian groups have suggested.[5] (For a discussion of the origin of races, see chapter 19.)

## Table 12: Potential Population Growth in Adam's Lifetime

According to Genesis 5, life spans from Adam to Noah averaged 912 years. Each of the patriarchs mentioned had "other sons and daughters" in addition to the sons recorded by name. The table calculations are based on these numbers:
- average life span = 900 years
- first child comes at age 40
- childbearing years = 600
- one child every four years during childbearing years

| Adam's age | Number of reproducing couples | Number of children born | Total population |
|---|---|---|---|
| 0 | 1 | 0 | 2 |
| 40 | 1 | 10 | 12 |
| 80 | 6 | 30 | 42 |
| 120 | 21 | 100 | 142 |
| 160 | 71 | 352 | 494 |
| 200 | 247 | 1,210 | 1,704 |
| 240 | 852 | 4,180 | 5,884 |
| 280 | 2,942 | 14,450 | 20,334 |
| 320 | 10,167 | 49,892 | 70,226 |
| 360 | 35,113 | 172,358 | 242,584 |
| 400 | 121,292 | 595,378 | 837,962 |
| 440 | 418,980 | 2,056,530 | 2,894,492 |
| 480 | 1,447,245 | 7,103,862 | 9,998,364 |
| 520 | 4,999,176 | 24,538,536 | 34,536,930 |
| 560 | 17,268,444 | 84,762,338 | 119,299,368 |
| 600 | 59,649,613 | 292,790,780 | 412,090,500 |
| 640 | 206,045,003 | 1,011,374,120 | 1,423,465,830 |
| 680 | 711,732,063 | 3,493,544,650 | 4,917,014,660 |
| 720 | 2,459,504,388 | 12,067,585,000 | 16,984,600,000 |
| 760 | 8,492,300,000 | 41,685,303,000 | 58,669,903,000 |

**Warning for Today**

In several Scripture passages, we read that horrible wickedness, virtually as bad as the wickedness of Noah's time, will again overtake humanity. The era when evil rises to such proportions are referred to as "the last days." One indicator that such a time may be approaching comes from current statistics on murder worldwide. In fact, for the first time we know of since the flood, murder has become the leading cause of death among humans.

This statistic may seem inflated compared with reports from law enforcement agencies. These information sources typically give numbers for their communities or for the United States only, and they fail to include the killing of living humans before their birth. Though the abortion rate has decreased somewhat in the United States, from a high of 1.6 million per year in 1990 to a current rate of 1.2 million per year,[6] still one in three pregnancies is terminated by parental "choice" in our civilized nation. The figures for the rest of the world's nations are, in many cases, even worse. The number of legally approved abortions performed worldwide is approximately 46 million per year.[7]

God waits patiently for our repentance, for an acknowledgement of our sin and of our need for divine mercy. But He will not wait forever, as the later chapters of Genesis demonstrate. These next chapters include even more difficult content to absorb than do the first four. But first, the question of biblical credibility in reference to the long life spans mentioned in Genesis 5 and in the shocking calculations presented earlier in this chapter must be addressed.

# 13

# POSSIBILITY OF LONG LIFE SPANS: GENESIS 5–6

Readers who make their way past the interpretive challenges of Genesis 1 through 4 meet an even more difficult hurdle here in Genesis 5. The long life spans recorded for Adam and his descendants clearly defy the credulity of twenty-first century people. Some decide the book must be fable or legend, whether in part or in whole; others, that the ancient Hebrew year must have been substantially shorter than 365 days. Or, perhaps the word for "year" can also represent some alternate (significantly briefer) time marker.

The life span of the patriarchs listed in Genesis 5 (omitting Enoch, whom God "took away" after 365 years) averaged 912 years. According to Genesis 5:27, Methuselah lived 969 years, about eight times longer than the oldest modern human on record to date—with all our technologically advanced means to extend life. How can these numbers possibly be credible?

### Defining "Year"

It seems worth noting that early Akkadian and Sumerian records also report extraordinarily long life spans. Only rough dates or ages appear in these accounts, but they claim their most ancient kings lived into the thousands of years.

Babylonian historian Berosus, a priest of Bel in the third century BC, mentions the names of ten kings from before "a great deluge" who reigned thousands of years each. The Weld-Blundell Prism and the Nippur tablets (cuneiform records dating back to the second and third millennia BC, respectively) also list multiple preflood kings who lived thousands of years.

No evidence can be found in either extrabiblical or biblical texts to indicate that pre- or postflood peoples counted their years significantly differently from the way we count them today. If a "year" in that era were equivalent to ten years today, making these ancient life spans roughly comparable to modern life spans, the ages given for fathering children (65 for Mahalalel and Enoch) would become an infeasible 6.5 years. What's more, the Genesis 6:3 reference to the shortening of human life spans to a maximum of about 120 years, where it remains to this day, would be meaningless and unnecessary.

Humanity's oldest astronomical and agricultural records indicate that the ancients counted years just as moderns do. Civilizations' survival depended on their ability to grow food, and their success in growing food depended on knowing the seasons, the times to plant and harvest. Biblical and extrabiblical references to the seasons show no possibility for confusion on this issue.

Mesopotamian and other early cultures also showed awareness that that a twelve-month, thirty-day calendar fell short of an actual year by a little more than five days. Ancient societies employed astronomers and equipped them with instruments, including "transits," for measuring time. Thus, early astronomers were able to measure a year's duration to within a few minutes' precision. Though some minor variations can be found from one society to another, the ancients typically celebrated a set of festival days every few years to make up the extra days and reset their calendars.

## Implicit Evidence for Long Life Spans

World civilization textbooks attest to the rapid rise of the most ancient civilizations in Mesopotamia's Fertile Crescent. The Bible itself describes rapid advances in preflood technology.[1] Long life spans, if true, would have promoted a high rate of advance. A 900-year life gives an individual ample opportunity to discover and apply knowledge, to pass along that knowledge, and to work with others to refine it, as well as to find new applications for it. Knowledge and experience would, thus, multiply, just as the history of ancient peoples actually did.

Postflood peoples, by contrast, show evidence of starts, stops, and restarts in their technological progress. The use of various metals, for example, frequently appears, then disappears, then reappears later in the archaeological record. This disruption or discontinuity in the rate of cultural advance makes sense if human life spans dropped dramatically around the time of the flood.

As noted in discussion of the first humans' food source (chapter 10), a vegetarian diet is essential for ultralong life spans. However, when God pronounced a change in life expectancy for people born after the flood, He also changed the dietary rules. People need no longer restrict their diet to plants. They were allowed to eat animals, although fear of humans would drive many creatures away from easy reach (Genesis 9:2–3). A diet including meat adds higher concentrations of heavy elements in the body (anywhere from 10–10,000 times more than a vegetarian diet). These higher levels would be detrimental, even life-threatening, after a few hundred years. However, for people living only 120 years or less (Genesis 6:3), the health risk becomes negligible—except where industrial pollution is extremely high.

### How to Live 900 Years

Until recently, no scientifically credible explanation could be given for how ancient peoples could have lived 900+ years. Some early proposals derived from mention of the "mist" or "streams" watering the Garden of Eden (Genesis 2:6) led to hypotheses about a protective water vapor canopy. However, these proved scientifically untenable (see sidebar, "The Canopy Idea" on page 126).

Genesis 6:3 indicates *what* God did and *why*, but not *how*. Answers to how human life expectancy dropped from the 900+ years down to 120 are left to scientific investigation. A reasonable place to start is to identify factors limiting human life span today. Seventeen such factors have been discovered thus far (see table 13). Among them, four alone could realistically account for the great survivability difference: (1) radiation from the decay of radioisotopes (uranium, radium, and thorium, for instance) in igneous rocks; (2) high-energy cosmic radiation; (3) telomerase activity (chromosome shortening); and (4) a high level of meat ingestion.

### Table 13: Major Factors Limiting Human Life Spans

1. killing (war and murder)
2. accidents
3. disease
4. famine or inadequate nutrition
5. high metabolism
6. internal oxidative stress
7. environmental stress
8. inadequate exercise
9. chemical carcinogens
10. heavy element accumulation in tissues
11. high caloric intake
12. high meat ingestion
13. ultraviolet radiation
14. solar x-ray radiation
15. radioisotope decay
16. high-energy cosmic radiation
17. telomerase activity (chromosome shortening)

## The Canopy Idea

In an attempt to explain long life spans prior to the flood, as well as Earth's huge hydrocarbon and limestone deposits, some Bible readers proposed that a thick water canopy surrounded Earth before the time of Noah. They claimed such a canopy would have been able to shield life from radiation, greatly extend human longevity, create a warm, humid environment to augment Earth's biomass and, once collapsed, would suddenly inundate Earth's entire surface, destroying all life (except on the ark) and even much of Earth's topography.

Such an idea stirred excitement because it seemed to explain so much at once. But the bubble burst when credibility tests were applied. First, a canopy with enough vaporous water to cover Earth would dissipate to interplanetary space before growing to such a size. A vapor canopy of such huge proportions, even one that existed for a short time, would set up a greenhouse (heating) effect so powerful that all ice and liquid water would evaporate from Earth's surface. With no water on Earth to sustain life, the flood would have been unnecessary.

A liquid or ice canopy would immediately crash down under gravity's influence. Even if such a canopy were somehow to defy the law of gravity, the conversion of that ice to liquid or liquid to vapor would have consumed so much heat as to freeze all life on Earth. Again, the flood would be unnecessary.

An increase in Earth's surface heat and humidity would increase the total living biomass of Earth by only a minor amount. Earth's surface area and the solar energy flow limit Earth's living biomass to a quantity far below what is needed to explain all Earth's measurable biodeposits in less than millions of years (see chapter 17). Although a vapor canopy would have provided some protection against ultraviolet radiation, it would not have impeded the hard cosmic rays that fundamentally limit human life spans.

Coal burning, building materials, paved roads, and even granite countertops guarantee our exposure, today, to igneous rock and the radiation emanating from it. Our high-tech civilization is built on such stuff. Because so many other factors hinder our longevity, we don't give this radiation much thought. Ancient people on the other hand, especially people living prior to the time of Noah, might have been well-protected. By dwelling in a sedimentary plain, using textiles and wood as building material, and burning fuels other than coal, their exposure to radioisotope decay could well have been kept to near zero. Such a scenario seems entirely plausible, on historical and biblical grounds (described in Genesis 6–11).

## Cosmic-Ray Damage

Cosmic radiation (not all of which is damaging) affects humans wherever they live. Harmful cosmic rays come from outer space—from objects such as quasars, black holes, and neutron stars, and from events such as novae (star explosions) and supernovae (giant star explosions). Of all these contributors, however, supernova explosions and the pulsars and radiation remnants they produce contribute by far the most and the deadliest radiation.

Except in our galaxy's halo (outer region), supernovae, supernova remnants, and pulsars are distributed fairly evenly throughout our galaxy. Until recently most astronomers assumed, on the basis of this even distribution, that the level of cosmic radiation all over Earth has been roughly constant throughout human history. This assumption was first challenged in 1995 by Russian astronomer Anatoliy Erlykin who noted an anomaly in the very high-energy region of the primary cosmic-ray energy spectrum.[2]

In 1997, British astronomer Sir Arnold Wolfendale joined Erlykin in observing "the signature of an extra component from a single source which protrudes above the 'background.'"[3] Together these researchers proposed that the "single source" of this intensely energetic radiation is "a local, young supernova remnant."[4]

Within a few years Erlykin and Wolfendale were able to show that virtually all the highest energy heavy nuclei cosmic rays (the most deadly to humans) currently showering Earth could arise from a single supernova—as yet unidentified—in the recent past (less than 100,000 years ago) relatively near (closer than 3,000 light-years away) to our solar system.[5]

## Identifying the Source

Initially researchers thought the Vela supernova might be the source, but further study ruled it out. In 2003 Erlykin and Wolfendale explained how the lack of gamma-ray radiation from any possible candidate for the source implied that the remnant of the supernova source must be so nearby that its extent occupies up to a 40° region of the sky.[6] The only supernova remnant close to that angular size is the Monogem Ring. It has an angular size of 25°. Its associated pulsar, PSR B0656+14, may contribute some of the radiation coming at us, but the Monogem Ring remnant would appear to be the dominant source.[7]

A team of five American and Irish astronomers confirmed that the age and distance of this pulsar are consistent with the age and distance of its associated supernova remnant.[8] They also confirmed that this distance and age match the predictions of a model in which the anomalous feature in the primary cosmic-ray spectrum is produced by "a single dominant source."[9]

The team also established the age and distance of this pulsar and remnant: approximately 100,000 years old and some 938±100 light-years distant.[10] The timing with which heavy nuclei radiation from this supernova and pulsar would begin arriving on Earth depends on a number of variables, which astronomers are currently working to narrow down.

Thus far, however, everything about the age and proximity of the Monogem Ring and its associated pulsar seems consistent with the possibility that God used these objects, at least in part, to shorten human life spans in the era after the flood. It seems possible that before Noah's time, the deadly cosmic rays that so significantly impact human longevity had not yet arrived from their supernova source.

**Effects of Telomerase Activity**
The most important life span limiting impact comes from inside, not outside, our bodies. As in all complex organisms, our cells can undergo only a certain number of replications. For cells that make up differentiated tissues, organs, and append-ages (the somatic cells), the "telomere" region of its chromosome is incompletely replicated during cell division. Thus, each chromosome becomes shorter and shorter as cell division continues. Eventually, chromosomes become so short that important genes fail to get replicated, and this failure can shut down cell divi-sion. Once cells are unable to reproduce, damaged cells cannot be replaced, so the organs, tissues, and appendages can no longer perform their life-essential func-tions, and death occurs. What this telomere shortening means for humans today is that no matter how healthy a person's lifestyle or how radiation-free a person's environment, he or she will not live beyond about 120 years.

However, one way past this biochemical life span limit may be found in an enzyme called telomerase. This enzyme adds nucleotide base pairs to the ends of DNA to counteract the shortening process. Allowing this enzyme to work in all somatic cells, however, carries a significant risk. Because telomerase sustains cell reproduction, if normal cells turn cancerous, then the resulting tumors would grow unchecked. In other words, the lack of telomerase in most somatic cells (other than the gametes) is one of the best defenses available to us against the development and spread of tumors and cancers.

In other words, too much telomerase activity typically brings about an earlier death for a complex organism due to the spread of cancers and tumors.[11] But, too little telomerase activity typically results in an earlier death from organ and tissue failure.[12] Given the cancer-inducing factors within our environment, telomerase activity level is currently ideal for maximizing complex organisms' life span.

## A Possible Explanation

In the earliest days of humanity, when exposure to radiation from radioisotope decay and from high-energy heavy nuclei cosmic rays was significantly lower than current levels, telomerase activity could have been much higher because the cancer risk would have been significantly lower. Later, when the radiation levels dramatically increased, God may well have intervened to limit telomerase activity so as to protect humanity from that radiation's damaging effects.

Other biochemical activity may have been different in that early era, as well. Certain genes appear to activate production of specialized proteins that magnify the longevity-enhancing benefits of caloric restriction and high antioxidant consumption.[13] Thus, by incorporating such features in His genetic design of humans God could have allowed for the long life span of vegetarian people inhabiting a low-radiation environment.

Genesis 11 indicates that the change in life span happened exponentially over time, not instantaneously. The recorded life spans decline over the multiple generations from Noah (who lived 950 years) down to Nahor (who lived 148 years).[14] This rate of drop in human life spans may reflect God's response to the exponentially increasing effects of radiation from a nearby supernova and from increasing exposure to igneous rocks, or it may reflect God's allowance for humanity's difficulties in adjusting to change. Or it may reflect both.

## God's Good Purpose

None of these possible life span-shortening scenarios implies that God simply reacted to (or sat back and watched) natural disasters. Genesis 6:3 tells us that God acted purposefully to shorten human life spans. From what we observe of human behavior, shorter life spans serve to limit the destructive impact of human selfishness, greed, and lawlessness. Individuals bent on violence can harm or destroy a great many people in a 900-year lifetime, and their spiritual malignancy tends to spread like a cancer.[15] The lengthy life span of preflood peoples may help explain why only one family among the entire human race was deemed salvageable by the time of Noah's six-hundredth year.

The extent to which a supernova event and a resetting of telomerase activity account for a dramatic change in humanity's life span change is a question for ongoing research. Nonetheless, even our limited understanding of how these phenomena impact human longevity indicates that what has sometimes been considered a scientific and historical impossibility—the 900+ years of Methuselah and his peers—really can be considered scientifically and historically possible.

In certain instances, such as that of human life spans, providing a plausible explanation is the best an interpreter can do. As long as a reasonable scenario exists, one corroborated by evidence and logic, the truthfulness of the account cannot be dismissed. Some passages, however, such as the Genesis 6 account of the Nephilim, remain shrouded in mystery. Their truth remains difficult, if not impossible, to validate. So an assessment of their plausibility rests on that of the larger story around them.

### Genomics and Humanity's Origin

The possibility that God intervened to alter the makeup of human genomes significantly impacts a current debate over humanity's ancestral population size. Some geneticists insist that genomics studies contradict the notion that Adam and Eve, a single human pair, could have given rise to all the genetic diversity presently manifested in the human population.[16] They claim that humanity's ancestral population must be comprised of at least 10,000 individuals.[17] However, these same authors explicitly point out that their calculations yield only estimates of humanity's ancestral population size, estimates that are dependent on the assumptions undergirding their models.

Biochemists Fazale Rana and Patricia Fanning have challenged these assumptions. In their assessment of the genomics data they see no basis for denying the biblical claim of humanity's descent from a single couple.[18] If God did intervene to alter the genomes of Noah's offspring, then, of course, greater genetic diversity could be and would be evidenced in the current human population. The plausibility of such an intervention is affirmed if we accept the account of God's creation of Eve using a biopsy taken from Adam. This act required an alteration of the DNA in that biopsy.

# 14

## SONS OF GOD AND THE NEPHILIM: GENESIS 6

Genesis 6 opens with contextual details that set the scene for the expansive flood narrative that follows. Yet these details seem so strange, so mysterious, as to present an interpretive and apologetics challenge nearly as great as the flood story itself. In this case, unlike that of the Genesis 5 life spans, the solution to the mystery comes largely from Scripture's pages, though science does come to bear.

The time frame is characterized by an increase in population. Apparently, at least some of the exponential population growth one would expect from Adam's long-lived descendants (see table 12, page 121) had begun to occur, despite metastasizing violence. Key characters in this story initially include the "sons of God" and the "daughters of men." Verses 1 and 2 tell us these sons were so captivated by the daughters' beauty they "married any of them they chose." Thus far, the story seems straightforward, though we may wonder who these "sons" are.

Then the story line is interrupted with a divine declaration of judgment: human life will be shortened from hundreds of years down to a maximum of about 120, because God will not "contend with man forever." Contention implies a struggle. It appears humanity has resisted God's authority and guidance at every turn. Here is our first clue that relations between the sons of God and daughters of men have provoked God to anger and to action.

Then, in Genesis 6:4, comes mention of some characters called the Nephilim:

The Nephilim were on the earth in those days—and also afterward—when the sons of God went to the daughters of men and had children by them. They were the heroes of old, men of renown.[1]

Because references to the Nephilim appear in other (later) biblical narratives, most notably in the accounts of King David and his exploits, modern readers can turn there for help in discerning who these beings may be. A reasonable inter-pretation will offer consistency—biblical, historical, and scientific. The existence of a reasonable interpretation is sufficient, in and of itself, to defend against the skeptic's challenge that this story is pure fiction or legend. What follows are three different plausible explanations.

### Identifying the Nephilim

According to the prevailing view among Bible commentators, the sons of God, the daughters of men, and their offspring, the Nephilim, are strictly human in every respect.[2] They read the account as an expression of God's provocation over wholesale violation of His prohibition against marriage between the sons of God, presumed to be male descendants of Seth, and the daughters of men, presumed to be female descendants of Cain. While no mention of this specific prohibition appears elsewhere in Genesis, it is deduced from passages in both Old and New Testaments, such as Ezra and 2 Corinthians.[3]

Additional support for this view is drawn from Genesis 4:1–24, which deals exclusively with Cain and his descendants, and from Genesis 4:25–5:32, which deals exclusively with Seth and his descendants. The Genesis 4:1–24 passage as-cribes nothing good (as in godly) to the line of Cain, and Genesis 4:25–5:32 pas-sage ascribes nothing bad (ungodly) to the line of Seth. Additionally, the text says that Enosh's people (Enosh is Seth's son) "call on the name of the LORD" (Genesis 4:26) and that the name of wicked Lamech's daughter, Naamah, (Genesis 4:22) means "beautiful."

The Nephilim, who appear both before and after the flood, are considered in this view to be wicked men of great renown for strength and skill in battle. The Hebrew root of the word "Nephilim" means "fall" (together "Nephal" and "yim" literally equals "fallen ones"). This name, then, suggests the Nephilim were morally flawed. In the post-flood era, the Bible speaks of them as residing among and fighting for the ungodly Canaanite and Philistine populations (1 Samuel, 2 Samuel, and 1 Chronicles).

A check of cross-references to the Nephilim in other parts of Scripture where they are identified by various names, including sons of Rapha, Rephaim, Anakites, and Anakim (KJV) raises some questions, however, about the source of their strength and other features.

The chilling descriptions of these beings focus on their enormous, argu-ably superhuman, size and strength. The Goliath whom David fought and killed (identified in 1 Samuel 21 and 1 Chronicles 20 as a descendant of Rapha) stood six-and-a-half "cubits" tall (at least nine feet, nine inches) and demonstrated remarkable agility while carrying at least 250 pounds of armor and weapons.[4] Og, the king of Bashan, another of these giants, is said to have slept in an iron bed measuring nine by four cubits (at least 13.5 feet by 6 feet).[5] The Hebrews used three different "cubit" units: the common, royal, and long, measuring (respectively) about 18, 20, and 22 inches.[6] By these measures, Goliath could have been nearly 12 feet tall and Og's bed, as much as sixteen-and-a-half feet long.

Ancient extrabiblical literature makes plentiful reference to giants. The Greeks, Romans, Phoenicians, Mesopotamians, and Egyptians, for example, all told stories of great and terrible heroes, men of supernatural size and strength. Greek literature is especially rich in this respect, and the Philistines who settled in Canaan's coastal plain came from Greece or Crete. In all these nonbiblical accounts, the "supermen" sprang from the sexual union between immortal "gods" and mortal humans. These giants certainly resemble the biblical Nephilim in their penchant for fighting[7] and in their tendency to manifest birth defects, such as extra fingers and toes.[8] The extrabiblical stories clearly differ from the biblical ones, however, in attributing honor and immortality to at least a few of the giants. The biblical Nephilim are mortal and thoroughly evil, without exception.

**Nephilim as Superhumans**
From a scientific perspective, the stature of Nephilim, Raphaim, and Anakim exceeds human physical capabilities as well as the limits of biological engineering. The bone mass necessary to support muscles and resist gravity's effects rises geometrically with a person's height (just as the weight of a building's supporting beams goes up geometrically with the length of the spans they support). This ratio implies an increasingly severe loss of mobility and stamina once human height exceeds about eight feet.

The story of the tallest documented modern human, a victim of a growth-hormone malfunction who reached a height of 8 feet, 11 inches demonstrates the point.[9] This man moved so slowly and with such difficulty that his day-to-day activity was severely limited, and he certainly could not participate in sports. He died at age forty from physical exhaustion.

The physics of basketball provides further corroboration. The ease with which a player can score a basket rises with the square of his height (because the range of shooting angles that will score increases with the square of the height from which the ball leaves the player's hands). Thus, even a one-inch height advantage is huge. This advantage explains why seven-foot tall players tend to be higher percentage scorers than six-foot tall players. However, basketball players who are seven-and-a-half feet tall or taller tend to move, jump, and dodge with less speed and agility than those only a few inches shorter. The shooting advantage gained from that extra height is counterbalanced by the reduced mobility and stamina associated with it.

Given human physiological limits, the description of the Nephilim—if mere men—must be exaggerated. Strictly natural bodies cannot manifest the stated combination of size, power, agility, load-carrying capacity, and endurance. The only other way to maintain this interpretation would be to question the weights and measures of Moses' and David's time. This approach presents difficulties, however, in view of archaeological evidence confirming their consistency, and it raises the additional problem of why Saul, a soldier who was "an impressive young man without equal" and "a head taller" than any other Israelite,[10] was so terrified of Goliath. Likewise, it raises questions as to why ten of the Israelite spies sent into the Promised Land by Moses exclaimed, "We saw the Nephilim there… We seemed like grasshoppers in our own eyes, and we looked the same to them."[11] Such words could be taken as hyperbole, but the measurements cannot.

## Sons of God in the Old Testament

The Hebrew phrase translated "daughters of men" refers consistently to humans, but the phrase for "sons of God" may be used to refer either to humans or to angels[12] and, thus, points to another possible interpretation of the text.

Outside the Genesis 6 passage, the only Old Testament references to "sons of God" appear in Job. In 1:6 and 2:1 the sons of God are said to have presented themselves before the Lord, with Satan alongside them. The location, "before the Lord," indicates a realm beyond Earth. When God asks Satan where he has been, he replies, "From roaming through the earth and going back and forth in it." Job 38:7 says the sons of God were witnesses to the laying of Earth's foundations. No human was present when that event took place. Many modern translations of Scripture simply render the "sons of God" phrase in each of these Job passages as "angels."

One Old Testament verse, Hosea 1:10, mentions the "sons of the living God." This phrase refers to humans, Jews in particular, but in a future context. It denotes those Israelites who will partake in salvation through the redemptive sacrifice of the coming Messiah.

Old Testament references to "children of the LORD your God"[13] and "his children,"[14] found in Deuteronomy, and to "my sons" and "my daughters," in Isaiah,[15] do refer to humans. The Hebrew word for "children" is the same as the word for "sons." However, neither of the two Hebrew phrases used in the Deuteronomy passages is identical to the "sons of God" phrase used in Job and Genesis. The two Deuteronomy expressions appear to fit well as variants of the 357 references in the Torah (Genesis–Deuteronomy) to "children of Israel." Thus, the Old Testament provides no conclusive evidence that the phrase "sons of God" must always and only refer to humans (see appendix C).

It does seem strange that "sons of God" would be used in reference to fallen angels. Job 38:7 describes the sons of God as shouting for joy over God's creative work—hardly the kind of behavior associated with fallen angels. However, the Bible never specifies exactly how long before Eden the angelic rebellion occurred. So the expression could include all angelic beings generically. The psalmist uses a nearly identical Hebrew phrase, often translated "heavenly beings" (see Psalm 29:1), with reference to angels.

Outside of Genesis 6, Moses refers to angels fifteen times in the Torah. He identifies them in these other instances using the Hebrew word *mal'āk*, translated "angels." In none of these other passages does he use the phrase translated "sons of God." This raises the question: If these verses in Genesis 6 do refer to angelic beings, why would he not use *mal'āk*? By the same token, if these two verses refer to Seth's descendants, why would Moses not say explicitly "the sons of Seth?"

### Insight from the New Testament

The New Testament usage presents a contrast that reflects the change Christ brought through His death and resurrection. All eight uses of the Greek phrase "sons of God" in the New Testament refer to humans. The equivalent expression, "children of God," (used six times) also applies exclusively to humans. Four more passages refer to "sons" without including, but certainly implying, "of God": Luke 6:35, Galatians 4:4–7, Hebrews 2:10, and Hebrews 12:7. In all cases (see appendix C), however, the designation "sons of God" (or "children of God") applies to people who trust in Jesus Christ as their Savior and are indwelt by the Holy Spirit. Luke 6:35 and John 1:12 point to future fulfillment of the promise that those who welcome and receive Christ *will* gain the right to become sons of God. Even the apostles were not called sons of God until after Christ's resurrection. These texts indicate that *only* post-Resurrection, post-Pentecost believers may be called the "sons of God" (or "children of God").

This title went into effect when the Holy Spirit "sealed" the new covenant God established with all those who put their trust in Him (see Acts 2, 8, and 10). Once Jesus' atoning work was done, the Spirit came to live among and *in* all people who answer God's call upon their lives, and, for the first time since Eden, humans regained the right to be called sons and daughters of God. Even great men of God such as Ezekiel and Daniel never bore that title. Only once in Scripture, previous to the Resurrection and to Pentecost, is a human being called a son of God. As we see in the Luke 3 genealogy, Adam began life with that title. Nevertheless, the argument that only Christians can be called sons of God comes by way of scriptural pattern, not by way of explicit doctrinal statement.

**Angels and Sex**
The primary objection to identifying the sons of God in Genesis 6 as (fallen) angelic beings comes from the typical perception of angels as asexual beings. Genesis here indicates that these sons of God engaged in sexual intercourse with women and impregnated them. Resistance to the angelic interpretation arises from three points: (1) nowhere in the Bible is sexual capacity expressly attributed to angels; (2) at no time has anyone documented a case of a demon's impregnating a woman; and (3) Jesus said, "At the resurrection people will neither marry nor be given in marriage; they will be like the angels in heaven."[16]

Many scholars have pointed out that Jesus' statement can be interpreted two ways: (1) it may mean that angels have no capacity for sexual relations; or (2) it may simply mean that in heaven humans will not engage in sexual relations, just as angels in heaven now do not engage in sexual relations. It seems reasonable that angels living in God's presence and experiencing His perfect love at every moment have neither need nor desire for sex.[17]

Angels who have broken their relationship with God through rebellion and who follow Satan instead of God have lost that unity, that oneness, and all the pleasures and joys of heaven that go with it. Their loss of place, purpose, and, more importantly, of relationship with God may possibly tempt these beings to seek the kind of intimate union they observe among humans. A subtle hint at this possibility comes from the observation that sexual acts of various kinds have been part of most pagan worship practices, including those of the Greeks and Romans, in the ceremonies and the temples devoted to false gods.

A similar focus on sexual acts seems consistent with a great body of documentation on occult practices. Evil spirits, and humans operating under their influence, manifest an obsession with sex to a far greater degree than the population at large.[18] The incidence of rape and sexual assault on women (as well as on men) seems particularly high among those involved in overtly occult encounters and occult worship practices.[19]

Most people think of angels as "bodiless, purely spiritual-beings and sexless."[20] However, the idea that angels have the capacity to take on human form and to perform physical functions such as walking, talking, eating, and drinking finds ample support in various biblical accounts from Genesis to Revelation.[21] In their reported encounters with humans, angels were sometimes mistaken for men (though not for women).[22] The men of Sodom apparently viewed Lot's angelic guests as desired objects of homosexual rape.[23]

## Two Possible Explanations

One major question remains, however, even if reasons exist for believing that the sons of God who fathered strange, superhuman offspring by the daughters of men could have been fallen angels: Why is there no evidence in modern times for the impregnation of women involved in demonic encounters?

The argument for interpreting the "sons of God" in Genesis 6 as fallen angels rests heavily on this question, and the Bible offers no explicit answer. However, Jude 1:6–7a offers relevant insight:

> And the angels who did not keep their positions of authority but abandoned their own home—these he has kept in darkness, bound with everlasting chains for judgment on the great Day. In a similar way, Sodom and Gomorrah and the surrounding towns gave themselves up to sexual immorality and perversion.

Jude here associates the angels' offense with sexual debauchery of the worst kind and scope known to humans.

Given the punishment Jude describes for these fallen angels' behavior, we can better understand the reaction of various demons Jesus cast out of people during His earthly ministry.[24] In many instances the demon (or demons) shrieked with terror at the prospect of being sent to the place of darkness and chains of which Jude spoke—also referred to as the "Abyss," or "Tartarus." The demons begged Jesus not to send them there, pleading that they had done nothing to deserve such horrific punishment. In each case, the demons were rebuked and sent away. Jesus appears to have accepted their appeal, reserving their ultimate judgment until a later time.

If demons have the capacity to bear offspring by women, their inclination to do so might be restrained today by the threat of that terrible penalty—consignment to the Abyss—for doing so. Such an interpretation would contribute to our understanding of society's degradation and the flood's necessity. The flood would have rid the earth of anyone inclined to engage in sexual relations with demons and of their evil, destructive offspring.

Yet even the flood did not eradicate the Nephilim for good. The sin that produced them recurred after the flood. We see Nephilim mentioned again in Numbers, Deuteronomy, Joshua, Judges, and 1 and 2 Samuel. After the flood, they seem to appear only in the region of Canaan. God destroyed these later "giants" by sending Abraham's descendants into Canaan. He sent Joshua and, finally, David, with his thirty mighty warriors to finish the job. Since the time of David's conquest, we see no evidence or hint of their return. One possible explanation, then, based on what we read in the New Testament, is that the threat of special punishment for those who cross the line was instituted or perhaps intensified at that time to prevent a recurrence.

One other proposed interpretation of Genesis 6 represents a blending of the two views outlined above. This approach attempts to solve the biological issues by hypothesizing a certain kind, or level, of demon possession. According to this view, the sons of God in Genesis 6 were humans invaded and possessed by fallen angels in such a way as to alter the genes transmitted via intercourse. In this way they produced offspring with the physiological characteristics associated with Nephilim. Further development and discussion of this alternate view seems warranted, but to date little appears in print.

### Who's Judged for Whose Sin?

The three interpretive options addressed here leave many questions unanswered, but they do fit the available information with some level of consistency. The existence of an element of uncertainty detracts no more from the reliability of the larger text than does an unanswered question of science undermine confidence in the entire body of established scientific knowledge.

One as yet unaddressed concern for interpreters of Genesis 6:1–4, however, springs from its implications about God's judgment. On the one hand, the condemnation of all humanity and animals—except those on the ark—seems unjustly extreme as a response to (apparently unapproved) marriages and childbearing between Seth's descendants and Cain's. On the other hand, it seems unjust to make humanity pay for immoral acts perpetrated by demons.

I am persuaded by what follows in Genesis 6, verse 5 and onward, that the sins of the sons of God, the daughters of men, and the Nephilim, whoever they may be, represent just part of the picture of moral disintegration that pervaded Noah's world. Earth's entire human population apparently had grown thoroughly and irreparably wicked. As the text records, "all the people on earth had corrupted their ways," and "every inclination" of every human heart "was only evil all the time."[25] That mind-boggling scenario carries us to a deeper study of what occurred during the great flood and why.

# 15

## BOUNDARIES OF GOD'S WRATH: GENESIS 6

**A**s much ridicule as skeptics heap upon the Genesis account of creation and of early humanity, even more derision takes aim at the Genesis flood story. What most people have heard or read about Noah and the ark from childhood storybooks onward strikes them as utterly preposterous. Not only does the story seem to contradict multiple disciplines of science, but it also seems to contradict the Christian doctrine of an all-knowing, all-loving God.

Let's begin with the latter of these two challenges. The appropriate starting point is to look at the *who, how, when,* and *why* questions surrounding God's severe act of judgment. Without such an inquiry, the scientific questions raised by Genesis 6–9—questions of geology, meteorology, paleontology, biology, anthropology, and more—cannot be answered satisfactorily. The themes of divine judgment and mercy provide the essential guide to our understanding of the text's content.

### Sin's Damage

The word *sin* describes the heart condition with which every human being is born,[1] the tendency to rebel against God's authority. Sins are the acts that reflect that heart condition. Each act of sin, according to Scripture, does damage to the one who commits it.[2] Sin "defiles," the Bible says, and we can easily recognize that some sins do more damage, or are more "defiling," than others.[3] Some sins are so serious that they damage not only the person committing them but also the people, animals, and even things around that person. Sins against the body (murder, assault, fornication, adultery, and so on) do deeper harm than do sins outside the body (stealing, lying, cheating, and so on).[4] But all sin damages, and all sin grieves and offends God's heart.

The extent of a sin's damage depends on the degree of degradation it manifests. Multiple and repeated sins compound the damage. Defilement begins and then spreads in this order:

1. in the sinner (Romans 7:8–11)
2. then to his progeny (Exodus 20:5)
3. then to his soulish animals (Joshua 6:21)
4. then to his material goods (Numbers 16:23–33)
5. then to his inhabited land (Leviticus 18:24–28)

Defilement reaching as far as people's possessions and lands has not been seen on Earth since ancient days, long before Jesus' earthly ministry and the spread of the Holy Spirit's restraining influence. Even during Old Testament times, evil rarely descended to such depths. In the centuries since Christ came, horrible atrocities have occurred, not just among "primitive savages" but among savages in modern garb with technological tools of torture. But the world has not seen a repeat of Sodom, for example, where a city's entire male population, young and old, violently pursued honored guests to commit homosexual rape against them.[5]

People sometimes struggle to believe that the God of the Old Testament could be one and the same as the God of the New. They read accounts of wholesale destruction ordered by God and cannot imagine His actions as expressions of mercy or love. They cannot fathom that God's judgment in such instances compares with the work of a skilled surgeon removing a dangerous malignancy. God has not changed, but conditions have.

In the Old Testament era God operated as needed to prepare and protect the way of His coming deliverance, more specifically of His coming Deliverer, from sin's penalty. In the postflood era, social structures began to exist to support the restraining influence of the conscience, and these, along with shorter life spans, limited the havoc wreaked by those whose conscience is seared.

Today, in New Testament era, we look back on the deliverance Christ brought. We can receive the "deposit" guaranteeing our ultimate deliverance, the indwelling Holy Spirit, who enables us to resist sin's power.[6] The Spirit works in and through us to protect life and prepare the way for that ultimate deliverance from sin's penalty, power, and presence.

All human behavior has been impacted, at least to some extent, because of God's presence among people in a new way, by the Holy Spirit's indwelling those who receive the Deliverer as their only hope. As Jesus explained, His followers are the salt of the earth,[7] a preservative protecting all society from the kind of reprobate (extremely wicked) behavior that occasionally plagued people during Old Testament times.

## Dangers of Reprobation

Reprobation, such as that which plagued the whole of preflood society (except Noah and his family), developed over time and spread. Romans 1:18–32 outlines, step by step, how reprobation develops and gains momentum. Verse 32 describes the final step of those who will not, and no longer can, turn back from evil:

> Although they know God's righteous decree that those who do such things deserve death, they not only continue to do these very things but also approve of those who practice them.

Reprobates not only do evil, they also cheer on others who do evil. They enjoy recruiting others to live as they do, according to Peter:

> They seduce the unstable….by appealing to the lustful desires of the sinful human nature, they entice people who are just escaping from those who live in error. They promise them freedom, while they themselves are slaves of depravity.[8]

Anyone exposed to depravity at close range for enough time will be affected, and infected, by it. Reprobates, as Paul said, are Satan's captives.[9] They share Satan's desire to drag others into captivity.[10]

When God gave Adam and Eve the responsibility to manage the earth for the good of all life, part of their task was to preserve and protect, calling upon divine wisdom and courage as necessary. They failed, and the result was a world in which oppression and violence and all manner of evil grew totally out of control.

Since the time of the flood, and still today, we see outbreaks of horrific oppression and violence, and the responsibility given to Adam and Eve remains in our hands. It is our job to take action against mass starvation and against atrocities of all kinds, on whatever scale. He calls upon us to protect and preserve life within our homes, our neighborhoods, our regions, and our nations.

Furthermore, when God calls, he also provides. We have been given the ways and means to do what is right and just, *if* and *when* we draw upon the wisdom and courage God makes available to us. Our failures are glaring, around the globe, but not since the time of the flood has the world seen total moral collapse.

God's intervention at that time became essential to preserve the human race and to fulfill His plan for our ultimate good. He worked as a surgeon to remove a deadly malignancy, and His skill exceeds that of the best human physician. He knows when and how to wield His scalpel. He knows how much or how little to remove to protect whatever viable tissue can be preserved. He is an enemy to disease and a friend to health. He operates from the motive of mercy and love.

### Extent of Depravity

Though we have no experience that enables us to picture the situation, Noah's contemporaries reached a degree of depravity that threatened to contaminate the world irreversibly. The Hebrew language has two words to describe such utter evil, *shāḥat*, meaning "wicked violence," "extreme wickedness," "cruel hatred," and "oppression";[11] and *ḥāmās*, which means "to act wickedly," "laying waste," "corruption," or "destruction."[12] No other people or society warranted the use of such strong language. Their evil was, and remains, unprecedented (though the New Testament warns that society may be on its way to a similar condition at "the time of the end"[13]).

Genesis 4 describes some of this wholesale reprobation. Contributing factors include violence and murder, initiated by Cain and copied by others. The long life spans favored the spread of these evils. The percentage of perpetrators rose as more and more victims died, the righteous among them. We are not told in Scripture why God allowed conditions to reach such a deplorable state, but one of His reasons may have been to demonstrate to all future generations that we humans lack the inner resources to save ourselves, to overcome evil with good. Another reason may have been to persuade us that short life spans benefit us under current conditions, as we await His ultimate deliverance from all contact with those who reject His lordship.

The flood account also tells of God's grief and agony over humanity's corruption. With a heavy heart He cleansed the world to keep it from utter ruin. He found one man, just one, who with his family could keep the human race from self-extermination and further suffering in the process. The story has as much to do with rescue as with the wrath that arises from love. God, the divine surgeon, saved one hundred percent of the potentially viable tissue in humanity's dying body.

### Boundaries of God's Wrath

The limits of defilement identified above also define the limits of God's judgment. His purging never goes beyond the boundaries of sin's damage. This principle becomes clear not only in this flood account but also in God's instructions for the Israelite invasion of Canaan under Joshua's command. In the conquest of some Canaanite cities, God instructed the Israelites to kill only the Canaanite adults. For other cities, God decreed death for the entire population but not for the soulish animals, the *nepesh* creatures owned by the inhabitants. (The damaging impact of abusive people on the birds and mammals living with them is well-documented, as noted in the Bible.[14])

In the conquest of a few cities, God told the Israelites to destroy everything: people, their soulish animals, and, in still rarer cases, the people's possessions too. The extent of destruction was determined by the extent of defilement.

Such destruction always resulted, of course, in the loss of some insects, plants, bacteria, and the like within the immediate area. To save them was neither practical nor necessary. Unlike birds and mammals, these species multiply and reestablish themselves rapidly enough that any limited region of destruction would quickly recover.

In the rarest cases, such as Sodom and Gomorrah, even the land was laid waste. To this day, despite the land's former fertility and abundant water supply, no crops or herds are raised in the area where these ancient cities existed.

One of the stories Moses tells later in Genesis recounts a dialogue between the Lord and Abraham, an exchange that helped Abraham, and helps its readers, identify the limits of God's judgment.[15] The Lord promised Abraham that if only ten righteous people could be found in Sodom and Gomorrah, He would save the entire populace for the sake of those ten. In destroying the cities the Lord did first rescue the (fewer than ten) righteous people and any relatives who chose to go with them. God's wrath never falls upon the righteous (other than on Jesus Christ, for our sake).[16]

In a previous conversation also reported in Genesis, the Lord told Abraham that the time had not yet come to destroy the Amorites.[17] Their wickedness had not yet developed to a degree that warranted destruction. His judgment would be held back until the Amorites' wickedness reached totally reprobate proportions. This degradation process, Abraham was told, would take another four hundred years.

### Application to the Flood
This principle of conservation, or limitation, in God's acts of judgment clearly applies to the Genesis flood. It means that if humans had spread as far as Antarctica, the flood would have covered Antarctica, destroying the Emperor penguins along with the people, except those aboard the ark. If no people lived in Antarctica, God would have had no reason to destroy the place or its penguins. Nor would Noah be required to take a pair of Emperor penguins aboard the ark.

The extent of the Genesis flood, according to the principle laid out in Scripture, would have been determined by the spread of human sin. If humanity had spread throughout Africa, Asia, and Europe, then those continents would have to be destroyed by the flood. If people remained only in the region of Mesopotamia and the Persian Gulf, only that region would have to be flooded. Whatever area it covered, the flood must still be "worldwide," given that people, not the globe, defined "world" (until a much later era). Any flood that exterminates all humans and their the soulish animals—except those on board Noah's vessel—would be considered worldwide and would achieve God's purpose in pouring out judgment to cleanse the earth of reprobate defilement.

# 16

# GLOBAL OR WORLDWIDE FLOOD?
# BIBLICAL EVIDENCE

O ne of the most hotly debated biblical issues among Christians of the past few centuries focuses on the geographical extent of the Genesis flood. This topic generates as much heat as the mention of biological evolution or the age of the universe. For some Christians, belief that the flood covered the entire planet and its highest mountains has become a litmus test of biblical orthodoxy and of belief in the inerrancy of Scripture.

This line in the sand is based in large part on the wording used in Genesis 6–8 to describe how the flood impacted *all* humans, *all* animals, and *all* the mountains. The words "all," "every," and "everything," appear more than 40 times in these three chapters (a few more or a few less, depending on Bible version). On this basis, it seems no wonder belief in biblical truth demands belief in a global deluge.

## Historical Perspective
In the past century or two, nearly everyone on Earth has begun to think globally. With a sufficient travel budget, a person today can visit virtually any location on the planet. Even those who cannot afford travel typically possess the technological means to see or hear what's going on in many other parts of the world. Decisions vital to our personal life often take into account conditions on other continents.

Our global perspective naturally colors our interpretation of Scripture. When we encounter such phrases in Genesis 7 as "under the entire heavens" and "every living thing on the face of the earth," we understand that "face" as the surface of a spherical body, a planet within a larger system of planets. But what did the people of earlier times understand? What constitutes "the entire heavens" and "the face of the earth" from the perspective of ancient peoples? We must interpret the passage in light of *their* frame of reference, not ours.

**Other Worldwide Events in Scripture**
In addition to the flood of Noah's day, six other worldwide events receive mention in the Bible. The first is Joseph's feeding the whole world. Genesis 41:57 says, "And all the countries came to Egypt to buy grain from Joseph, because the famine was severe in all the world." Genesis 42:5–6 makes clear that the famine had spread to all the nations subject to Egypt's sovereignty and influence, including the land of Canaan. Egypt was a powerful force in Joseph's day, but its sway fell far short of impacting the Maoris in New Zealand and the Incas in Peru.

The second is the coming of foreign dignitaries to receive wisdom from Israel's King Solomon. 1 Kings 4:34 says, "Men of all nations came to listen to Solomon's wisdom, sent by all the kings of the world, who had heard of his wisdom." 1 Kings 10:24 adds, "The whole world sought audience with Solomon to hear the wisdom God had put in his heart." However, we read in 1 Kings 4:31 and 2 Chronicles 9 that these visitors came from as far away as Sheba (modern-day Ethiopia) and all the lands of Arabia. Evidently, the whole world of Solomon extended roughly 1,300 miles from Jerusalem in any direction.

The third is a decree from Caesar Augustus at the time of Christ's birth. In Luke 2:1 we read, "In those days a decree went out from Caesar Augustus that all the world should be registered" (ESV). Given that Augustus' authority extended only as far as the Roman Empire, this reference to "the world" is understood to mean the Roman world.

The fourth is what happened at the time of Pentecost, following Jesus' resurrection. According to Acts 2:5, "Now there were staying in Jerusalem God-fearing Jews from every nation under heaven." According to genetic studies of the Jewish people as well as of other ethnic groups around the world, none of the people mentioned in this verse came from Bolivia or Australia.[1] For Jewish people living in first-century Jerusalem, "every nation under heaven" would likely refer to all the provinces of the Roman and Parthian empires.

The next is recorded in Paul's encouraging words to the Christians in Rome. He writes, "Your faith is being reported all over the world."[2] Here again, the world of Paul and of the Roman Christians was the vast, but not global, Roman Empire. Paul in no way implied that the Inuit or sub-Saharan peoples had received news of the Christians in Rome.

One more appears in Paul's letter to the believers in Colossae. To this group Paul writes, "All over the world this gospel is producing fruit and growing, just as it has been doing among you."[3] Again, the Roman Empire constitutes the whole world of Paul and the Colossians.

Each of these biblical references to a worldwide occurrence points to an area less than Earth's entire surface or entire land area. Therefore, phrases such as "the entire heavens" and "the face of the earth" in the context of Noah's flood may also refer to an area or region smaller than the whole of Earth's surface.

With respect to the use of the words "all," "every," and "everything," some interpreters comment that it's their repetition that matters.[4] I agree. But rather than signify anything about geography, this repetition more likely emphasizes that the flood impacted all of humanity. Once again, if humans had not yet begun to occupy all of Earth's landmasses, the flood could be worldwide, or universal, without covering the globe.

### Oceans' Boundaries

The permanence of "dry land" and ocean boundaries is affirmed in Job 38, Psalm 33, 104, and Proverbs 8, all passages elaborating on the creation days. Job records God's challenge, "Who shut up the sea behind doors when it burst forth from the womb…when I fixed limits for it and sets its doors and bars in place."[5] These metaphors paint a picture of permanence.

Psalm 104 says of creation day three, "You [God] set a boundary they [the waters] cannot cross; never again will they cover the earth."[6] This explicitly states that never again, from the time God raised up continents and sent the oceans to their place, would water cover all the land. Again in Proverbs 8:29 we read that "he [God] gave the sea its boundary." These verses seem to indicate that Earth would never again return to the watery state in which it began, described in Genesis 1:2.

### New Qualifiers

The apostle Peter twice comments on the Genesis flood in his epistles. In 2 Peter 3:6 we read, "By water also the world of that time was deluged and destroyed." The Greek word translated "world" is *kosmos*, and alongside it stands the word *tote*,[7] which means "at the time." By modifying *kosmos* with *tote* Peter communicates to his readers that the world of Noah is not their world, the Roman world.

Some Bible interpreters who view the flood as global in extent argue that because the coming judgment by fire, referred to in 2 Peter 3:7 will be a global event, the judgment by water mentioned in 2 Peter 3:6 must be global as well.[8] The weakness of this argument is that Peter here is speaking not about geography but rather about people. He points out that judgment comes from God upon all the ungodly. That is the extent of it.

This comment about the flood echoes his earlier reminder, seen in 2 Peter 2:5. He wrote, "...[God] did not spare the ancient world, but preserved Noah a preacher of righteousness, with seven others, when He brought a flood upon the world of the ungodly" (NASB). In the original Greek text, the two relevant phrases are *archaiou kosmou* and *kosmo asebon*.[9] They literally mean "the ancient world"[10] and "the world of those who were destitute of reverential awe towards God."[11] According to Peter, God's judgment came against a world as defined by its spiritually dead people, not by geography.

Peter's understanding of the flood and its purpose no doubt came from conversations with Jesus Himself. Matthew 24:38–39 and Luke 17:26–27 record some of Jesus' teaching about the flood of Noah's day. Both gospel accounts capture Jesus' message about those who ignore God, focusing entirely on maintaining the status quo and remaining utterly oblivious to God's call upon their lives. Their spiritual decay crept up slowly, but their judgment came suddenly when God "took them all away" and "destroyed them all." His reference to "all" refers to the people of Noah's day, other than Noah and his family.

Jesus goes on to reference God's similar action toward the people of Sodom. As recorded in Luke 17:29, Jesus said, "But the day Lot left Sodom, fire and sulfur rained down from heaven and destroyed them all." Once again he clarifies that God's wrath came against reprobate people and limited to their location. Lot and his daughters, still only a short distance beyond Sodom's gates, were spared when judgment fell upon the "all."

**Failure to Disperse**

God's earliest command to Adam and Eve was that they "multiply and fill the earth." His plan for humanity called for global occupation. God's later words and actions, as recorded in Genesis 9–11, imply their failure to follow through. Humanity failed to spread out.

In Genesis 9:7 God repeats the command to multiply and fill the earth first given in Genesis 1:28, and in doing so (9:4–6), He speaks directly and sharply to Noah about the need to restrain murder. The firmness in His tone cannot be missed.

In Genesis 11 we see that God's command was still being ignored many generations after Noah.[12] So recalcitrant were our progenitors that God intervened directly to move them from their home base for their own survival's sake. Since that time God has kept the nations geographically and politically separated to prevent a recurrence of wholesale rebellion. When nations are dominated by worldly rather than godly values, their proximity and "harmony" become dangerous. The lesson of Babel must not be missed.

We can deduce from these passages that humanity had remained firmly entrenched in only one geographical area. Not until many generations after Noah did humans begin to disperse and settle throughout the rest of the planet.

## Geographical Markers

Biblical clues to the geographical limits on human habitation can be found in the place-names Genesis records. In Genesis 1–9 all the places mentioned belong to settlements in Mesopotamia and the Persian Gulf Oasis. From Genesis 10 onward, the text refers to places throughout much of the Eastern hemisphere.

This sudden shift to a wider geographical focus after Genesis 10 strongly suggests that until the time of the flood (and even afterward), humans and the animals on which they depended remained in and around the area often referred to in textbooks as the cradle of human civilization. Thus, to fulfill God's purpose, the deluge would be as vast as that region but need not go beyond.

## Highest Mountains

The wording, in English, of Genesis 7:19–21 helps shed light on why so many readers of English-language Bibles conclude that the flood must have covered the entire globe. This passage indicates that the floodwaters inundated all the mountains "under the whole heaven." In the King James Version, the text says this:

> And the waters prevailed exceedingly upon the earth; and all the high hills, that were under the whole heaven, were covered. Fifteen cubits upward did the waters prevail; and the mountains were covered. And all flesh died that moved upon the earth.

The New International Version reads this way:

> They [the floodwaters] rose greatly on the earth, and all the high mountains under the entire heavens were covered. The waters rose and covered the mountains to a depth of more than twenty feet. Every living thing that moved on the earth perished.

The text would appear to say that all land life on the planet was destroyed and that even Mount Everest was covered by more than twenty feet of water. But is that what the original Hebrew words literally convey? Is it possible that translators have been influenced by tradition or by their own historical context, which includes awareness of Earth as a planet? A careful look paints a less (geographically) expansive picture.

The Hebrew verb translated "to cover" is *kāsâ*. R. Laird Harris, the lead editor for the *Theological Wordbook of the Old Testament* wrote:

> The usual usage of the verb *kāsâ* I is the literal meaning "to cover." Frogs covered Egypt (Exodus 8:6 [H 2]). The pillar of cloud covered the tabernacle (Numbers 9:16). It is also used more generally to mean "conceal" (Genesis 37:26; Proverbs 10:18, KJV "hide") or "overwhelm" (Proverbs 10:6, 11, NIV "overwhelm"). In Genesis 7:19–20 the hills were "covered;" the Hebrew does not specify with what. The NIV specification of water goes beyond the Hebrew. The Hebrew may merely mean that the mountains were hidden from view by the storm.[13]

Even if the covering or concealment was by water, three possibilities exist. The water could reside upon, run over, or fall upon the hills. In these scenarios the word *kāsâ* can be interpreted to mean that more than twenty feet of water stood, that is, remained, over the high hills or mountains; or it could mean that this quantity of water ran over them, as in a flash flood, or fell upon them as rainfall. The context gives no clear indication which of the three meanings to choose. Not that the choice is insignificant for understanding the effects of such "covering." Any of the three scenarios would guarantee destruction, with no survivors.

The Hebrew words for "all the high mountains" are *kol heharim hugebohim*. Here again, because of a limited vocabulary the Hebrew words carry a range of meanings. The word *har* is used for "hill," "hill country," "mount," or "mountain."[14] It could refer to a towering peak such as mountaineers love to ascend, or it could mean a small hill that children climb in their playtime. Any landform in between these two extremes is also a possible definition.

The Hebrew adjective *gābōah* means "high," "exalted," "elevated," or "lifted up."[15] It applies to any elevation above the plains, from a landmark hill to a peak such as Mount Ararat. Genesis 7:19 describes Noah's inability to see anything but water, horizon to horizon, from his viewpoint on the ark's upper deck. If the ark were floating anywhere near the middle of the Persian Gulf or the vast Mesopotamian plains on water as much as two or three hundred feet deep, no hills or mountains would be visible from his position.

From there Noah would see only water. The high mountain ranges surrounding the Mesopotamian region and the Persian Gulf would lie beyond Noah's line of sight. His view would have been limited by Earth's curvature, by atmospheric conditions, and by his aging eyes, among other factors. Those who travel through California's San Joaquin Valley (much narrower than the Mesopotamian valley) typically cannot see the towering peaks to the east or the coastal range to the west, at least not from the valley's center.

Further support for belief that the flood covered only the limited, humanly inhabited region of the planet rather than the whole globe comes from Genesis 8:5, which says,

> The waters continued to recede until the tenth month, and on the first day of the tenth month the tops of the mountains [or hills] became visible.

Although Noah could see land, neither the raven nor the dove he released could fly far enough to reach a landing place. A week later, however, when the dove went out again, it recovered a leaf from an olive tree. Where do olive trees grow? Not on high mountains. We can reasonably assume from this detail that the *har* Noah could see and that the dove was able to reach were low-lying hills or foothills.

It's significant to note that from the perspective of the dove as it flew, "the waters were still on the face of the whole earth" (Genesis 8:9, ESV). Right here in the context we have a clear indication that "the face of the whole earth" can and does mean a particular less-extensive-than-global region.

Genesis 8 also tells us how God removed the floodwaters from the land: He sent a wind. This drying technique perfectly suits what a flooded plain such as Mesopotamia would require. Water of nearly any depth in such a flat region would flow very inefficiently toward the sea, but a wind would significantly accelerate its movement. Wind also speeds natural evaporation. Thus, wind would prove an effective means for removing water from an expansive, low-lying plain. It would prove of no use, however, in removing the waters of a global flood. Such a quantity of water could not possibly recede to any location on or around the planet by the means described in a time period as brief as eleven months. A flood universal to all humanity inhabiting one geographical region certainly could, especially with a supernaturally guided assist from the wind.

## Floodwaters' Sources
Another way in which the flood chapters themselves argue against a globally extensive flood is by reporting where the water came from (Genesis 7) as well as where it returned (Genesis 8). Genesis 7:11–12 says the floodwaters came from "the springs of the great deep" and "the floodgates of the heavens." The Hebrew

phrases used here are *ma'yenoth tehom rabah* and *'aruboth hashamayim*, respectively.[16] The first refers to subterranean reservoirs, or aquifers, and the second, to heavy rain clouds. The quantity of water on, in, and around these earthly sources measures vastly less than the quantity required for global inundation—even if the highest preflood hills or mountains were no more than 500 feet above current sea levels.

Like most desert plains, the Gulf Oasis and Mesopotamia possessed geological features that favor formation of large aquifers. Certain geologic events can bring that water to the surface. And, while rain falls only rarely in Mesopotamia and the Persian Gulf region, an "act of God" could bring about the 40-day torrential downpour Genesis records.

To describe the receding of the floodwaters, Moses employed these four Hebrew words: *shākak* ("to subside" or abate"), *shûb* ("to return"; i.e., to return to its original place or condition), *kaser* ("to diminish" or "to be lessened"), and *qālal* ("to be diminished...i.e. had flowed away").[17] These verbs suggest that the floodwaters returned to the places from which they came, the aquifers and the clouds, where they remained for millennia and, presumably, until today. God moved the water from one location on Earth to another and then returned it. So what we see is what we have to work with in deriving our interpretation of the text.

### Ark's Landing Place

How often have you heard a speaker or teacher or documentary narrator say that Noah's Ark came to rest on Mount Ararat? Given Ararat's elevation, 16,945 feet (5,165 meters) above sea level, no wonder people envision the flood as covering all the high mountains of Earth. But that is not where the Ark landed.

Genesis 8:4 reports that the ark came to rest on the "mountains" (plural *har*) of Ararat, not on Mount Ararat. This distinction makes a significant interpretive difference. The entire Ararat range, actually a complex of ranges, extends from the north and east of Mount Ararat all the way south to the foothills skirting the Mesopotamian plain. This range encompasses an area measuring more than 100,000 square miles (250,000 square kilometers) with elevations ranging from the hundreds to the thousands of feet (or meters).[18]

According to the biblical text, Noah's ark could have come to rest anywhere within this vast region (see figure 18, page 181).

### Meaning of Earth

One recently developed argument for interpreting the flood as a global event is based on the use of the Hebrew words *'ereṣ* and *'ădāmâ* for "earth" or "world" throughout Genesis 6–8. Although each of these words can, and often does, denote "a specific territorial designation" (according to theologian Victor Hamilton[19]), this new argument says that if Moses intended to refer only to a portion of Earth's surface, he could have and would have chosen from among three other Hebrew nouns, *ḥārābâ, yabbāshâ,* or *ṣayôn.* These nouns' definitions never include the entirety of Earth's surface.

Ironically, *ḥārābâ,* which means "dry land"[20] does appear within the passage. It is used in Genesis 7:22. But, even apart from this weakness, the argument lacks credibility on other grounds, both linguistic and contextual.

A quick look at a biblical concordance reveals that *'ereṣ* is an often-used noun—the fourth most frequently used noun in the Old Testament, in fact. Only the words *yhwh* (LORD), *bēn* (son), and *'ĕlōhîm* (God) appear more often. It may be used for Earth in the cosmic sense, but most often it indicates a specific territory or land area. By contrast, *ḥārābâ, yabbāshâ,* and *ṣayôn* are used only rarely in the Old Testament. Given Moses' desire to communicate clearly to a broad audience, his preference for familiar nouns over obscure ones makes sense.

The English equivalents for *'ădāmâ* include "ground," "land," and "earth."[21] Theologian Leonard Coppes points out, "Originally this word signified the red arable soil. From this it came to denote any cultivated, plantable ground and/or landed property."[22] Given that only a fraction of the world's continental landmass may be described as arable, it seems unlikely that *'ădāmâ* could refer to all the land on Earth's surface. Rather, the use of *'ădāmâ* in Genesis 6–8 more likely implies that preflood humans limited their habitation to plantable land.

**Context as Key**

If we approach Genesis 6–8 from the perspective of both the author and the audience, we can understand why its language seems so strong as to evoke images of a global inundation. The flood was, indeed, a massively cataclysmic event, a total destruction of humanity and the animals associated with them, except those sheltered by Noah's unique craft. It was the most catastrophic event—and potent warning of sin's consequences—ever delivered to humankind.

Perhaps because English-speaking, English-reading people have for several centuries pictured Earth, its peoples and geographic features, in global terms, we forget that the ancients had no such images in their minds. The world meant people, the land meant the ground under their feet stretching from horizon to horizon. The highest mountains would be those within sight or walking distance of their homes.

Throughout the Bible, both Old and New Testaments, all references to and depictions of the Genesis flood support this ancient perspective. Not one passage indicates that the story should be understood otherwise. Even without considering the scientific evidence of the flood's extent, a compelling case can be made for seeing the event as worldwide, or universal, with respect to humanity, but less than global with respect to geography. For a glimpse at the scientific support for this biblical account as a plausibly truthful story, look to the next chapter.

# 17

# GLOBAL OR WORLDWIDE FLOOD? SCIENTIFIC EVIDENCE

The credibility of the biblical flood story has been called into question for all the wrong reasons. A misrepresentation of what the Bible actually says has been so widely disseminated for decades and so adamantly defended by sincere believers, including some with advanced degrees, that the real story seems all but drowned out. From a careful study of the Hebrew text, giving appropriate attention to its theological message and historical context, a clearer picture emerges. As it does, it reveals that to assert a global deluge is wholly unnecessary for upholding biblical inerrancy—as unnecessary as it is inconsistent, both internally and externally.

From a scientific standpoint, the assertion of a relatively brief, relatively recent global cataclysm that accounts for all of Earth's major geologic features flatly contradicts the physical evidence. The worldwide flood from which God rescued Noah and his family cannot—and need not, for defense of biblical truth—be put forth as a global scenario. That's not to say, however, that no evidence exists for an event as devastating as the Bible describes.

### Availability of Flood Evidence

The Genesis flood must have been enormous by anyone's understanding of the biblical account. To float a vessel 450 feet long by 75 feet wide by 45 feet high or larger (based on cubit measures given and assuming the short cubit measure[1]) takes a lot of water. For a time Noah could see no land from horizon to horizon.[2] According to best estimates, such a flood would require about six billion acre-feet of water or more.

Most readers assume that a deluge of such proportions would leave behind substantial evidence, a deposit or other markers that geologists today *should* be able to identify definitively. Several large alluvial flood deposits have been found in the Mesopotamian plain.[3] One or more could possibly (though not likely) fit the time range for the Genesis flood. However, the lack of a precise date for the flood hinders any firm conclusions.

More importantly, the assumption that clear evidence "should" remain must be challenged. The flood, though massive for sure, lasted a mere year and ten days. A major flood of such brief duration typically does not leave a deposit substantial enough to be positively identified thousands of years later.

The Mississippi River flood of 1927 and the Mississippi and Missouri Rivers flood of 1993 provide an example of this point. Several regions, some larger than 100 miles long and 50 miles wide, were inundated. Parts of the flooded area remained under more than thirty feet of water for several months. Yet, just a few decades later, all evidence of flood deposits from these disasters has disappeared. On this basis (among many others) geologists would not expect a 150-day long flood covering the Persian Gulf, Mesopotamia, and parts of the Arabian Peninsula even by as much as several hundred feet to leave behind sufficient evidence for a positive geological identification some tens of thousands of years later.

**Geographical and Other Markers**
Despite a lack of direct geological evidence, other indications for the flood's timing, location, and extent do exist. Some of these have been addressed in the discussion of early human history, also in dates for Adam through Noah (see chapter 7) and of Eden's most likely location (see chapter 10). Evidence suggests a thriving civilization developed thousands of years ago in a region called the Gulf Oasis (see chapter 10), a place that was dry during the last ice age but now sits under the Persian Gulf.

Biblical place names and other descriptive details in the first two chapters of Genesis, including the mention of four major rivers, point to this locale as the likely vicinity not only of Eden but also of the world in Noah's time. Based on humanity's refusal to disperse even after the flood we can surmise this is where many of Noah's descendants continued to dwell. The archaeological remains of ancient human settlements there would, of course, belong to postflood people, given that any traces of preflood habitation would have been destroyed in the inundation.

From a geographical perspective, this location makes sense as the region where the flood occurred. It was habitable and arable roughly 40,000 years ago, a rough estimate of when Noah lived (see chapter 7). Huge aquifers reside under this region, the potential "springs of the deep" mentioned in the account, and high mountains surround it. In addition, it offers a fairly easy migration route into eastern Africa, where genetic diversity is high.

Taking all these factors (and more) into account, the latest scholarship proposes that the Genesis flood covered all of Mesopotamia, the entire Persian Gulf region, and much of southern Arabia, as well (see figure 17.1).

### Global Argument Overview

Advocacy of the global flood perspective has an intriguing history in itself, briefly reviewed in chapter 21. The emergence of what is called "flood geology" accompanied development of "creation science," a recent-creation perspective founded on belief that the Genesis creation days consisted of six consecutive 24-hour periods. As a globally catastrophic event of immense proportions, the flood could be invoked to explain away a host of geophysical markers for Earth's old age, thought to be a foundational pillar supporting biological evolution.

Global flood models have grown more and more complex as evidence for Earth's 4.566-billion-year history has mounted. Sadly, the more vigorously Christians have promoted such models, the more virulent the reaction of the scientific community and of the culture influenced by it. For this reason, the models' major tenets must be explained and addressed. The discussion may become technically challenging, but a thorough response may help deflect unnecessary ridicule and rejection of biblical truth.

Arguments for—and responses to—various global flood scenarios focus primarily on these topics, each of which will be addressed in the sections that follow:
- Widespread marine fossils and sediments
- Water source and rapid plate tectonics
- Radiometric decay rates
- Biodeposit quantities, and
- Animal "diversification"

Some require more scientific depth than others to evaluate, but each raises questions and issues frequently presented in books, articles, and public presentations advocating the global flood interpretation.

### Widespread Marine Fossils and Sediments

The existence of sedimentary layers and marine fossils on all seven continents and in multiple mountain ranges may seem a convincing sign that the flood covered the whole Earth, but they are not. Vast regions of the continents and larger islands lack any fossils or sedimentary layers. Likewise, fossil fuel deposits are found on just a small percentage of Earth's landmasses.

While it is true that Earth's highest mountains, the Himalayas, including even

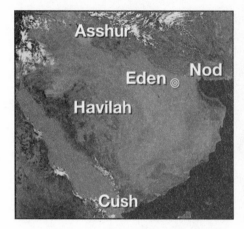 

## Figure 17.1: Extent of Noah's Flood

The top left map shows probable landmasses around Arabia just prior to the Genesis flood. With ice still covering much of North America, Siberia, and Europe, global sea levels would have been lower, leaving most of what is now the Persian Gulf and Red Sea dry. The top right map shows the probable extent of Noah's flood at its peak, a little over 300,000 square miles. After the flood, people would have had an easy migration route into east Africa. An early migration could explain the relatively high genetic diversity of present-day sub-Saharans. The bottom map shows the current sea levels around the Arabian Peninsula. The target symbol indicates the proposed location of the Garden of Eden.

Credit for the satellite image of Arabia: NASA

Mount Everest, are littered with marine fossils, geophysicists recognize these fossils as evidence of something other than a global inundation. They see the power of plate tectonics.

For example, the Indian subcontinent bears little resemblance, geologically, to central Asia—adjacent to it—because it belongs to a different piece of Earth's crust. From its past location adjacent to Madagascar and Antarctica in the south Indian Ocean, the Indian subcontinent drifted northward (and still does). As it approached Asia, the ocean floor between it and the Asian plate buckled upward to form the Himalayas. This rising piece of ocean floor that still rises at an average uplift rate of 15 mm annually carried marine fossils with it.

The uplift and northward movement of the Himalayas shows no major discontinuities. Consequently, geophysicists conclude that both the movement of the Indian Plate into the Eurasian Plate and the uplift of the Himalayas have been proceeding almost continuously for approximately the past 15 million years.[4] Thus, major portions of this plate movement and marine layer uplift predate the Genesis flood by many, many years.

Likewise, North America's vast alluvial plain arose from events of the far distant past. The prairies lay under a huge shallow sea for tens of millions of years. This ancient sea is largely responsible for the region's abundant sea fossils and huge limestone and fossil-fuel deposits, deposits far too vast to be laid down in just one year. Also, a number of independent dating techniques show that the prairies emerged from under water more than 200 million years ago, long before the Genesis flood.

**Water Source and Rapid Plate Tectonics**
Global flood models face a serious water shortage. To inundate all of Earth's surface would require more than four times the sum of all the water currently present in Earth's oceans and lakes, in Earth's atmosphere, and within Earth's crust. Therefore, global flood proponents have conjectured that Earth's mountains before the flood were no more than a few hundred feet above sea level. Even if that were the case, however, our planet's water supply is insufficient to completely cover them.

The water problem for global flood models led, in part, to the canopy idea, the hypothesis that a thick water canopy once surrounded Earth and collapsed at the time of the flood (see chapter 13). When this canopy idea essentially fell through, a second proposal came forward: a sudden uplift of Earth's ocean basins as the cause of tsunamis that flooded all Earth's landmasses just as a torrential downpour occurred.

The torrential-downpour hypothesis poses a problem in itself. The laws of physics and the temperature of Earth's surface place a hard limit on how much water can evaporate from Earth's oceans and lakes. Hard limits also apply to the percentage of the evaporated water that at any given time can condense as rain. These physical limitations would permit torrential rain to fall for forty consecutive days on one region of Earth's surface but not on all of Earth's surface at the same time.

The favored solution to the water problem in the latest and best-developed global flood models, therefore, is to posit extremely aggressive tectonic activity, both vertical and lateral. Global flood proponents well-versed in paleontology and geology recognize the certainty of the scientific case for Earth's continents' once being joined to form a single landmass, the supercontinent Pangaea. Because their models require a geologic time frame of ten thousand years (or less) and humanity's presence throughout all the years of Earth's existence, the supercontinent breakup must occur within the 375-day flood episode.

All this uplift and lateral tectonic activity would have been accompanied, in the global deluge scenarios, with equally aggressive erosion forces. The claim is that virtually all of Earth's tectonic activity, geological formations, fossilization, coal, oil, natural gas, gypsum, and limestone deposits, and more must be attributed to one flood event, which lasted one year and ten days.

In other words, many of Earth's mountains must have been pushed up by tens of thousands of feet and many of Earth's ocean trenches and basins pressed down by still more tens of thousands of feet in that time period. Meanwhile, Pangaea must have split apart, with the resultant continental pieces quickly separating by 5,000 miles or more. At the same time, virtually all Earth's biodeposits must have been laid down and all volcanic action, crustal layering, sedimentation, metamorphosis, and visible erosion squeezed into the flood's 13-month time window.

One of many challenges to the plausibility of such a scenario comes from the fact that the energy required to make these radical alterations in such a brief time exceeds by many orders of magnitude what the laws of physics permit—and what the planet could actually survive. To address this problem, global flood models assign temporary radical changes to the "constants" of physics during the flood's time frame. For example, the models assert that normally long-lived radiometric isotopes such as thorium-232, uranium-235, and uranium-238, must have decayed about a billion times faster in that period than what we can measure today.[5] Thus, ultrarapid decay would supposedly generate sufficient energy to compress all this transformation activity into a period barely longer than a year—and yield radiometric dates for Earth's age in the thousands rather than billions of years.

**Radiometric Decay Rates**

Virtually all global flood models are framed in the context of a recently created Earth and all these models depend fundamentally on extremely aggressive plate tectonic activity, which, in turn, depends on vastly accelerated radiometric decay rates. However, from a biblical perspective alone, this radical, temporary acceleration can be ruled out. Scripture tells us that the laws of heaven and earth are "fixed,"[6] unchanging from the moment God put them in place (see chapter 11). Further, because God's purpose is to make Himself known to humanity, He does not deceive. When He acts to interrupt the normal order of reality, He leaves evidence for us to find. Even in the event of Christ's bodily resurrection from death, He provided ample physical evidence so that people would know with profound certainty what His power had accomplished.

From a scientific perspective, multiple independent lines of evidence contradict the hypothesis of a radiometric decay-rate change during Noah's flood. A brief overview of this evidence is provided here for those who wish to review it.

**a) Astronomical evidence:** Because astronomers routinely observe stars, nebulae, and galaxies hundreds, thousands, millions, and billions of light-years distant, they *directly* observe radiometric isotopes as they existed hundreds, thousands, million, and billions of years ago. Through straightforward measurement of these isotopes' abundances, astronomers verify that radiometric decay rates have remained the same throughout cosmic history. Likewise, astronomers, through their observations of hyperfine spectral lines in distant stars and galaxies, have established that light's velocity has never varied throughout cosmic history.[7] Furthermore, they have demonstrated that the constancy of light's velocity is essential to life's existence.[8]

**b) Core drill evidence:** By drilling deep into the ice of permanently frozen regions of Earth, scientists can remove "cores" and directly observe annual layers. Three ice cores from Antarctica have been most revealing. The Dome C core provides a continuous record of the past 800,000 years; Dome F, of 720,000 years; and Vostok, of 420,000 years.[9] Three additional ice cores from northern and central Greenland (NGRIP, GRIP, and GISP2) show us the past 105,000 to 123,000 years of Earth history.[10]

Confidence that each layer corresponds to a year comes from two validation approaches: (1) by identification of the dust signatures of known volcanic eruptions, and (2) by observation of subtle variations in ice layer thickness. With respect to volcanic dust, we know the Krakatoa eruption took place in 1883 and many eruptions of Vesuvius, including the one that destroyed Pompeii in 79 AD. By counting layers between the layers that contain the dust signatures of these eruptions, researchers have confirmed that each layer does, indeed, correspond to one year.

Variations in the layers' thickness correlate with changes in the eccentricity of Earth's orbit. (Eccentricity is a measure of the noncircularity of an elliptical orbit.) As Earth's eccentricity varies according to a well-established 100,000-year cycle (due primarily to the gravitational influences of Jupiter and Saturn on Earth's orbit), seasonal temperatures change in direct proportion. These changes affect layer thickness. The cyclical changes in Earth's orbit about the Sun are clearly seen in the thickness fluctuation within the Antarctica ice cores (see figure 17.2), further demonstrating that these layers represent years.

In some glaciated regions ice melts and refreezes several times within a year, generating multiple ice layers per year. For example, at a location in southern Greenland, World War II fighter planes were found under 250 feet of ice.[11] The ice cores mentioned above, however, all were drilled in high altitude interior regions of Greenland and Antarctica, hundreds of miles from the nearest seacoasts. There, only one melting and freezing episode occurs within a year, as confirmed by the signatures of volcanic eruptions and Earth's orbital eccentricity cycle.

One of the many benefits these ice cores offer to researchers is the opportunity to study radiometric isotopes contained within the annual layers. This analysis has provided further confirmation that radiometric decay rates have remained constant throughout the past hundreds of thousands of years of Earth's history. (Carbon-14 decay is an exception. Cosmic rays are the primary stimulator of carbon-14 decay. The ice core data reveals the expected small variations in the carbon-14 decay rate in response to changes in the cosmic ray flux.) What's more, no evidence of a flood event appears in the ice cores' record for either Greenland's past 123,000 years or Antarctica's past 800,000 years.

Still more validation comes from a study of a marine sediment core drilled off the coast of South Island, New Zealand. Its layers reveal some 3.9 million years of the southern hemisphere's climatic history.[12] This sediment core shows the same 100,000-year cycle of variation in Earth's eccentricity as do the three deep Antarctic ice cores, as well as the same evidence for the constancy of the radiometric decay rates and the same lack of evidence for a massive flood. By all indications, the flood did not extend as far as Greenland, Antarctica, or New Zealand.

c) Tree ring evidence: Analysis of tree rings, the work of dendrochronologists, cannot reveal the same length of history as ice and sediment cores show us, but they do provide a view of the period most relevant to global flood models.

The bristlecone pine chronology of the American Southwest now exceeds 8,500 years (5,000 years from living trees and an extra 3,500 years by overlapping the ring data of living trees with that from dead trees in the same area), and some 3,000 years may be added as research continues.[13] The European oak and pine chronology, a composite of work done in Germany and Northern Ireland, now extends over the past 11,000 years.[14] And botanists have discovered that a Palmer's Oak in the Jurupa Hills of Rubidoux, California, reproduces through generating exact clones near its (original) trunk. The dimensions of that cloned stand and tree ring counts within it show that this particular oak tree is the world's oldest known living plant at 15,600±2,500 years.[15] Here, too, volcanic eruptions in recorded history have left their signatures in specific tree rings, verifying that the rings correspond to years.

Again, as with layers in the ice and sediment cores, the annual rings of these ancient trees contain radiometric isotopes. Analysis of these isotopes confirms that radiometric decay rates (other than that of carbon-14) have remained invariant throughout the past 15,000 years. This study also demonstrates that the American Southwest and Western Europe have not experienced a flood of continental proportions within the past 15,000 and 11,000 years respectively.

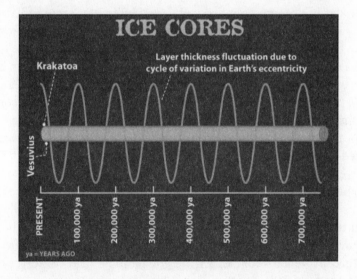

**Figure 17.2: Earth's Eccentricity Cycles Seen in an Ice Core**
The 800,000 layers in the Dome C Antarctic ice core reveal layer thickness variations (schematically drawn) corresponding with the 100,000-year periodic variation in the eccentricity of Earth's orbit. Also evident in the annual layers are dust signatures of volcanic eruptions that occurred throughout recorded history.
Credit: Phil Chien

**d) Biological evidence:** With respect to complex life, and even some relatively simple life-forms, radiometric decay is not benign. Had the ark's passengers been exposed to vastly accelerated radiometric decay, they would not have survived. Yet they did. Genesis 11 says that Noah lived an additional 349 years after the flood, and Shem for an additional 502 years.

Given the life-exterminating impact of greatly accelerated radiometric decay rates, some global flood models suggest that the great depth of water underneath the ark protected the life on board.[16] One problem with this response, however, lies in the variation of the water's depth, not to mention the high levels of floodwater turbulence. This turbulence would bring sediments up to the surface, and these sediments, loaded with radiometric isotopes, would have killed all creatures on the ark—if, in fact, radiometric decay rates were greatly accelerated.

Sediments in the floodwaters would not have been the only concern for the ark's inhabitants. Radiometric isotopes would have existed throughout the ark's wood and pitch, the supplies on board the ark, and even in the bodies of every life-form on the ark. The ark's life also would have been exposed to deadly radiation from atmospheric dust and even from the Moon.

The water itself represents a concern. Currently, 80 percent of Earth's internal heat comes from decay of radioactive isotopes.[17] The heat flow from Earth's interior to its surface is such that each square meter of Earth's surface is warmed by about a tenth of a watt, just a tiny fraction of what it receives from the Sun.[18] However, with radiometric decay rates as much as a billion times greater during the flood episode, each square meter of Earth's surface would have become about 100,000 times warmer than it is today. The Sun itself would have been hotter as a result of exponentially higher radiometric decay. This much heat would have evaporated all of Earth's water and melted all of its crust, not to mention how it would have impacted conditions on the ark.

In light of this data, some global models invoke a cooling of Earth through a hyperexpansion of the universe during the flood episode. Others hypothesize cooling through a volumetric expansion of the Earth and the Sun. The problem with the first proposal is that cosmic expansion is irrelevant to Earth's physical temperature. In such a situation Earth's gravitational field conserves terrestrial heat energy and, thus, is not a heat sink.[19] The problem with the second proposal is that while a major increase in the volume of the Sun and Earth could have the potential to cool things down for the ark and its inhabitants, the necessary expansion factors would have catastrophic effects. They would rip Earth apart and extinguish the Sun's fusion furnace. Meanwhile, they would do nothing to diminish the radiation and heat emanating from radioactive isotopes in the ark's wood, the ark's supplies, or in the bodies of the animals and humans on board the ark.

## 1. Implausible Plate Tectonics

Global flood models rely heavily and universally, as already stated, on plate tectonic activity as the one known mechanism to account for the formation, movement, and restructuring of Earth's oceans and continents and for the location of Earth's fossils.[20] The difference between these models and mainstream geophysical models is that global flood scenarios squeeze several billion years' worth of tectonic activity into an extremely brief time window, one *less* than a year wide.

Genesis 8:2–4 tells us Noah's ark came to rest on the mountains of Ararat just 150 days after the floodwaters first began to rise. Any major tectonic activity after that time would have destroyed the ark and killed its occupants. The same would be true in the earliest stage of the deluge, as water is just beginning to lift the ark above the ground. Thus, a period somewhat briefer than 150 days is the total time available for tectonic arrangement of all Earth's geological features, according to global flood geophysics.

Such a perspective requires lateral continental movement of as much as 5,000–8,000 miles. All this movement must be compressed into less than a 150-day time frame. This amount of movement averages out to 125–200 feet per minute. Such a rate of continental movement can be compared with that observed in the March 11, 2011, earthquake that struck off the northeastern coast of Japan. During the 5–6 minute duration of that magnitude 9 earthquake, a 500-mile strip of Honshu Island running from Tokyo to Sendai moved laterally by no more than 8 feet.[21] The average rate of continental movement demanded by global flood models is 80–125 times greater.

In other words, for about 150 days Earth would have been battered by the force of about 42,000 consecutive magnitude 11 earthquakes (a magnitude 11 earthquake releases 100 times the energy of a magnitude 9 earthquake). However, the structure of Earth's crust is not conducive to continual steady movement of crustal plates. Instead, the plates lock, then lurch, lock again, and lurch again. Thus, rather than earthquakes being a continual phenomenon, they are episodic. Therefore, global flood models propose what amounts to hundreds of magnitude 13 earthquakes or thousands of magnitude 12 earthquakes, accompanied by hundreds of supervolcanic eruptions, hundreds more volcanic island collapses, and hundreds of devastating tsunamis (see "The Tsunami Problem" on page 165).

The effects of such concentrated volcanism, erosion, and tectonics, had they occurred during the past few thousand or tens of thousands of years, would surely be observable and measurable by geophysicists today.[22] Fault lines scarring the planet would be more numerous and much larger, by far, than what we see. Although researchers see ample evidence of geological catastrophes in Earth's history, these major catastrophes date long before the arrival of the first humans. Meanwhile, many more of Earth's features testify of long-enduring gradual processes.

### 2. The Aftermath

Genesis 7–9 gives no indication that the ark or its inhabitants suffered any physical trauma either during or after the 150 days. Noah and his family exited the ark without noteworthy injuries.

Genesis 8:11 reports that the dove Noah released from the ark plucked an olive leaf and carried it to him while the floodwaters were still receding. No olive tree, let alone its leaves, would have survived thousands of miles of tectonic movement, thousands of feet of erosion, and violent volcanic eruptions packed into less than a year's time.

Genesis 9 tells us that Noah began productive agriculture immediately after leaving the ark—impossible if extreme erosion and tectonics had rearranged the landscape. Aftershocks from large tectonic events would have continued for many years, making agriculture, buildings, and even basic existence impossible for many decades beyond the flood event itself. The absence of these ongoing aftereffects in the Genesis 8–9 narrative further contradicts the notion of a global cataclysm.

### Biodeposit Quantities

Perhaps the most difficult challenge facing global flood models arises from research into the quantity of Earth's biodeposits—coal, oil, natural gas, kerogen, clathrates, gypsum, limestone, phosphates, insoluble metals, topsoil, and more. Global flood models propose that the sum total of all these materials came from plant and animal death on Earth at the time of the flood.

Fossil fuels alone present an insurmountable obstacle to such a proposal. Total known oil reserves prior to the industrial revolution amounted to 8.3–11.3 trillion barrels—some 3.0–4.5 trillion barrels of conventional oil, 2.5–3.5 trillion barrels of tar sand oil, and 2.8–3.3 trillion barrels of shale oil.[23] These figures include only the conceivably recoverable oil. Preindustrial revolution known coal reserves, including both currently economically and potentially recoverable coal, amounted to 4.0 trillion short tons (equivalent to 17 trillion barrels of oil).[24] Natural gas reserves prior to the twentieth century were an estimated 9.4–10.8 quadrillion cubic feet (equivalent to 1.7–1.9 trillion barrels of oil).[25] Thus, total known fossil fuel reserves before the industrial revolution stood at 27.0–30.2 trillion barrels of oil equivalent.

## The Tsunami Problem

History shows that ships in the middle of deep oceans easily ride out tsunamis generated by magnitude 8 and 9 earthquakes. Such tsunami waves, though moving at the speed of sound (768 miles per hour), typically measure only about a foot high amid deep oceans. And, because the wavelengths of tsunami waves in the deep ocean are typically 100–200 miles, a single wave takes from 8 to 20 minutes to pass by. Thus, people on board ships in deep oceans rarely notice a passing tsunami.

However, a series of magnitude 11 (or greater) earthquakes would generate significantly larger tsunamis. And, if all the earthquake energy proposed by global flood models were distributed throughout the time the ark was adrift, the ark's inhabitants would likely have experienced unending seasickness or injuries from falling. Seasick creatures find it difficult to eat and retain food.

As an additional problem, severe tectonic activity generates erosion events of devastating proportions. Indeed, calamitous disasters are a core feature of every global flood model. The more dramatic erosion events include landslides and volcanic cone collapses, both above and below water. Such events produce a whole new category of tsunamis. For example, the 1958 Lituya Bay landslide caused a tsunami wave over 1,700 feet high. Thus, the ark's inhabitants would have faced a far greater threat than ceaseless seasickness. Tsunamis of this kind inevitably would have pushed the ark into shallow seas where any type of tsunami could easily destroy it.

Unlike reserves, resources represent the world's total fossil fuel deposits, regardless of their commercial accessibility. Geologists have a reasonably good measure for pre-industrial revolution coal resources, namely 10.5–14.5 trillion short tons.[26] Likewise, they have determined that conventional natural gas resources stood at about 13 quadrillion cubic feet[27] while shale natural gas resources equaled 16–20 quadrillion cubic feet.[28] American geologist Richard Nehring placed the measure of known conventional oil resources at 7.0 trillion barrels, tar sand oil at 4.1 trillion barrels, shale oil at 3.2 trillion barrels, and mature source rock oil at 5–20 trillion barrels, a total of 19.3–34.3 trillion barrels.[29] Thus, the quantity of pre-industrial revolution fossil fuel resources stood at 58.8–81.8 trillion barrels of oil equivalent.

Traditionally recognized fossil fuel resources, however, comprise just a minor component of the residue of once-living matter. The major components are kerogen, clathrate, and limestone. Kerogen includes the remains of diatoms, spores, planktons, bacteria, and pollens embedded in sedimentary rocks. Clathrate is a crystalline combination of natural gas and water. It can form under below-freezing temperatures or high-pressure conditions. Thus, it is found under oceans and in polar permafrost. Limestone is composed primarily of various calcium carbonate crystals from the skeletal fragments of marine organisms such as coral, mollusks, ooids, peloids, intraclasts, extraclasts, and foraminifera. Many limestone deposits also contain siliceous fragments from diatoms, sponge spicules, and radiolarians.

Geochemists estimate that the total quantity of kerogen in Earth's crust equals 100–10,000 times the total quantity of traditional fossil fuel resources. This estimate accounts for only some of the kerogen that has ever existed on Earth. Bacteria continuously consume huge quantities of kerogen.[30]

As for natural gas trapped in clathrate, a "central consensus" estimate obtained from multiple independent investigators using varied estimation methods determined the quantity to be at least 742 quadrillion cubic feet.[31] Theoretically, as much as 270,000 quadrillion cubic feet of natural gas could exist in hydrate deposits.[32]

## Table 17: Inventory of Biodeposits

| Source | Quantity (in quadrillions of tons) |
|---|---|
| coal, oil, and natural gas | 0.009–0.013 |
| clathrates | 0.020–7.17 |
| kerogen | 0.9–90 |
| organics in limestone | 75–120 |
| **total** | 76–217 |

Sedimentary rock makes up 7.9 percent of the total volume of Earth's crust.[33] Limestone and marble comprise at least 6 percent of this sedimentary rock.[34] The skeletal fragments of marine organisms comprise 80–90 percent of this limestone and marble.[35] Given that the average thickness of continental crust is 40 kilometers (about 25 miles) and of oceanic crust, 7 kilometers (a little more than 4 miles),[36] the quantity of biological material present in Earth's limestone is at least 29 million cubic kilometers (roughly 7 million cubic miles), or 6.8 x $10^{16}$ tonnes (75 quadrillion tons).[37]

As table 17 shows, the minimum quantity of Earth's biological material—not including topsoil, phosphates, or sulfate-reduced (insoluble) metal ores—equals 76 quadrillion tons. In other words, the biological material embedded in Earth's crust exceeds Earth's current living biomass (625 billion tons[38]) by at least 122,000 times (maximum of 348,000 times).

If this quantity seems small in view of Earth's 3.8-billion-year biological history, the explanation comes from the second law of thermodynamics—in biblical terms, "bondage to decay."[39] Because God has subjected everything in the universe to the law of decay,[40] no transfer of energy (for example, solar energy into sugars and fats) proceeds with 100 percent efficiency. Biodeposits are laid down with far less than 0.1 percent efficiency. Even if life were considerably more abundant on Earth when the flood began, and if all that life were laid down as biodeposits with the maximum efficiency the laws of physics permit, its sum total in Earth's crust would fall far short of what is known to exist.

### Model Adjustments

The challenge presented by the quantity of Earth's biodeposits has propelled some adjustments to global flood models.[41] The first is to suggest that only a tiny fraction of Earth's limestone, clathrates, and kerogen are biological in origin. Another is to propose that prior to the flood Earth's land and atmospheric conditions were structured in such a way as to sustain a biomass a hundred times greater than it carries today. A third is to hypothesize that the flood transformed a huge quantity of dead biological material accumulating on Earth's surface from the time of Adam to the time of Noah (in their models 1,656 years) into biodeposits.

The first adjustment falters on carbon isotope evidence. Biologically derived material manifests a lower carbon-13 to carbon-12 ratio than does nonbiological material. Geophysicists find ubiquitous evidence for this lower ratio in deposits of limestone, clathrates, and kerogen.[42] Researchers also note that methane hydrates (clathrates) occur predominantly near continental margins, at water depths of 350–3,000 meters and none at all below 5,000 meters. Those are the depths at which sufficient organic material is deposited into the sediments and where the temperature and pressure conditions permit biologically derived methane to be converted into methane hydrates. If the methane in the hydrates were not mainly biogenic, clathrates would be much more broadly distributed.

The second adjustment, which posits a single, vast continent near the equator with growing conditions similar to those of the Amazonian rainforest and enhanced by a water vapor canopy, would yield an even distribution of biodeposits across all continental landmasses. Such is not the case. Biodeposit distribution is, in fact, highly uneven. Coal and oil, for example, are found within just a few locales on each of Earth's continents. More than 90 percent of the planet's continental landmass area is devoid of *any* deposits of oil, coal, or natural gas.

Still another problem with this proposal, apart from the failure of all canopy hypotheses (see chapter 13), lies in the quantity of ice overlaying Antarctica and Greenland. If these lands had belonged to tropical climate zones before the flood, their current quantity of ice must have accumulated in just the last few thousand years (4,300–5,000 years, according to global flood models).[43] The measured thickness of Antarctic ice exceeds 4,770 meters (15,650 feet)[44] and the average annual precipitation for the Antarctic continent is 6.5 inches, even less in the regions of thickest ice.[45] Even if none of the snow and ice in Antarctica were to sublimate (pass from solid to vapor state) and none of it were to undergo compression from overlying ice, the ice is still 12 times thicker than what global flood models allow.

The third adjustment rests on the assertion that under benign conditions, dead biological material could accumulate without any substantial loss from decay processes. However, God has designed Earth's organisms in such a way that after death, when exposed to the elements, they degrade. And that degrading is rapid, on the order of months and years, not centuries or more. This rapid process is crucial to the nutrient recycling that a biologically diverse, biologically rich planet such as Earth requires.

Furthermore, much of Earth's biomass is comprised of detritivores (species that feed on dead biological matter) and decomposers. Detritivores play the major role in clearing the environment of dead organic material. Decomposers convert what is left over, such as bone and fur, into raw soil nutrients such as carbon, nitrogen, calcium, and magnesium compounds. Thus, under benign conditions only a small percentage of dead biological material accumulates.

### Animal "Diversification"

A global inundation would mean, of course, that all land animals (plus sea animals and plants, too, given the devastating plate tectonics) alive today or at any time since the flood descended from the pairs aboard Noah's vessel. Because the biblical account (Genesis 6:15–16) gives us the ark's dimensions—about 450 feet long, 75 feet wide, and 45 feet high—and recent research provides a determination of the number of land-dwelling animal species on Earth today—5.8 million[46]—we have a basis for testing the model.

If the ark carried pairs of the birds and mammals Noah and his family would need to quickly reestablish both their livelihood and their worship practices after the flood, anywhere from hundreds to a few thousand species, its space would be sufficient, and eight people could potentially look after them. No one questions that the number of current species, minus the many species that have gone extinct in the past 5,000 years or more, would not fit. Even if one-tenth of these species were aboard the ark and if most went into some kind of hibernation, the idea that eight people could care for their needs, feeding them and cleaning up after them, defies reality.

To address this issue, global flood models propose that Noah saved only pairs of each family or order, rather than a pair of every species of land animal (disregarding plants and sea creatures). Earth's current 5.8 million land animal species arose after the flood, according to this perspective, through biological "descent with variation."[47] By this strictly natural process, a few thousand pairs rapidly evolved into millions. Zebras, horses, and several other horselike creatures are said to have evolved (or "diversified"[48]) from a single horse-like pair.[49] The entire cat family—tigers, lions, leopards, cheetahs, panthers, bobcats, and more, including the ancestors of housecats—likewise are claimed to have evolved from a single cat pair on the ark.[50] These proposals would seem to trade one implausible hypothesis for another. Animals, especially those as advanced as horses and felines, simply do not—and cannot, by any observed or postulated mechanism—evolve or diversify at such a rapid rate (see chapters 6 and 9). Not even the most optimistic nontheistic evolutionary biologist would support this possibility because it contradicts firmly established biological limitations.[51]

### The Point

Behind this lengthy though still incomplete discussion of issues relevant to the Genesis flood stands a dual purpose. The first is to offer a theologically sound, biblically consistent, and scientifically plausible interpretation of the flood account for any Bible reader. The flood demonstrates God's care in preserving humanity from self-extermination. The deluge extended only as far as necessary to impact the entire world, as defined by its human population. The scientific evidence supports the plausibility of a sufficiently devastating inundation and a sufficiently sizeable watercraft with a sufficient collection of animals to fulfill God's purposes.

The second aim of this dual goal is to remove one major barrier to belief in the Bible as God's Word, the geophysically impossible *global* flood. As demonstrated in this chapter, such an event defies plausibility. While God can and does, on occasion, perform miracles that override the laws of physics (which He established)[52] He would have no reason to remove the evidence of His having done so. For example, when Jesus raised Lazarus from the dead, He did not hide Lazarus so that no other human being could determine Lazarus was alive. Nor did Jesus conceal Lazarus' grave clothes so that no one could see the man had truly been buried. Why would God speed up radiometric decay rates by a factor of a billion and then remove the evidence of that acceleration from ice and sediment core layers, radiation output of the Sun and stars, and isotopes observed in the Sun, stars, and on Earth's surface? God's revelation through nature's record is trustworthy, not deceptive. Consequently, skeptics cannot use either the biblical flood account or nature's record as an excuse for rejecting the inerrancy of Scripture.

# 18

# THE ARK'S PASSENGERS:
# GENESIS 6–9

Depictions of giraffes, lions, alligators, elephants, pythons, polar bears, kangaroos, penguins, Komodo dragons, monkeys, jaguars, and more marching up the ramp of a big ship or posing on its deck remain firmly fixed in most people's minds and rise to the surface when the name Noah is mentioned. These images, as appealing as they may be in children's picture books, raise questions and doubts, too, and draw ridicule from skeptics. Even those who get past questions about the flood's intent and extent face challenges from a host of additional issues needing plausible explanations:

- Where did Noah obtain the technology and resources to build such a huge vessel?
- How could eight people possibly care for all the ark's animals?[1]
- How could a wooden ship of the dimensions outlined in Genesis possibly be seaworthy?[2]
- If the flood was less than global, why bother to build an ark rather than move Noah's family and animals to high ground?

Learning about these issues—the ark's design and construction, its passengers, and its cargo—can help answer doubts about the credibility of the flood story *without* resorting to the conclusion that it must be allegorical—or a borrowed legend.

## Why an Ark?
Given the flood's geographically limited (though worldwide) destruction, a reader may wonder why God did not deal with Noah's situation as He did with Lot's later on—rescue by evacuation.[3] God could have instructed Noah to pack up and depart to a region far away where he and his family and livestock would be out of harm's way.

Two reasons stand out. First, when God pours out judgment, He gives ample warning. He sends a spokesperson, a prophet, and gives that prophet some kind of platform, pulpit, or dramatic device for drawing people's attention. Prior to the flood, Noah was that prophet and the scaffolding around the ark served as his platform.

The efforts of a distinguished patriarch, to build an enormous vessel in the middle of a desert plain that receives scant rainfall certainly would have commanded attention. Noah's persistent devotion to an immensely challenging project for a hundred years would have heightened the drama. As crowds gathered to jeer, Noah patiently preached. He warned his listeners of impending doom if they refused to repent of their evil ways. He freely offered passage to anyone who would heed his warning and call upon God for mercy. Perhaps one reason for the enormous size of the ship was to demonstrate the sincerity of this offer.

The New Testament confirms that Noah gave time to being "a preacher of righteousness."[4] Noah "condemned the world,"[5] not so much in words as by the example of his faith while he, like God, "waited patiently."[6] He could have built the ark much faster if he had spent less time preaching, but the magnitude of the coming disaster compelled him to provide ample warning to his contemporaries.

**What about Lot?**

Lot's circumstances contrast with Noah's in several ways. Noah was faced with ubiquitous moral degeneration. Lot was not. For Lot, the moral degeneration was limited to Sodom and the adjoining cities of the plain. Lot was not a native to Sodom. He moved there as an adult and served for some time as a "judge" at Sodom's city gate. Thus, Lot had a ready platform from which to preach.[7] Sodom was small compared to Mesopotamia, and its population tiny by comparison with the whole of humanity. One short trip would remove Lot and his family from danger and from an area not necessarily vital to humanity's survival.

As it was for Noah and Lot, so it was for Moses, Isaiah, Jeremiah, Ezekiel, Jonah, and every other righteous man facing a wicked society. God always sends a warning of impending judgment. He always sends a prophet and a pulpit in advance. He always offers rescue to those who will repent.

**The Building Project**

Some skepticism about Noah's ability to construct the ark comes from the fact that until the late nineteenth century, no person or nation had ever built such a huge vessel. The largest commercial wooden ships were the mid-nineteenth century clipper ships, a little more than three hundred feet long. Given the tensile strength of oak lumber, shipbuilders of the past recognized the impracticality of building larger vessels. How, then, could Noah's engineering capability and resources outstrip those of much later shipbuilding professionals?

Again, we must look closely at contextual details. First, Noah's ark was not intended for sailing speedily across oceans. Rather, it simply had to float on flooded plains. Engineering requirements for a barge-type vessel with no particular destination differ greatly from those of a three-masted schooner. Second, Noah faced none of the economic constraints pressuring nineteenth-century shipbuilders, whose goal was to transport as much cargo for as little money as possible over vast distances. They did not push their oak shipbuilding designs very far, for they eventually discovered that for very large vessels, steel offered greater economy. Unlike the nineteenth-century shipbuilders, Noah could consider various options for his building materials.

According to the Genesis text, Noah used "gopher wood" to build the ark. This type of wood cannot be identified today with any certainty. We have no way to know all the different kinds of trees that might have grown in and around the regions of the Persian Gulf Oasis and Mesopotamia. We do know that hardwoods such as walnut are much stronger than oak. Some tropical timbers are denser than water with tensile strengths matching that of certain metals. Woods like these would have been more plentiful, we can surmise, in the era before widespread construction of huge buildings and palaces. Therefore, access to timbers of the necessary strength probably presented no big problem for Noah.

Both Old and New Testament passages indicate that Noah held considerable stature in his community. From these hints we can surmise that his personal and personnel resources were abundant, certainly adequate (with God's help, of course) to complete the construction project. In addition to enlisting his sons, Noah may have employed many more people to assist in the work. We can easily imagine the opportunity this workforce would provide for attracting large crowds to hear Noah's message.

Whether he used a large building crew or not, workers were available for Noah's use—as were all the necessary materials—from hardwoods to a natural waterproofing sealant. No insurmountable obstacles stood in Noah's way for successful construction of an ark of the dimensions the text describes. While no one today would or *could* invest the years and other resources Noah did, Noah acted in response to an urgent mission given him by God. He obeyed God's call, whatever the cost.

**Animals Rescued**

Help in identifying the creatures the ark sheltered comes from two sources: first, from biblical teaching about God's judgment; second, from consideration of the Hebrew nouns used for animals in the account. Chapter 15 discusses the limits of God's judgment to the extent of sin's defilement. God always preserves and protects whomever and whatever can be redeemed. This principle is consistent with the Hebrew words used in Genesis 6–9 to describe the animals spared for future purposes. The text includes these seven words, defined in the *Theological Wordbook of the Old Testament,* to indicate which animals went onto the ark:

- *bāśār*: "flesh" (can refer to animal musculature, mankind, and animals used in Jewish sacrifices)[8]
- *bᵉhēmâ*: "beast, animal, cattle" (usually refers to large four-footed mammals)[9]
- *ḥayyâ*: "living thing, animal" (usually used to denote wild, instead of domestic, animals)[10]
- *nepesh*: "life, soul, creature, person, appetite, and mind" (can describe soulish creatures, particularly land creatures with the breath of life and capable of expressing yearnings, emotions, passions, will, and self-awareness)[11]
- *'ôp*: "bird, fowl, insect"[12]
- *remeś*: "creeping organisms" (usually includes small land mammals, such as rodents, and can also include small reptiles)[13]
- *ṣippôr*: "bird"[14]

All these words refer to birds and mammals, though some can be used a little more broadly. A high correlation exists between this list and the list of soulish animals God created on the fifth and sixth creation days, animals significant to preparing Earth for humanity and, according to Job 38–39, crucial for the launch and support of human civilization.[15] Clearly, the survival of these creatures would be important to the restoration and progress of human society after the flood. Nothing in the Genesis text compels us to conclude that Noah's passengers included anything other than the birds, mammals, and perhaps a few of the higher reptilian species that lived in the regions then inhabited by humans.

**Bird and Mammal Migration**

Given birds' and mammals' ability to migrate, the question often arises as to why God would complicate Noah's task by including them in the ark. Why not let them flee the flood zone and then migrate back later, or why not replace them with birds and mammals outside the flood zone after the waters receded? No specific explanation appears in the text for Noah's massive rescue effort, but some reasons can be surmised.

For one, birds simply cannot fly long distances during a torrential downpour. The weight of the rain falling on their bodies overcomes the lift they need to fly. And as warm-blooded creatures, birds have high body-surface-to body-weight ratios. Thus, they are vulnerable to hypothermia. This vulnerability explains why birds are wary of oncoming rainstorms and seek shelter when a storm is imminent. During the flood, the rain and rising waters hindered the birds from finding a place to survive. So God brought some of each species onto the ark.

A similar challenge faced the land mammals, also. The flood would have been so severe, with water pouring rapidly from both the ground below and the skies above—and so unfamiliar within their habitat—that none would have been able to escape it. Given the narrow habitat range of some species, many may have been permanently lost if not protected on the ark.

The region impacted by the flood, although something less than global, still must have been large (see chapter 17). Its impact on the land and vegetation should not be minimized. Birds and mammals are notably inefficient colonizers. Those from outside the flood zone would have taken several decades or more to move into this region, adjust to their new habitat, and repopulate it.

By including the regions' bird and mammal species in the rescue, God enabled Noah and his family to rapidly restore ecological balance in the flood zone and, just as rapidly, to relaunch civilization. These goals are reflected in God's instructions to Noah, telling him to take seven pairs of the bird and mammal "kinds" most critical for resettling the land and rebuilding society and one pair of all remaining kinds of birds, mammals, and higher reptiles for regenerating the ecosystem.

## Animals Not Protected

Two additional Hebrew nouns apply to the creatures that were *not* specifically designated for rescue from the flood. They and their expanded lexical definitions are as follows:

- *shereṣ*: "teeming, swarming things" (usually refers to prolific small, "non-soulish" animals such as amphibians, smaller reptiles, flying insects, and wriggling water animals, but can sometimes include small mammals, such as rodents) [16]
- *yᵉqûm*: animals with standing; animals which subsist [17]

While *shereṣ* can refer to small mammals, most often it is used for small nonsoulish animals. Likewise, *yᵉqûm* can refer to all animals or just those that merely subsist.

In the destruction of Jericho, for example, or in any other conflagration, other life-forms, in addition to those targeted for judgment, died in the catastrophe. So, too, bacteria, insects, amphibians, and other creatures would have died in the floodwaters. Their death does not mean, however, that their kinds would be eradicated from Earth. Though many years would pass before the Mesopotamian plain and regions in and adjacent to the Persian Gulf Oasis—now stripped of its soulish life (other than the creatures saved by the ark—would be fully repopulated, the bacteria and insects and other life-forms would return in a matter of weeks or months, at most.

**Noah's Future**
In addition to building the ark and preaching repentance, Noah's job included caring for breeding pairs of the various *nepesh* species living in the vicinity of humans. The text indicates he did not need to go out and find them, capture them, and bring them in. God apparently intervened to send these creatures to him. These animals would be crucial for reestablishing both the environment and the economy of the region. Domesticated animals are a vital source of milk, as well as of clothing and other materials, and some animals are a source of pure delight.

Certain of the creatures on board would have had a habitat range as limited as or even more narrow than that of humans. These would have faced imminent extinction from the flood had they not been protected, but most others would not. Yet God commanded Noah to take on board not just one pair but rather seven pairs of some species. These birds and mammals seem the ones most significant for agricultural (thus, economic) purposes and also for resumption of sacrificial worship.

In all likelihood, more *nepesh* species existed in Noah's day than are alive on Earth today. So a reasonable estimate of the number of animal pairs aboard the ark may have been many hundreds of species at a minimum, and perhaps as many as several thousand. Noah faced the task of making provision both for housing this floating zoo and for feeding it (not to mention cleaning up after it)—not only during the flood, but also until postflood land began producing sufficient food for them. The same went for his own family, too.[18] Therefore, he needed to pack about an 18- to 20-month food supply. The weight of food and fodder must have exceeded the weight of animals and people by several times.

In addition, Noah's family needed to carry all the supplies and tools for rebuilding their homes and farms. The availability of wood might not be problematic, given the lumber in the ark itself and the olive leaf retrieved by the dove (signifying the proximity of at least some surviving trees). Nevertheless, the rebuilders would need equipment and simple machines, ropes, precut stones, timbers, and pegs, plus materials for clothing, cooking, and sleeping.

## Caring for the Ark's Passengers

A vessel of the ark's dimensions would have been spacious enough for the three decks God instructed Noah to build.[19] Constructed in this way, it would offer generous cargo space, pens or stalls for the animals, and adequate quarters for the human passengers. Fodder could have been stored close to the animals, fertilizer saved for future agricultural use, and still the ark would allow room for exercising the animals. At the same time, the ark would be small enough that eight people could tend to these chores. (The image of Noah drowning in the excrement of the ark's animals is based on a faulty understanding of how many animals were on board.)

Given their hundred-year building, planning, and preparation time, Noah and his family could possibly have adapted and installed many labor-saving devices. Dumbwaiters, carts, chutes, rails, and simple plumbing may well have greatly streamlined their work as animal keepers. In the course of using and modifying such things, Noah's family may have been planning and preparing for their days back on land—building better homes, farms, and future industries.

## Searches for the Ark

In 1995 CBS aired a two-hour, prime-time documentary on the Genesis flood and the search for Noah's ark titled, *The Incredible Discovery of Noah's Ark*. Many similar productions have appeared since then. In addition to confirming the widespread impression that Christianity requires belief in a global flood (producers typically reject Christians' requests that they present alternate views), the CBS program claimed to prove Noah's ark was discovered near the summit of Mount Ararat. Atheists and skeptics had a field day exposing the supposed "evidences" presented in the documentary.[20] Their exposés *all* stated or implied that evangelical Christians rely on deception, fraud, and sloppy scholarship to promote their beliefs.

Rather than explaining why the wood fragments displayed in that program could not be legitimate ark remnants, I prefer to focus on explaining why we should *not* expect archaeology to recover any such artifacts. First, the text gives no specific location for the ark's landing site. The Genesis text identifies the "hills/ mountains" of Ararat—a huge region bordering the Mesopotamian plain—as the area where the ark came to rest.

A better place to look would be the Ararat hills just a few hundred feet above sea level some 20 to 50 miles (35 to 80 kilometers) north of Nineveh's ruins (see map below). But I do not recommend any search. The ark's gopher wood timbers would have been huge and enormously valuable. No enterprising postflood society would have failed to exploit such available wood. Given the proximity of the ark's probable resting place to later cities, including Nineveh, built by Nimrod's generation shortly after the flood,[21] this high-quality precut lumber would surely have been used for construction. In fact, all the ark's timbers may have been raided even before Nimrod's time.

To search the ruins of Nineveh and other ancient sites for ark remains would represent a further waste of time and money. All the ancient Mesopotamian cities were burned to the ground more than once. Even if archaeologists found traces of burned wood and sealant, they would have no way to make a positive identification of this material as belonging to the ark. The plausibility of the flood story itself and the supernatural accuracy of the entire biblical record is evidence enough that the Genesis flood really did occur as described.

## Other Ancient Flood Stories

More than 200 distinct flood stories exist in the lore of ancient civilizations, just as do creation stories. The majority of these mention a large vessel that saved the human race from extinction. The abundance of these flood stories would seem to point to something more than just a widely shared fantasy. It suggests that the memory of some unprecedented flood catastrophe was etched in the minds of ancient peoples.

One explanation connects these flood accounts with a common source. As with creation accounts, we see faint traces of a trend: typically, the greater the story's distance (in time and geography) from Mesopotamia, the greater the distortion relative to both the biblical account and established facts of nature. The least distorted of the nonbiblical account is the Babylonian flood story.

The same library of Ashurbanipal that contained the Babylonian creation story also contained a flood story, the Gilgamesh Epic.[22] It is a lengthy poem like the Enuma elish and, like the Enuma elish, the Gilgamesh Epic seems a reworked version of the apparently older Atrahasis Epic of Old Babylon.[23]

The Babylonian flood poem more closely resembles Genesis than does the Babylonian creation poem. It describes the building of a large multideck ship sealed with pitch or tar. Like Noah of Genesis, Utnapishtim of the Gilgamesh Epic boards the ship with his whole family. The Gilgamesh flood, like the Genesis flood, destroys all humanity except those on board the ship, and its waters come mostly from a furious rainstorm.

At this point the similarities end. The Genesis ark had a stable shape for flotation. Utnapishtim's cubical ship (200 feet by 200 feet by 200 feet) was neither seaworthy nor water stable. The rain of the Gilgamesh account lasts only six days, and instead of rescuing eight people and pairs of all bird and animal species associated with humanity aboard his boat, Utnapishtim ferried to safety all his kinsmen, all his society's craftsmen, all the cattle and beasts of the field, and the seed of all living things.

The poem differs most profoundly from the Genesis story in its portrayal of the power(s) behind the flood. The gods of Gilgamesh send the deluge not to protect mankind from its own evil but to destroy mankind for no apparent reason. Their action is arbitrary. Once the inundation is under way, the gods flee in terror to the upper reaches of heaven, where they crouch in fear like traumatized dogs. Then the flood suddenly ends, in a matter of hours.

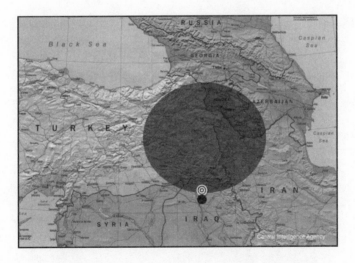

## Figure 18: Possible Location of the Ark's Resting Place

The shaded area is the region identified in Genesis 8:4 as the "mountains of Ararat." The target symbol at the bottom of the shaded area shows a likely landing location for Noah's ark. The small solid circle just below the target symbol indicates where the ruins of the ancient city of Nineveh have been found.

Credit for underlying map: Central Intelligence Agency

The Gilgamesh gods, like those of the Enuma elish, seem obvious anthropo-morphic beings. They manifest ignorance, weakness, fear, and other human foi-bles. This difference, in addition to the obvious departure from scientific plausi-bility, separates the Gilgamesh Epic from the Genesis flood account, which stands all the more distinctly alone. The epic's very existence, however, lends some ad-ditional credence to the Genesis story.

## New Beginnings

Out of this horrific encounter with death comes a fresh beginning for humanity. The future rests in the hands of Noah and his family. What will they do with it? Will they fix their hearts on the One who saved them, or will they again go their own self-centered way? The answer to that question comes into focus as we con-tinue to navigate the unfolding story.

# 19

## ORIGINS OF NATIONS AND RACES: GENESIS 9–11

**G**enesis 9–11 tells of the restart of humanity and of generations that repopulated Earth soon after the flood. These Genesis chapters document man's persistent autonomy despite having witnessed or heard all about the dire consequences of spiritual rebellion. First, Adam and Eve's progeny failed to "fill the earth" as God had commanded (Genesis 1:28). Then Noah's descendants failed to obey that command.

As chapter 16 points out, Adam and Eve's descendants neither multiplied to their potential nor moved beyond the environs of the Persian Gulf Oasis and Mesopotamia. So when Noah left the ark to start over, God spoke to him in clear, direct terms about the importance of multiplying and spreading throughout the earth (Genesis 9:5–7). God also instructed Noah to curtail murder, a significant hindrance to the multiplication and migration of his descendants.

Sadly, Noah's immediate descendants fared only slightly better in fulfilling God's command than did Adam's. While achieving some success in restraining murder, they still resisted settling beyond Mesopotamia and the Persian Gulf region. Unity and conformity seemed more important to them than did following God's plan.

### Dangers of "Peace and Unity"
All generations of humanity, including our own, have dreamed of political peace among all peoples as the solution to humanity's ills. Of course the world would benefit from peace, safety, and harmony within homes, communities, nations, and, better yet, on a global scale. As history makes abundantly clear, however, these ideals cannot be achieved and maintained through human effort alone—even with the help of experienced leaders, better-managed economies, checks and balances in government, a system of just laws, and attention to social justice.

It is the hearts and actions of leaders, economists, legislators, lawyers—and the citizens—that are the problem. Only God can provide the necessary change of heart and then of action.

The yearning for world peace and unity seems especially strong among those who have personally witnessed or been directly impacted by the horrors of military conflict and terrorism. For example, an estimated 50 million people (and possibly more) died in World War II.[1] And the former Soviet Union—which suffered more losses during the war than any other nation (around 14 million civilians and soldiers killed[2])—murdered approximately 55 million of its own people in the "peace" times afterward.[3]

So-called peace and unity can, because of human nature, lead to as much (if not more) evil and suffering than does conflict and disunity. This sad fact does not mean citizens of any nation should fail to advocate for peace, but we would do well to remember that lasting peace and true unity are available in Christ alone, as we live to serve Him.

One reason for such carnage in times of political peace is that people driven by greed and power always rise up to exploit and oppress others. The disaster that befell humanity and led to the Genesis flood should serve as a strong warning to all generations of what happens when people unite to serve their own interests rather than God's. Because we see some good in people, even in those who are not yet serving God, we assume human goodness will somehow prevail. But history shows otherwise.

### Marketing Analogy

A marketing analogy may help explain the risks of worldwide peace and unity (under human leadership, apart from submission to God). If one corporation acquires full control over a product everyone needs and wants, the outcome is an increase in price and a decrease in quality. Free-market economies enact antitrust laws to prevent monopolies and limit exploitation. Competition among corporations forces, at least to some degree, fair product prices and desirable product quality.

Typically, nations compete with one another for citizens and for economic strength. "Brain drain" describes the loss of brilliant, talented citizens from their nation to one that offers them more opportunity for reward. Similarly, many nations lure corporations to relocate through tax incentives and educational programs designed to provide larger pools of well-trained, efficient, and cost-effective personnel.

Eliminating national boundaries and uniting nations under a global banner may seem the best way to establish world peace and unity; however, it would eliminate competition for citizens and corporations. If only one nation exists, that nation could—and would, *under any leadership other than Christ's*—oppress its citizens and corporations. The oppressed would have no recourse. The one government, really a ruling elite, would become the final arbiter of what is "good" for itself and for everyone. Human pride and selfishness would then command the world.

These principles reveal the tragedy of the all the world's totalitarian regimes. Consider, for example, North Korea, which has isolated itself and its people, effectively locking them in and the rest of the world out. For some time now, its leaders have gotten away with oppressing—some might say enslaving—its citizens.

## Biblical Warnings

The prophet Isaiah described what the world becomes as a result of human nature, wherever people are committed to their own ways rather than to God's:

> The way of peace they do not know;
>     there is no justice in their paths.
> They have turned them into crooked roads;
>     no one who walks along them will know peace.
> So justice is far from us,
>     and righteousness does not reach us.
> We look for light, but all is darkness;
>     for brightness, but we walk in deep shadows.[4]

The Bible speaks of several occasions on which God supernaturally intervened to protect the world from the dangers of unification. One is reported here in Genesis, another in Daniel. In a vision Daniel learned that God had halted the Babylonian attempt to dominate the world and that He would block the Medo-Persian Empire as well as three future empires (Greece, Rome, and an empire still to come) in their attempts.[5] The history of civilization documents the failure of one empire after another in its quest to control the world.

The danger of superficial peace and unity among peoples helps us understand Jesus' peculiar and disturbing statement to His disciples:

> Do you think I came to bring peace on earth? No, I tell you, but division.[6]

These words seem to contradict what the angels sang on the night of Christ's birth.[7] But He is anticipating the conflict that will arise between those who acknowledge His authority and embrace His kingdom, a kingdom of the heart, and those who reject it. He reconciled the seeming contradiction with these words to His disciples just before His crucifixion:

> Peace I leave with you; my peace I give you. I do not give to you as the world gives.[8]

Jesus came to offer humanity a very different kind of peace. He knew that real peace among humans is possible only if people first make their peace with God.

### Origin of Nations

The opening verses of Genesis 10 tell us that after the flood, human population did multiply and civilization advanced. Not many generations after Noah's sons' time, a powerful prince, named Nimrod, built eight cities throughout southern, central, and northern Mesopotamia.[9]

Genesis 11 also reports that the postflood population resumed a dangerous preflood trajectory. As they maintained a single language and a single society,[10] they embarked on an ambitious building project, the construction of a huge city and a high tower in pursuit of two stated goals: (1) to express overweening pride in their own achievements; and (2) to discourage human emigration beyond Mesopotamia's boundaries:

> Come, let us build ourselves a city, with a tower that reaches to the heavens, so that we make a name for ourselves and not be scattered over the face of the whole earth.[11]

If God were to tolerate this blatant, persistent rebellion against Him,[12] and if humanity were to succeed in its stated goals, only another great disaster, such as the flood, would curb humanity's evil and oppressive ways.[13]

So, God acted again. The text tells us He "confused their language."[14] No longer did everyone understand the same words. No longer could all the people come together in building their ideas and plans. Amid the confusion, people were compelled to find and stay close to anyone with whom they could meaningfully communicate. Nations likely formed along language lines.

Separation was achieved, but the scattering of the different language groups from Mesopotamia and the Persian Gulf Oasis to all the habitable lands throughout the entire globe still lay ahead. Still ahead, too, was a set of events that would both help them scatter and keep them scattered.

According to the text, God assigned each people group its own territory, as noted in the table of nations in Genesis 10, and the people groups finally began to move. If the life span shortening event (see discussion of the "Monogem Ring," chapter 13) gives a hint as to when the flood occurred (some tens of thousands of years ago) we can estimate that the movement of peoples from Mesopotamia and the Persian Gulf region to the far reaches of Asia, Africa, Europe and beyond began sometime relatively soon afterward. Initially, however, certain natural barriers, such as a frigid Bering land bridge, stood in their way.

## Ancient Land Bridges

God had a plan for keeping the newly emerging nations apart. He had created the world and formed it in such a way as to produce landmasses and oceans in just the right balance for life. This balance constitutes the "fixed limits" he set for the oceans and land. He also fashioned its geography and geophysical forces so that, at just the right time and in just the right places, conditions would facilitate the separation of the peoples and ensure their staying separated.

Geographers note that virtually all Earth's continental landmass lies in climatic zones suitable for human habitation. Moreover, with the exception of frozen Antarctica, the continents and major islands are nearly contiguous. Yet certain physical barriers present a formidable challenge to people lacking modern transport vehicles. Indonesia is separated from mainland Asia by the Strait of Malacca. Australia is divided from Indonesia by the Torres Strait. The English Channel flows between Britain and the rest of Europe. North and South America are cut off from Eurasia by the Bering Strait.

A closer look at one of two examples illustrates how these barriers existed, broke down, and then rose again. The Bering Strait, for instance, constitutes an expanse of cold, treacherous sea between Alaska and Siberia (at its narrowest point it is about 53 miles, or 85 kilometers, wide). Even with modern ships, attempts to cross that body of water can be a risky venture. Previous to the nineteenth century, except for one special moment in history, the Bering Strait effectively discouraged peoples living in Asia from emigrating to the Americas, and vice versa.

In 1996, a geological and paleontological study discerned that a land bridge in that area actually joined North America to Asia between 40,000 and 11,000 years ago. A team of Arctic researchers discovered the remains of land vegetation across the full length of what is now under the Bering Strait.[15] During most of these 29,000 years, temperatures remained too frigid to permit human migration across this land bridge. For most of this epoch, Siberia and Alaska were as heavily blanketed with ice as Greenland is today. (The existence of these huge ice sheets explains why sea levels were so low.)

For a brief time, however, just before the Bering land bridge became inundated by rising seas (from the melting continental ice sheets), a warm, moist climate blanketed the Bering bridge and significant portions of Alaska and Siberia. Insect assemblages and plant fossils indicate that the period between 14,000 and 11,000 years ago was especially favorable for human migration. The mean summer temperature at that period, as indicated by the insects and plants, ranged between 53°F and 56°F (11.5°C and 13°C),[16] not exactly balmy, but certainly survivable. More importantly, these temperatures were warm enough to support food-bearing plants migrating people would need, and the research team found the remains of such plants.

A relevant study by another research team working in British Columbia indicates that other land bridges opened and closed at about the same time as the Bering. The Hecate Strait, a stretch of rough, cold sea that ranges from 40 to 80 miles (65 to 130 km) wide, separates Queen Charlotte Islands and mainland of British Columbia. Challenge enough for large modern boats, it would have proved more than a little daunting to natives in dugout canoes or other small vessels. Yet evidence of human habitation in the Queen Charlottes dates back to 10,200 years ago.[17]

A team of geologists and paleoenvironmentalists combined data to reconstruct the environmental and sea-level history of the Hecate Strait region. They found that the strait's floor, relative to sea level, had once risen by as much as 502 feet (153 meters),[18] about half due to falling sea levels and half from a bulging of the undersea floor in reaction to the Cordilleran ice sheet's pressing down on the British Columbian coastal mountain range.[19] With this much continental landmass pressed down by as much as 820 feet (250 meters), naturally something else had to go up, such as the adjoining crustal material.

The team's results demonstrated that a land bridge between the Canadian mainland and the Queen Charlottes formed as early as 14,600 years ago,[20] although the necessary plants and climate for long-term human habitation did not come until about 1,600 years later.[21] Between 10,000 and 9,500 years ago, the bulge in the Hecate Strait subsided and sea levels rose again, destroying the bridge.[22]

The speed with which the bridge formed and disappeared came as a surprise to the research team. The sea level rose and fell as rapidly as 33 feet (10 meters) per century,[23] giving credence to the Haida people's legends of fast-rising seas in their early history.[24] The rapidity of the rise apparently prevented them from implementing a means to evacuate the Queen Charlottes and return to the mainland.

### Time of Peleg

The Haidas were not the only people cut off. Everywhere in the world sea levels shifted rapidly, first eliminating barriers then widening them again, separating continents and large islands. The world became geographically accessible and then divided, keeping humans geographically separated. However, the team of geologists and paleoenvironmentalists were not the first to mention such a transition. More than 3,400 years ago, Moses wrote:

> Two sons were born to Eber: One was named Peleg, because in his time the earth was divided.[25]

While the biblical statement of the earth's division seems consistent with new discoveries about the geographical separation and with the timing of the Genesis 9–11 account of God's scattering humanity over the whole face of Earth, no firm conclusions can be drawn. Genesis 10:25 simply says that the earth was divided in the time of Peleg. However, because this name appears halfway down the list from Shem to Abraham, the estimated biblical date for Peleg does seem to match the scientific dates for the collapse of the world's land bridges.

### Great Dividing

Here is the scenario that emerges from integrating the biblical and scientific data: When Noah's descendants refused to "fill the earth," God intervened to scatter them far beyond their land of origin. Thousands of years later, that scattering reached the geographical limits of the eastern hemisphere. Approximately 14,000 years ago, a passable land bridge formed from the eastern to western continents. For a few thousand years the scattering of humanity into all the habitable landmasses continued. When that scattering was complete, roughly 11,000 years ago, the land bridge broke, preventing humanity from reuniting and repeating the sins of the preflood and early postflood peoples.

As for Australia, Indonesia, New Guinea, and the British Isles, archaeological evidence shows that humans settled them thousands of years prior to the settling of the Americas. The straits separating these lands from larger nearby landmasses are warmer and calmer than the Bering and Hecate, for example. They may well have been passable in boats. Some evidence suggests that earlier land or semi-land bridges did exist in these locations. However, when the Bering and Hecate land bridges were disappearing, absolute sea levels were rising by about seventeen feet (five meters) per century.[26] This rise would have sufficiently broadened the straits separating Australia, Indonesia, New Guinea, and Britain from the Asian and European mainland to hinder the return of their inhabitants.

**Origin of Races**

The origin of humanity's racial groups remains a mystery. Neither the Bible nor scientific research offers a direct explanation. One fact can be derived from Scripture: skin color differences did exist by the time of the Jewish exodus from Egypt. Moses' relatives rebuked him for marrying a dark-skinned woman.[27] In some passages written later, the Bible contrasts the dark skin color of the Nubians and Ethiopians with the lighter complexions of the Egyptians, Jews, and Mesopotamians.[28]

This question cries for an answer: How did the human species develop such distinct skin colors as well as other more subtle differences in the relatively brief time between the days of Noah and the time of Moses? The usual answer that it happened in response to natural selection seems inadequate.

Genetic and anthropological research shows that natural selection works more slowly than necessary to offer a plausible explanation. Sun sensitivity, for example, works poorly as a selection effect. While dark-colored skin offers more protection against solar ultraviolet radiation damage and vitamin-B or folate deficiency, the advantage is too small to discourage people of light-colored skin from settling in the tropics. Nor is the lower production of vitamin D relative to sunlight intensity as observed in dark-colored skin sufficient to give light-skinned people a survival advantage over dark-skinned people in the polar regions. Evidence for how weakly natural selection favors one skin color over another comes from the observation that dark-skinned Eskimos live in the arctic and fair-skinned Greeks live on Mediterranean isles. Apparently, Eskimos overcame their skin color problem by consuming vitamin-D rich fish oils while Greeks used hats, clothing, and umbrellas to maintain their folate levels and avoid sunburns.

These findings imply that natural selection falls short of explaining the development of racial diversity over just a few tens of thousands of years. At the risk of employing what may seem a "God-of-the-gaps" approach, I would propose an alternate explanation.

Given that Genesis 11 explicitly describes God's personal intervention in breaking up destructive unity and in motivating people to spread throughout

Earth's habitable lands, God may have done more than diversify language. Perhaps He introduced some external changes—those we recognize as distinguishing racial features—to facilitate the peoples' separation.

The types of change would seem to work together to motivate and maintain separation of various people groups. An indication that this separation was God's intent comes from Genesis 10:5, 20, and 31, where the world's peoples are said to be differentiated according to clan, language, territory, and nation.

Questions about how God introduced these changes, as well as questions about how He "confused" the languages cannot be answered from the biblical data. The *how* holds less importance for us than the *why*.

Genetic research shows the extent of change through selective pairing. Highly selective pairing among humans might have yielded some development of racial diversity. On the other hand, God might have intervened, as He seems to have done in changing telomerase activity, by miraculously introducing something new, in this case new genetic material that would generate racial features. God may have used a combination of these two methods or another entirely different means, but the changes happened in a way and in a time frame that scientists acknowledge as inexplicable by natural means alone.

God's plan to separate peoples reflects His desire to restrain the evil that inevitably emerges from a political "monopoly" as well as to encourage the "filling" of the earth and "subduing" (or managing) of its resources. This plan cannot be taken as an indication of any prohibition against different peoples cooperating and intermingling, as in trade and in marriage. Indeed, God's objective was that while the barriers separating the nations would be high enough to prevent pervasive, oppressive totalitarianism, they would be low enough that if one or more nations unduly oppressed the citizenry, those citizens would be able to overcome the barriers to leaving their nation.

### Ham's Penalty

For many centuries certain religious sects have held the deplorable racist view that Noah's "curse" on his youngest son, Ham, marked the beginning of dark-skinned peoples. The incident for which Ham was penalized occurred shortly after the flood when Noah was harvesting fruit from a vineyard he had planted (Genesis 9:18–27).

Noah became drunk from the wine of the harvest and slept off his drunkenness "uncovered," in the privacy of his tent. Ham walked in on his father, gazed on his father's nakedness, and then told his two brothers all about it. The two older brothers respectfully picked up a garment, walked into Noah's tent backward, and covered their father without looking. When Noah recovered and found out what Ham and his brothers had done, he pronounced this curse (and blessing):

> Cursed be Canaan [Ham's son]! The lowest of slaves will he be to his brothers.... Blessed be the Lord, the God of Shem! May Canaan be the slave of Shem. May God extend the territory of Japheth; may Japheth live in the tents of Shem, and may Canaan be his slave.[29]

These words imposed servitude on Ham's descendants through Canaan. However, the Genesis 9 text gives no hint, not the faintest implication, that skin color marked or even accompanied the change in Canaan's future. Nor does any Bible passage contain such a suggestion.

We recognize that many details have been omitted from the report of this incident. For some unspecified reason, the penalty fell only on Canaan, one of Ham's sons. Ham's other sons, Cush, Mizraim, and Put, were excluded. The historical record shows us that few if any of Canaan's descendants lived long on Earth. The Old Testament and extrabiblical records document that the nations moving in to occupy the ancient land of Canaan, the land held by Canaan's clans,[30] wiped out all of these people.

There is no archaeological evidence that Canaanites had dark skin. Those who associate Canaan's curse with race invariably harbor a political agenda. Typically, they and their followers seek a basis for imposing a second-class or servant-class status on one or another of the peoples around them. Some, identifying Caucasians as descendants of Shem and Japheth, say Canaan's curse applies to certain African people. Some turn the tables and claim the sign of Canaan's curse is white skin. Both groups trump up a biblical excuse for oppressing other racial groups. Political ideology—and spiritual evil—rather than exegetical principles, drive their blatant misinterpretation.

**Origin of Fermentation**
Because some Christians look upon wine or other alcoholic consumption as sin, they have proposed an unlikely and unscientific interpretation of this Genesis 9 story about Noah. They suggest Noah was surprised by his experience of drunkenness. Given Noah's righteous standing, they say, Noah could not have known that the beverage he consumed would make him drunk. They imply, by this interpretation, that fermentation never occurred on Earth until after the flood. Just as some believers look upon entropy (the law of decay) and physical death as evils introduced by humanity's sin, so also they view fermentation as the result of

reprobate behavior at the time of the flood. Specifically, some speculate that different atmospheric conditions before the flood somehow would have inhibited the fermentation process.[31]

The Bible in no instance labels fermentation or wine as evil. Jesus provided wine at the wedding feast in Cana, His first public miracle.[32] Paul instructed his disciple Timothy to take a little wine for his stomach's sake and not confine his fluid intake to water only.[33] The Bible does forbid drunkenness, any drinking beyond "moderation." The text gives no indication that Noah was taken by surprise by anything other than his one son's behavior.

Shem and Japheth's actions also seem to demonstrate a prior familiarity with fermentation's effects. They responded to Noah's condition appropriately, not with expressions of bewilderment or concern that their father might be seriously ill. They showed confidence that, if their father continued to sleep, he would be better soon.

The view that fermentation began after the flood contradicts abundant evidence for continuity in the operation of physical laws (see chapter 11). The laws of physics are not changed at any point in the Genesis chronology. God's Word in Genesis and God's Word in nature (see Psalm 19:1–4) agree in testifying to the stability of such laws. Bacteria, molds, fungi, and yeasts, all operating according to the laws of physics, play a vital role in the survival of higher plants and animals. God created them in time to support the existence of these other plants and animals. According to what we learn in Genesis 1, neither they nor the physical processes involved in fermentation could have been new at the time of the flood. For many domesticated animals, including some mentioned in Genesis previous to the flood, fermentation actually constitutes an essential part of the digestive process.

### Civilization's Spread

DNA "fingerprinting" helps with investigations other than those relevant to coroners or criminal trials. One study compared the genes of wild wheat to those of cultivated wheat.[34] Study results showed that the launch of organized, large-scale agriculture began at about 9000 BC near the Karacadaq Mountains in southern Turkey, where the Tigris and Euphrates Rivers run close together. This site is consistent with what has long been called the cradle of human civilization, namely the center of Mesopotamia's Fertile Crescent—and with the probable landing site for Noah's ark. The date is also consistent with the Bible's claims for the dawning and spread of civilization after the flood.

The same DNA analysis additionally mapped the spread of organized agriculture throughout Mesopotamia's Fertile Crescent (9000 to 8000 BC), to Persia, the Nile Delta, India, and Greece (8000 to 6000 BC), and beyond to south central Europe, the remainder of Egypt, southern Russia, and Arabia (6000 to 5000 BC). As the map in figure 19 shows, this expansion is consistent with the biblical chronology outlined in Genesis 10–11 for the spread of the nations, or people groups.

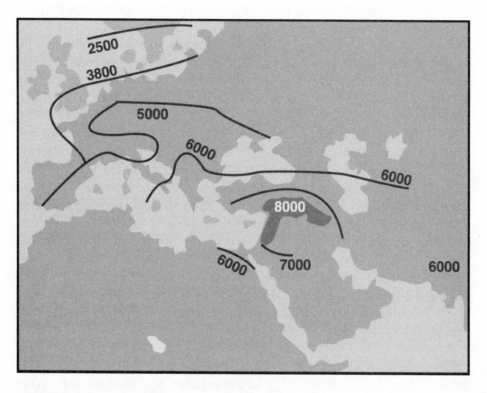

**Figure 19: Spread of Wheat Cultivation**
Wheat cultivation expands from its launch point in northern Mesopotamia to the Fertile Crescent, then to Persia, Egypt, India, Greece, and beyond. Dates on the map are in years BC.

Two American anthropologists, Melinda Zeder and Brian Hesse, through their study and dating of goat skeletons, pinpointed the initial domestication of goats as taking place 10,000 years ago in the Zagros Mountains located in western Iran and northeastern Iraq.[35] The timing and location for the origin of goat domestication matches the date and location for wheat domestication. The Karacadaq highlands are just slightly west of the Zagros highlands. The two dates match. Thus, both the wheat and goat domestication evidence as does the birth of large-scale plaster manufacture,[36] fits consistently with the biblical record for the spread of human civilization after the Genesis flood.

## End of Primeval History

The Genesis 11:10–32 genealogy provides a bridge from the primeval past to a past that feels—and indeed *is*—much nearer to us. Noah and his immediate descendants likely lived 30,000–50,000 years ago. The scattering of peoples following the Tower of Babel incident most likely took place between 40,000 and 11,000 years ago. Abraham, on the other hand, was born only about 4,000 years ago. Thus, the biblical events that occurred from Abraham's time onward have been considered, by some, more believable than the biblically described events preceding Abraham. Historical and scientific evidence has long been abundant for the former and extremely limited for the latter. But that situation has changed to a significant degree in recent years.

Scientific research has provided a burgeoning body of evidence that corresponds with and affirms the accuracy of the Bible's first eleven chapters. We need not fear what future scientific advance will bring to light. Neither should we accept an uninformed dismissal of biblical claims. Science supports the biblical message that God made the universe, including our solar system and Earth and life, that He protected humanity from self-annihilation, and that He continues to work out His plan for the ultimate triumph of good over evil.[37]

Nevertheless, the majority of Christian scholars reject this demonstrable correspondence and virtually all attempts at integration. Thus, my objectives would not be complete without some brief responses to the more significant criticisms arising from these scholars. Given that their criticisms fall into three distinct categories, I've prepared chapters to address each one of the three categories.

# 20

# HIGHER CRITICISM

The first scholars to mount a serious attack on the Genesis creation account for its supposed "internal inconsistency" were Richard Simon, an Oratorian priest, writing in 1678,[1] and Campegius Vitringa Sr., a Dutch Reformed theologian, writing in 1707.[2] Their argument fell on deaf ears, for the most part. Contemporaries ignored it and later generations dismissed it. But the seeming "discrepancy" they pointed out eventually caught the attention of others.

This question of an internal contradiction with the first two chapters of the creation story continues to emerge despite having been answered. One cannot help but wonder why. Its persistence suggests some reason exists other than open, honest inquiry for keeping it on the table. The discussion first became active in eighteenth century Europe.

## Emergence of Higher Criticism

Jean Astruc, a professor of medicine at Montpellier, France, and a regius professor of medicine at Paris, had the means, influence, and motivation to develop and disseminate his own personal perspective on the Genesis creation accounts. Though the ideas he presented originated with others, he garnered fame as the founder of Old Testament "critical" studies.

In 1753 Astruc published his first treatise aimed at undermining the credibility of Genesis. His education and position kept many people from questioning his integrity. Even a cursory glance at his personal history—his recanting of his family's Huguenot faith, a series of illicit relationships, and his swindling of several widows and their families—reveals motive for discrediting the authority of the Bible.[3] Enough of his peers had similar motives to make them eagerly receptive to his work.

Astruc asserted that in writing Genesis, Moses borrowed and embellished material from various independent sources. To support this conclusion, he claimed that Genesis contained two contradictory creation narratives, which must have come from different sources.[4]

Soon after Astruc's ideas began circulating, Johann Eichhorn, perhaps the most famous theologian of his time, published the same conclusions, though he credited a later-born scribe, not Moses, with compiling the conflicting narratives.[5] Eichhorn's initial publications made no reference to Astruc, but in a later book, *Historical and Critical Introduction to the Old Testament*, he acknowledged his dependence on Astruc's material.[6] Eichhorn then popularized the notion that emerging geological research not only contradicted the two Genesis chronologies but also the creation dates for the universe and Earth—namely 4004 BC—proposed by Irish Anglican Archbishop James Ussher.

Soon Eichhorn and his German colleagues theorized that much of the Old Testament represented a compilation of late, unreliable documents dating from 800 to 500 BC.[7] They argued that the biblical accounts of creation were edited versions of myths the Hebrews borrowed from neighboring cultures.

Astruc, Eichhorn, and the emerging "higher critics" presumed that the order in which various creation events appear on the page represents the intended chronology in the text. For the most part, they ignored verb choice, verb forms, contextual cues, indicators of parenthetical comment, and virtually all other syntactic features. The order of Genesis creation events they deduced[8] appears in table 20.

### Table 20: Higher Critics' Genesis Chronology

| Genesis 1 order of events | Genesis 2 order of events |
|---|---|
| 1. heavens and earth created | 1. heavens and earth created |
| 2. light created | 2. plants created |
| 3. light divided from darkness | 3. man (male only) created |
| 4. heaven (firmament) created | 4. animals created |
| 5. land separated from water | 5. woman made from man's side |
| 6. plants created | |
| 7. sun, moon, stars created | |
| 8. animals created | |
| 9. man (male and female) created | |

These critics placed the creation of virtually everything but the "heavens and earth" in discrepant positions on these two lists. And, they exposed the apparent "errors" using the latest scientific concepts available to them. Their work influenced many theologians and other intellectuals worldwide to reconsider their view of the Bible as divinely inspired, authoritative truth.[9] For some, the search for God as revealed in Scripture either ended entirely or took a significant turn toward subjectivity—toward a "faith" divorced from fact and reason.

This subjective version of faith still pervades the teaching of many theologians and religious leaders. Many Christian churches fail to teach biblical faith. The Hebrew and Greek words used in Scripture for "faith" all denote firm conviction—leading to action and decisions—based on established facts and compelling evidence for what God has done. Biblical faith encompasses the mind as well as the emotions and the will. It implies trusting on the basis of being "convinced," not on the basis of wishful thinking or a separation of mind from heart—as if that were possible. (See Isaiah 50:10; 1 Thessalonians 5:21; Hebrews 11:1; also examples in Exodus 4:5; 19:9; Isaiah 41:20; 43:9–10; John 11:15, 42; 13:19; 14:29; 19:35; and 20:31.)

### Early Response to the Higher Critics

Some Protestants took what seemed a less drastic, more reasonable position than promotion of blind faith. They deemed the Bible an extremely complex set of books, each composed of several documents varying in quality and from disparate sources. Thus, they viewed their critical task as sifting God's truth from the human myth and error, separating the wheat from the chaff, the gold from the dross. Their conservative constituents formalized this theological position: the Bible is true and reliable as a guide to doctrine and practice (practice of worship and human relationships, responsibilities, and government), but not as a depiction of history and the natural realm.

Individuals and churches holding the view that the Bible is the inspired, inerrant Word of God immediately reacted. They condemned the notion that people can stand in judgment over the Bible, choosing which parts are true and worthy to be followed and which parts can be ignored justifiably. While seeing through many of the obvious interpretive errors in the higher critics' conclusion, they made little comment about supposed external contradictions. Perhaps because they felt uneasy about opposing science and scientists, they initially made little if any response to claims that Genesis and science irreconcilably contradict each other.

Most Christian fundamentalists of the nineteenth and twentieth centuries clung to the Protestant formal principle *sola Scriptura*, which they interpreted to mean that a believer needs only the Bible's words, for these alone are true and trustworthy. Typically, they regarded what science and scientists had to say as irrelevant or suspect.

## The Great Divide

These contrasting positions on faith and Scripture reflected a growing schism in the Protestant community. One camp, labeled fundamentalist or conservative, resolutely held the Bible as their sole authority, taking what they called a "high" (or inerrant) view of Scripture. Distrustful of science, these Christians tended to weigh their understanding of the Bible's words far more heavily than the facts of nature emerging from the scientific enterprise.

The other camp, labeled liberal or modernist, viewed the Bible as an important literary work, "inspired" perhaps, but not in the strictly divine sense. They looked elsewhere for truth about history, geography, anthropology, astronomy, or many other matters of life.

The higher critics and their scholarly peers seemed astounded at first that so many Christians willingly ignored their claims of internal inconsistency and external contradiction. They viewed the fundamentalist response of dismissing science as a defensive maneuver. Apparently assuming that traditionalists had tacitly recognized science's insurmountable challenges, they assessed their own position as strong and the others' as hopelessly weak. They touted "the 'assured results' of the higher criticism."[10] From their perspective, Christian conservatives appeared naive, unsophisticated, and intellectually inferior.

Agnostic and deistic scholars at European universities heaped praise on the higher critics for their "ground-breaking scholarship." These accolades were received as further testimony to their own intellectual and academic prowess—and of the strength of their theological perspective. Meanwhile, nontheistic and antitheistic scholars exulted in what they considered a "triumph" over Christian theism.

## Scientific Reaction

While more than a few Christians of the late nineteenth century adopted Darwin's theory of biological evolution,[11] many saw it as a rejection of biblical creation theology. The scientific enterprise, which had been launched from the foundation of biblical principles, now began to appear as a danger to biblical faith. This reaction seemed troubling to scientists, especially those active in church.

Many researchers could not fathom how their work, which they saw as contributing to the body of truth, could be so readily dismissed. They were stunned that Bible verses promoting the study of God's existence and attributes as seen in nature would be glossed over. The latter move seemed to resemble the higher critics' tactic of choosing which parts of the Bible to follow and which to ignore.

The result? Many Western scientists in the nineteenth century; for example, most of the scientists who were members of either the Cambridge Network or the British Association for the Advancement of Science, adopted the views of the higher critics or left the church altogether. This move further convinced the higher critics they were right. Meanwhile, the polarization and alienation between scientists and conservative Christians led to increasing distrust between them, and both groups have missed out on the benefits of interaction and dialogue.

The alienation sharpened as a group of twentieth century science-educated Christians chose to defend biblical truth by arguing against scientific discoveries demonstrating the age of the universe and of the Earth. In this way they could challenge the claims of evolution and take a new approach to answering the age-old problem of evil and suffering: blame everything on Adam's fall. Their efforts, discussed in the following chapter, have only widened the rift between the Christian community and the scientific community and set both sides up for an ongoing series of attacks and counterattacks that continues to this day. Sadly, even now in the twenty-first century, many Christians remain unaware of the growing body of scientific evidence that supports their conviction about the Bible's reliability.

**Critique of the Critics**
A number of Christian theologians have devoted their careers to researching the theological and exegetical claims of the higher critics. Multiple papers and books present a thorough history along with new research findings and careful analysis of the higher critics' flawed suppositions.[12] While I recommend a study of these resources, my approach in this book is to remove the basis for conflict. The apparent "need" for either the well-intentioned revisionist science of the past century or the well-intentioned twenty-first-century version of higher criticism (discussed in chapter 22) can be eliminated by demonstrating that a straightforward reading of the Genesis creation chapters, a "literal" but not a wooden "literalist" reading, integrates perfectly with the established scientific record, especially in light of all biblical passages relevant to creation.

# 21

# "CREATION SCIENCE"

A champion arose shortly after the dawn of the twentieth century to battle the Goliath of modern science. His work gave rise to a movement of creation scientists, also called scientific creationists, whose strategy was to fight fire with fire. Having accepted the higher critics' claim that no resolution is possible between the established scientific record and a literal reading of Genesis, these Christians launched an effort to discredit accepted scientific theories and to rewrite science in terms that would support their interpretation of the Genesis 1 text.

## Flood Geology

The founders of scientific creationism initially mobilized to defend their view of the Genesis flood as a global event. George McCready Price, a Seventh-day Adventist layman and amateur geologist, sought to combat the incursion of "evolutionary" teachings, which he equated with belief that the universe, Earth, and life date back millions of years, in a book called *The New Geology*, published in 1923.[1]

Price thought he had come up with a winning weapon not just for the destruction of evolutionism (belief that life-forms progressively advance through natural processes) but also for any interpretation of Genesis that accepted the scientific time scale of millions or billions of years. These views included the gap theory, which proposed a lengthy interval between Genesis 1:1 and 1:3, and the day-age interpretation, which took the Genesis 1 creation days as six long time periods. He referred to such views as "creation on the installment plan"[2] and denounced them as "heretical"[3] and as a "libel on Moses." He considered the day-age view, in particular, as a direct assault on the Seventh-day Adventist doctrine of the Sabbath.[4]

According to Price's view, the best way to counter the claims of geology was to claim that the flood described in Genesis 6–9 could account for all geologic features on all continents, all the fossils ever found, and all Earth's limestone, coal, oil, gas, and topsoil deposits. According to Price, these sediments, fossils, and fossil fuels were laid down within several months during Noah's flood, not through hundreds of catastrophes over hundreds of millions of years.

Price cared little that his views found no support in the scientific community. He had already stated his opinion that scientists typically suffer from a severe case of "university-itis."[5] In other words, their findings and conclusions would *always* and *only* fit the reigning paradigm.

The Scopes Trial (1925), in which a Tennessee public school teacher was prosecuted for presenting biological evolution in the classroom, provided ample publicity to Price's book and ideas. Fundamentalist and conservative Christians, stinging from the humiliation of their hero, prosecuting attorney William Jennings Bryan, desperately sought some way to bring the evolutionists down a notch. Price's book, his fervor, and his considerable skills as a public orator made him the new David, courageously taking on the Goliath of biological evolutionism.

## Ramm's Appeal

By the 1950s, a number of credentialed scientists in the Christian community had become alarmed at the growing popularity of Price's book and ideas. Bernard Ramm, a noted philosopher of science, wrote *The Christian View of Science and Scripture* (1954)[6] to alert Christians working in the sciences that "flood geology" had already become "the backbone of much Fundamentalist thought about geology, creation, and the flood."[7] He urged his readers to act quickly to repudiate Price's notion of a recent creation packed into 144 hours less than 10,000 years ago. Ramm described this notion as "narrow bibliolatry"[8] and urged scientists to adopt what he termed "progressive creationism."

Ramm's appeal backfired. His reference to "narrow bibliolatry" was taken as an attack on the truth of the Bible, and his broad definition of progressive creationism[9] seemed too closely parallel to the higher critics' position. Ramm denied 24-hour creation days as well as long creation periods, or "day-ages."[10] He also denied humanity's recent appearance[11] and the scientific relevance of Genesis 1,[12] preferring to view this story as something other than a factual chronological account.[13] For these reasons—and because the list of "great creative acts" Ramm and his followers accepted continued to shrink through the years—Ramm's work served to heighten rather than limit the popularity of Price's teaching in conservative Christian churches.

## Reaction to Ramm

Ramm's slide toward higher criticism and acceptance of theistic evolution (the view that God somehow invisibly guides the natural processes of biological evolution) so thoroughly upset John C. Whitcomb Jr., a theologian at Grace Theological Seminary, and Henry M. Morris,[14] chairman of the civil engineering department at Virginia Polytechnic Institute and State University, that they published a lengthy rebuttal in 1961, entitled *The Genesis Flood*.[15] This thick treatise sought to put scientific meat on the bones of Price's flood geology and to establish both flood geology and recent creation (as in the last 10,000 years or less) as the one and only orthodox interpretation of Genesis. Though many reviewers regarded the book as an update of Price's earlier work, the authors made scant reference to Price or his book. Perhaps they wanted to distance themselves from Price's Seventh-day Adventism and his lack of scientific credentials.

Science during the 1950s was experiencing huge success and contributing to a major economic boom. Christians felt the need of a scholarly response to what they deemed the anti-Christian science establishment. Their sons and daughters were being encouraged by school teachers to study science—in part, to meet cold-war-era competition with the Soviets—which now included textbooks affirming Earth's age and, along with it, evolutionary theory.

*The Genesis Flood* appeared to deliver the goods. Written by educators with earned doctorates (PhD and ThD) from accredited institutions, the book was filled with explanatory footnotes and citations to the scientific literature. Its thickness and small print gave it the look and feel of authority. To the layman, *The Genesis Flood* appeared a well-researched, well-documented science textbook. To the fundamentalist Christian community, Whitcomb and Morris seemed to offer the scientific and intellectual respectability they eagerly sought.

## Flood Geology Captures the Church

*The Genesis Flood* prompted geneticist Walter Lammerts to begin corresponding with Morris and eight other Christians in the sciences. In 1963 these ten formed the Creation Research Society (CRS). Together they brought about a spectacular revival of flood geology and recent creationism. Within ten years the CRS boasted 450 members with graduate science degrees, several self-sustained research projects, journals, books, and pamphlets distributed in the tens of thousands, and an educational program that had successfully penetrated the majority of America's fundamentalist and evangelical Christian churches and schools.

By the early 1970s the CRS began to splinter over differences in opinions and objectives. This splintering soon served to multiply the CRS's success. One organization promoting belief in recent creation became several organizations, reaching many more people in many more places.

The (then) rising star among these new creationist organizations, the Institute for Creation Research (ICR), was founded in 1972 by Henry Morris. Officially labeling its beliefs in flood geology and recent creation of the universe and Earth as "creation science" or "scientific creationism," ICR scientists began to promote their message aggressively not only in churches but also on university campuses. They sponsored public debates with nontheistic professors, drawing crowds of several thousand. Their "Back to Genesis" seminars at churches drew thousands, too. The ICR's team prepared dozens of books and other materials on scientific creationism covering the spectrum from preschool to college level.

By the next decade nearly every conservative church in America had been influenced by the teachings of the CRS and its daughter organizations. The movement had also begun to spread to other nations and continents. Henry Morris's books were translated into twenty or more languages, and societies similar to the CRS and the ICR formed in more than a dozen nations, including Australia, Canada, Russia, South Africa, and the United Kingdom.

By the 1990s these organizations' teachings had become so predominant that the news media, the American Association for the Advancement of Science, and the National Academy of Sciences began to define "creation," "creationist," "creationism," and even "evangelical Christianity" according to the tenets of flood geology. As science historian Ronald Numbers wrote in 1996, "[T]heir once marginal views, inspired by the visions of an Adventist prophetess [Ellen White], now define the very essence of creationism."[16]

## Creationism Grows

In the late 1980s Ken Ham, with a bachelor's degree in applied science, came from the Creation Science Foundation (now Answers in Genesis) in Australia, his homeland, to work for the ICR. In 1994 Ham left that organization to found Answers in Genesis–USA, which expanded to include other affiliates. Following internal turmoil, Answers in Genesis–USA and Answers in Genesis–UK separated from the remainder of the rest of the Answers in Genesis (AiG) family, retaining the name. The other groups took on a new name, Creation Ministries International (CMI).

Today, with its 60,000-square-foot Creation Museum in Kentucky, near Cincinnati, AiG has become the world's largest creationist organization, with over 150 employees and an annual income exceeding $22 million.

The efforts of both AiG and its competitor, CMI, seem to have shifted the focus of the creation science community in the last few years. In addition to taking aim at evolution and evolutionists, they now invest substantial effort criticizing Christians who accept the scientifically established ages of the universe, Earth, and life, regardless of these individuals' stance on the truth of the Bible. One tactic is to label such people (and I am among them) as "compromisers."

The popularity of young-earth creationism (YEC) seems understandable on many counts. For one, it appeals to the innate awareness that we humans hold a unique position among God's creatures as bearers of His image, the *imago Dei*. On this pivotal point, a great many scientists (including me) wholeheartedly agree, and it is completely unconnected with beliefs about the age of the universe and the earth.

For another, YEC offers a simplistic response to the problem of evil. Whatever appears flawed or painful or difficult or destructive in the world need not be attributable to God as part of His "very good" creation. All such things entered creation only after Adam and Eve sinned. Decay and death are assumed by the young-earth view to be evil in all contexts. Never mind that decay is essential to the digestive process or that the abundant biodeposits aid our spread of the gospel message.

This core young-earth belief may present a picture of God that feels safe and comfortable, and yet the heart of the gospel message rests in the truth that only through death is real life possible. Jesus used the analogy of a seed, a word picture echoed by the apostle Paul.[17] A seed cannot fulfill its destiny to become a plant or a tree unless it dies. Likewise, it is through Christ's death that humans have the opportunity to receive eternal life. Christ's gift of eternal life can be obtained only if we are willing to "die" to personal autonomy and allow Christ to live in and through us.

Perhaps another appeal of YEC lies in its choice of target. If science and scientists are the enemy of faith, no one need be concerned about the difficult and often challenging questions they raise. Their mistakes and weaknesses can be justifiably ridiculed, along with their sometimes arrogant, abrasive behavior. Christians can explain their lack of effort and effectiveness in reaching scientists with the gospel on a (supposed) nearly universal hardness of heart and darkness of mind, not on disrespect for their work and their motives.

### Antievolutionists Embrace Its Equivalent
One of the many ironies of creation science may be seen in its explanation of how life "diversified"[18] after the flood (see chapter 17). The doctrine they chose to crush evolutionism forces acceptance of dramatically more efficient evolutionary

processes than what any nontheist biologist would dare to propose.[19] As Philip Kitcher, philosopher of science at Columbia University observed, "the rates of speciation 'creation-science' would require to manage the supposed amount species diversification are truly breathtaking, orders of magnitude greater than any that have been dreamed of in evolutionary theory."[20]

Creation science teaches that all animals ate only plants until Adam and Eve rebelled against God's authority (see chapter 11).[21] Thus, creation scientists assert the meat-eating creatures evident in the fossil record (and living today) must have transformed rapidly through "descent with variation"[22] by natural processes alone, from the plant-eaters.[23]

## Denial

Perhaps this belief in superefficient biological change explains scientific creationism's extreme resistance to accepting the evidence of Earth's age. If natural evolutionary processes worked that efficiently, a millions- or billions-of-years-old Earth might seem to remove the need for God's direct involvement in life's history.

Most significantly, the young-earth creationist stance considers any concession that Earth (or the universe) may be substantially older than about 10,000 years as a denial of biblical truth and, thus, as a wrecking ball crashing into the foundation of Christian faith.[24] No wonder otherwise compassionate, morally upright people question anyone, even a fellow Christian, who accepts the evidence for an ancient universe and Earth.[25] No wonder they cannot allow themselves to appreciate scientific evidence for God's miraculous work throughout the whole of Earth's 4.5662-billion-year history.[26]

Sadly, this denial of millions and billions of years and rigid adherence to a particular interpretation has resulted in a loss of faith among many people raised within or exposed to the Christian community. Having heard no other way to sustain belief in the literal truth of Genesis, some turn away from any trust in the Bible altogether, while others retain that trust by developing new interpretations of the Genesis story. Some of these new approaches, which in some ways resemble a return to higher criticism, are discussed in the chapter ahead.

# 22

# NEW CRITICISM

Recognizing the damage caused by ongoing and often heated conflict over Genesis—not only among scientists and theologians, higher critics and conservatives, but also within Christian churches and schools—a growing coalition of evangelical leaders and scholars has stepped forward to offer new interpretive approaches. These approaches aim at the laudable goal of restoring peace. They encourage everyone involved in the battle over Genesis to back off from "overinterpreting" or "reading into" the text more than it was intended to communicate.

All the conflict and turmoil could end, they propose, if everyone would just acknowledge that the Genesis creation accounts are beautifully composed works of artistic prose. Some of these scholars argue that the Genesis creation texts communicate physical creation details but not a chronology. Others assert that the texts are limited to refuting the creation stories of the pagan nations surrounding the ancient Hebrews. Others claim physical creation activity is incidental to far more important themes in these passages. Some go so far as to say Genesis 1 and 2 are silent on matters pertaining to the physical aspects of creation. For this latter group, no need exists even to discuss Genesis 1 and 2 in light of established scientific findings. They view any attempt to do so as irrelevant and likely damaging to the Christian faith.

The appeal of these various approaches seems understandable, even laudable. Who, after all, would deny the beauty and artistry of Genesis 1 and 2? What's more, examples certainly exist of today's readers asking too much of the text by expecting it to match complex details of advanced and still advancing scientific knowledge. Letting the ancients speak to the ancients seems right and fair. But what do we relinquish if we embrace these limited interpretive approaches? That's the question this chapter explores.

**Framework Interpretation**

Among the first of the new critical approaches was introduced by such prominent theologians as Meredith Kline, Henri Blocher, and Bruce Waltke. It has been
referred to by various designations, but the most familiar is simply the framework interpretation. This view treats the Genesis creation texts as a basic theology of creation, not as a literal or scientific description of origins. Lee Irons
and Meredith Kline recently wrote, "We do not equate a nonliteral interpretation
with a nonhistorical interpretation of the text....We affirm a historical creation,
a historical Adam, and a historical Fall."[1]

Framework interpreters see the seven days as a literary device, or framework,
designed "to bring out certain themes and provide a theology of the sabbath,"
but *not* "to supply us with a chronology of origins."[2] Their perspective invokes
a "two-register" cosmology. The upper register is seen as heaven, the dwelling
place of God and His angels, and the lower register as "earth," meaning the entire
physical universe. Each of the creation days is said to frame the description of
some aspect(s) of the lower register as a way to communicate important truths
about the upper register. Consequently, framework interpreters view the time
indicators in Genesis 1 as nonlinear.

As another textual indication of the text's nonchronological nature, the
framework model notes a distinct parallelism between the first three and the
subsequent three days of creation. The first triad they view as defining realms of
habitation while the second triad describes the filling of these realms with inhabitants.

Additional themes of the Genesis story highlighted by framework proponents include God's sovereignty, the power of God's spoken word, the goodness
of creation, humans as bearers of the image of God, and the importance of the
Sabbath—themes on which anyone convinced of the Bible's divine inspiration and authority would wholeheartedly agree. But the manner in which these
themes are presented in the text would seem to me to suggest a more straightforward, less figurative (from a literary standpoint) intent.

To remove what appears an obvious chronology and literal intent from Genesis 1 is to strip away much of the apologetics power of the account. Would the
Holy Spirit be unable to express both the creation chronology and creation theology in the same inspired words? Would the Holy Spirit overlook an opportunity to
demonstrate how God's two books of revelation—the book of Scripture and the
book of nature—corroborate one another?

**Two (or More) Adams**

Another recent approach to reconciling the conflict between Genesis and science is the idea that the biblical creation story can and does accommodate biological evolutionary models. According to this approach, Genesis 1 addresses human history from about 6.5 million years ago until the Neolithic Revolution (circa 11,000 years ago), and Genesis 2 speaks of human history after the Neolithic Revolution.[3] In this interpretive model the Adam of Genesis 1 is not the same individual as the Adam of Genesis 2.

In agreement with standard evolutionary theory, proponents of this model say the hominid species evolved first into *Homo sapiens*, including *Homo sapiens idaltu* and other late-appearing, human-like *Homo* species, and finally into *Homo sapiens sapiens*, modern humans. Then, in the Garden of Eden, God selected a single pair of these creatures to receive the image of God, according to this interpretation. A subset of this evolutionary model proposes three Adams: the first Adam as the progenitor of the hominds; the second as the first Cro-Magnon (or *Homo sapiens sapiens*); and the third as the Neolithic individual to whom God imparted His image.

As intriguing as the two- and three-Adam models may be, they face some significant theological challenges. Genesis 1 seems explicit about God's direct involvement in creating the first human pair and endowing them with the divine image.[4] Both Jesus and the apostle Paul affirm that all humans descend from a pair of individuals named Adam and Eve.[5] The doctrines of original sin and redemption are closely tied to the one Adam from whom all humanity descends.[6]

On the science front, additional problems arise. Mitochondrial and Y chromosome DNA analysis confirms that *Homo sapiens sapiens* is a species distinct from other hominids.[7] The fossil record shows relative stasis, not change, within any of the hominid species during its time on Earth.[8] According to recent studies in neuroscience and cognitive psychology, a marked discontinuity exists between the capabilities of the human mind and the intellectual capacities of all other animals.[9] These findings, which present potent challenges to current evolutionary models, affirm the biblical description of Adam and Eve's creation. The biblical timing of humanity's arrival, several tens of thousands of years ago, receives further confirmation from the discoveries of a cluster of cultural "big bang" events roughly 50,000 years ago.[10]

**Only a Polemic**

A valid emphasis on identifying and understanding literary genre as a significant part of the Bible interpreters' task has been exploited by some theologians as a way around the debate over Genesis and science. Given the Israelites' exposure to the creation myths of Egypt, Babylonia, and of other heathen nations surrounding them, their approach is to treat the Genesis creation texts primarily as a polemic against ancient Near Eastern cosmologies.[11]

From this perspective, the scientific details and chronology of creation become largely irrelevant. What really counts is Moses' presentation of the difference between God's moral perfection and the foibles of the pagan gods. At the same time he contrasts God's plan with the blatant political agendas of pagan myths (see chapter 8).

Most Bible readers would agree that Genesis does, indeed, convey such a message, but the idea that it says only this much and no more is more difficult to support. To say that the Genesis creation accounts' purpose is essentially limited to a polemic against Near Eastern creation myths presumes that the ancient Israelites (not to mention the nations around them) cared little or nothing about how the world and they, themselves, came to be.

All humans, from children to the elderly, from those lacking in formal education to those with advanced degrees, throughout the ages have expressed intense curiosity about origins. The pervasiveness of this curiosity may be seen in the multiplicity of creation stories, legends, and myths across time and cultures.[12] Attempts to explain natural history appear in the written record or oral tradition of virtually every people group on Earth.

Meanwhile, the Bible declares itself a revelation to all generations, not just the generation alive at the time it was written.[13] Embedded in the inspired words of ancient prophets are additional messages bearing significance for later generations. As Peter says, "It was revealed to them [the prophets] that they were serving not themselves, but you."[14]

As a book for all generations, inspired by the One who knows the past as well as the future, the Scriptures would be expected to impart truth to each generation of humanity. We should anticipate that the Bible's creation texts, Genesis and others, will include content that becomes progressively clearer to successive generations as knowledge of the book of nature increases. Thus, it serves as a polemic not only against the pagan creation myths of Moses' generation but also against the distorted accounts of natural history promulgated by nonbelievers through all generations.

### Functional Origins

In his best-selling book, *The Lost World of Genesis One*, esteemed Wheaton College professor John Walton provides yet another inviting pathway around the

Genesis-and-science controversy. This new approach says that "Genesis 1 was never intended to offer an account of material origins."[15] Simply stated, no real conflict exists because "the text does not offer scientific explanations."[16] In other words, "Science cannot offer an unbiblical view of material origins because there is no biblical view of material origins, aside from the very general idea that whatever happened, whenever it happened, and however it happened, God did it."[17] Walton bases this conclusion on his belief that "the material cosmos was of little significance to them [ancient Israelites] when it came to questions of origins."[18]

Recently, two more evangelical theologians, Johnny Miller and John Soden, joined Walton in promoting this view of Genesis 1. In their book, *In the Beginning... We Misunderstood*, Miller and Soden declare, "The assumption that Genesis 1 is science is what we hope to lay to rest with this book."[19] They go on to write, "Genesis 1 was not intended to teach a scientific view of creation....Genesis 1 neither intends to answer nor speaks to scientific questions."[20]

What is the Genesis account all about in this view? Pure theology. According to Walton, it is "an account of functional origins, specifically focusing on the functioning of the cosmos as God's temple."[21] That is, Genesis describes the spiritual functions of the universe, not its material reality. It "looks to the future... rather than to the past."[22]

Walton's functional interpretation accepts the creation days as 24-hour days[23] but sees in this interpretation no conflict with the scientifically established 13.8-billion-year age of the universe or the 4.5662-billion-year age of Earth. According to this view, the creation days have nothing to do with natural history. Rather these days represent "the period of time devoted to the inauguration of the functions of the cosmic temple"[24] during which that inauguration is "accomplished by proclaiming its functions, installing its functionaries, and, most importantly, becoming the place of God's residence."[25]

The motivation to uphold the authority of God's Word and to eliminate conflict between the scientific record and the Bible I can and do fully appreciate. However, to do so by proposing that the Bible is totally silent on material origins seems a bridge too far. It also seems an unnecessary and false extreme to assert that science is powerless to address theological issues. On the basis of my own and other scientists' personal experience (see sidebar, "Can Science Access God?" on page 215), I must disagree with assertions that "science is removed from the realm of divine activity";[26] and "science is not capable of exploring a designer or his purposes";[27] "neither ultimate cause nor purpose can be proven or falsified by empirical science;"[28] "science cannot offer access to God and can neither establish his existence beyond reasonable doubt nor falsify his existence."[29]

In this functional origins approach I hear echoes of Stephen Jay Gould's separate, nonoverlapping magisteria.[30] By ruling out any overlap between nature's record and the Bible, people can compartmentalize science as the realm of the physical and factual as contrasted with the Bible, the realm of the spiritual and subjective, often deemed by skeptics as the realm of wishful thinking. Christians thereby lose a critically important evidential foundation for their faith. What's more, they risk conceding the origins debate to those who claim no need of a Creator.

The refusal to use scientific evidence as a way to verify that the Bible is wholly truthful and, thus, the divinely inspired Word of God can only weaken the church's evangelistic efforts. Without objective support, how can a Christian obey Peter's injunction to "always be prepared to give an answer to everyone who asks you to give the reason for the hope that you have"?[31] Often the questions nonbelievers raise are questions about the material world and its origins. For the Christian to respond by saying the Bible is silent on such matters would be to suggest that the Bible is irrelevant.

### Additional Response to the New Criticism

To say Genesis 1 "is not written to us"[32] but only addresses Moses' contemporaries closely parallels the assertion that the Genesis creation texts are merely a polemic against ancient creation myths. Just as God allowed Old Testament prophets to speak of future events in calling the Israelites to repentance, so, too, He is fully capable of inspiring scientifically accurate descriptions and predictions of future discoveries (unique statements about the material world that later prove correct) to demonstrate to later generations that the Bible is the divinely inspired and wholly trustworthy revelation from God.

The suggestion that the Israelites had neither interest in nor knowledge of the physical world, that they did not know "the sun was much further away than the moon, or even further than the birds flying in the air,"[33] seems unnecessarily demeaning and actually contradicts well-documented history. The ancient Egyptians, Greeks, and Babylonians invested more heavily (as a percentage of gross national product) in astronomy by far than any nation does today. The ancients built instruments capable of making astronomical measurements as precise as a fifteenth of the Moon's diameter. By noting that the Big Dipper drops lower in the sky the farther south one travels, the ancients discerned that Earth must be a sphere floating free within a sky of stars. By measuring the angle of sunlight at locations of known distances apart, they determined the diameter of Earth to within one percent precision. Measurements of the Moon's phases and the

## Can Science Access God?

Astronomers can and do directly observe cosmic history, from a split second ($10^{-34}$ seconds) after its beginning to its continual expansion ever since. Physicists have successfully produced a number of theorems confirming that space and time have not existed eternally but rather originated when the universe came into being.[34]

Such discoveries prompted astrophysicist Fang Li Zhi and his physicist wife, Li Shu Xian, to write, "A question that has always been considered a topic of metaphysics or theology—the creation of the universe—has now become an area of active research in physics."[35] Physicist and Nobel Laureate Arno Penzias remarked, "Astronomy leads us to a unique event, a universe which was created out of nothing, one with the very delicate balance needed to provide exactly the conditions required to permit life, and one which has an underlying (one might say 'supernatural') plan."[36] Cosmologist Edward Harrison acknowledged, "Here is the cosmological proof of the existence of God—the design argument of Paley—updated and refurbished. The fine-tuning of the universe provides prima facie evidence of deistic design."[37]

The scientific invasion of theological turf goes farther. Research in anthropology, astrobiology, biochemistry, genetics, geophysics, paleontology, and the origin of life yield an abundance of biblically relevant and theologically significant findings.[38] When asked what evidence persuaded him to abandon his public advocacy of atheism and acknowledge God's existence, philosopher Antony Flew responded that it was revelations from scientific research on the origin of the universe, the fine-tuning of the universe for life, and the origin of life.[39]

The Bible likewise asserts that nature's record provides unequivocal evidence for God's existence and personal attributes. According to Psalm 97:6, "The heavens proclaim his righteousness and all peoples see his glory." In Romans 1:20 we read, "For since the creation of the world God's invisible qualities—his eternal power and divine nature—have been clearly seen, being understood from what has been made, so that people are without excuse."

size and shape of Earth's shadow relative to the Moon's diameter during a lunar eclipse showed roughly how far away from Earth both the Sun and Moon must be and their sizes relative to Earth. Their inability to detect parallaxes for any of the stars told them that stars must be much more distant than the Sun.[40]

Recently, a team of Finnish astronomers and world culture experts in their examination of Egyptian astronomical records dating back to the thirteenth century BC discovered that Egyptian astronomers at that time and earlier had measured the periodicity of Algol's luminosity variability to a high degree of precision.[41] (Algol is the second brightest star in the Perseus constellation. It was known as "the raging one" to ancient Egyptians and as "Satan's head" to ancient Israelites.) By comparing Algol's thirteenth century BC period of 2.850 days with the modern value of 2.867 days the Finnish astronomers were able to confirm the validity of a particular theoretical model of stellar burning and stellar mass transfer and, thus, advance the discipline of stellar physics.

At least some of this knowledge of astronomy would have been available to the Israelites. Moses, a prince in Pharaoh's court, would have been well-educated in Egyptian science.[42] Moreover, curiosity about the heavens and the natural realm is an innate human trait. This curiosity is evident in little children, in stone-age cultures, and in the historical records of the most ancient civilizations.

Another parallel between the functional interpretation and the polemic view lies in their perception of science. Both views characterize science as shifting sand in "a constant state of flux."[43] Because "what is accepted as true today, may not be accepted as true tomorrow,"[44] divine intention should never be held hostage, they say, to transient scientific theories.[45]

Such a view appears out of sync with the two-books doctrine of historic Christianity, derived from Article 2 of the Belgic Confession.[46] Some portions of both revelatory "books" will be mysterious and unexplained while others will be perspicuous—crystal clear—to anyone who "reads" them with care in a spirit of humility.

Many scientific findings hold a level of certainty comparable to the findings of theology established as doctrine. For example, the second law of thermodynamics, also known as the law of decay or the law of entropy, is evident and unchanging throughout the natural realm. It is scientifically solid. It will not ebb and flow or change. It also is stated and affirmed in the pages of Scripture.[47] An overlap does, then, clearly exist between the two kinds of revelation.

## Pursuit of Truth

Science, like theology, is a truth-building enterprise. Obviously, not all the facts of nature may be discovered in the Bible any more than all the details of the Christian gospel may be discovered in the study of nature. However, the foundation of what is clear, evident, and undisputable helps guide research into that which is partially explored or partially understood. Thus, a disciplined application of appropriate interpretive methods can add to that foundation of understood truth and push back the curtain of ignorance and confusion (see appendix A).

On account of human limitations and biases, this truth-building enterprise has no end as long as humanity continues in its current state. There is always more truth to discover and always room to go deeper into the truth we know. For example, in astronomy, careful measurements of the motions of Jupiter, Saturn, Mars, Venus, and Mercury gave birth to calculus and Newtonian mechanics, which enabled more refined measurements of planetary motions, which led, in turn, to the discovery of Uranus and Neptune and, eventually, to tensor calculus analysis and special and general relativity.[48] General relativity then pointed to big bang cosmology.[49]

In the progress of knowledge relativity neither falsified nor replaced Newtonian mechanics. Relativity only refined it. In fact, the refinements are so small they can be safely ignored for the purposes of solar system space travel. Today, the reliability of special and general relativity in predicting cosmic dynamics has been confirmed to twenty-one and fifteen decimal places, respectively. As new discoveries occur and as measurements are made to even more places of the decimal, relativity may need to be refined but it will not be overturned, taking big bang cosmology with it.

In stating that general relativity *confirmed* big bang cosmology, I refer to the words of astronomer Robert Jastrow, who noted in his famous book, *God and the Astronomers*, that theologians beat astronomers to the big bang's discovery by many centuries.[50] This is not a case of a modern-day astronomer force-fitting "where the big bang fits into the biblical record."[51] At least seven centuries before any scientific evidence for a cosmic origin event came forth, Christian and Jewish theologians discerned from the Bible the central elements of big bang cosmology.[52]

The new critics' contribution to truth building by drawing out significant meanings from Genesis that others have missed deserves respect and attention. So does their warning to refrain from reading more into the biblical text than God intends to convey. However, to completely disconnect biblical revelation in Genesis from comment about the world of nature would be to overturn twenty centuries of biblical scholarship on Genesis.[53] Eliminating scientific evidence for the inspiration and trustworthiness of the Bible's message is tantamount to crippling Christians' endeavor to advance Christ's kingdom and fulfill the Great Commission.

## Peacekeeping v. Peacemaking

Each of the new approaches I have encountered for ending the conflict over the meaning of Genesis 1 requires limiting the Bible's revelatory power, nature's revelatory power, or both. In each case, it seems humanity is meant to receive less knowledge and understanding about creation. Such restrictive interpretations raise the question of why God would want us to remain in the dark about such matters. Is He not a God who desires to make Himself known?

These various attempts to "keep peace" among Christians may help temporarily, but they fall short of God's call to "*make* peace." What is the difference? Peacekeeping seeks to *avoid* conflict. Peacemaking seeks to *resolve* conflict. Peacekeeping serves to separate warring parties from one another. Peacemaking means laboring to transform warring parties into full allies. Perhaps most people learn the difference from their experience of family life.

God knows each of us needs trusted allies to live and grow in obedience to Him as well as to complete the disciple-making assignment He placed in our hands. While serving as a minister of evangelism I first observed that for most adults outside the church to become followers of Christ, they need to see God's handiwork, God's character, and God's plan revealed in both the words of Scripture and the record of nature, where the two join forces as allies to validate and reinforce each other. Most Christians will not even attempt to discuss their faith with educated non-Christians without being convinced that the two records convey a consistent message.

Admittedly, peacemaking demands much greater effort than peacekeeping. Diligent research is necessary to see possible pathways toward resolution and reconciliation. But, that is exactly the kind of research whereby we learn more about our Creator and our created realm, including our own life.

In this endeavor we need not and must not fear being forced to honor one revelation and reject the other. The God who inspired the Bible is the same God who made the universe, Earth, and all Earth's life. This God is the very definition of truth; therefore nature's record will never contradict Scripture and vice versa.[54] When a seeming contradiction confronts us, we can know with certainty we have either misunderstood (one, the other, or both revelations) or perhaps we have yet to dig deeply enough. Whatever the case, we can embrace the opportunity to gain greater knowledge and appreciation for the Bible, for nature, and for the God who is responsible for both.

# 23

# MORE THAN MYTH

Observers of human culture acknowledge that every society tells its own "story of beginnings." Such stories fit the definition of *myth*: "a traditional story, especially one concerning the early history of a people or explaining a natural or social phenomenon, and typically involving supernatural beings or events."[1] Widely held opinion among educated people, including many theologians, would categorize the Genesis creation story as myth, though it enjoys broader dissemination than other such stories. As part of that genre, they might say it reflects a universal psychological need.

Old Testament theologian Ellen van Wolde expresses this view in her book, *Stories of the Beginning: Genesis 1–11 and Other Creation Stories*:

> Without a story about the beginning, human beings face chaos, and their origin seems to be an abyss. In order to provide a foundation for existence, the beginning was filled with meaning. Moreover, every culture attaches a meaning to the beginning, often in the form of stories. These are not stories in the sense of tales, but realities in which people live. These are stories which give people roots. In Western culture Genesis is the story of the beginning. Other cultures tell different stories of how it all began, and we read them with great amazement. We follow their traces with fascination into the past. Where no person ever was, what no ear ever heard, we create by constantly reading afresh the story of our own beginning.[2]

Who can help but agree with Van Wolde's observation that the beginning is "filled with meaning," that it provides a foundation for existence? These words describe one of the themes of this book. My own movement toward personal faith in Jesus Christ, the Savior and Creator, began with a reading of Genesis. I had already read dozens of creation myths in my quest to put aside all religious beliefs and devote myself entirely to astronomy research. But the biblical account of the beginning of the universe, Earth, life, and human history arrested my attention. It compelled me to read on. Why?

According to Van Wolde, creation "stories" become "the realities in which people live," the realities "we create," in her words. How do stories *become* reality? Is humanly created reality, *reality*? These questions may be among the most important any of us ever contemplates. The answer spells the difference between subjective truth and objective truth. It also spells the difference between Christianity and other worldviews. The creation stories of other worldviews become reality through "blind faith," as distinct from "biblical faith."

Reading the Bible as a young scientist, I remember feeling thrilled, humbled, surprised, and enormously relieved to discover that God invites testing. He expects us to believe based on objective evidence. Biblical faith must be informed faith, belief rooted in testable facts and logic. Like the confidence scientists place in firmly established natural phenomena, faith is based on adequate evidence, not *absolute* proof. Many people accept the erroneous notion that absolute proof is what scientists seek and find. Some demand absolute proof of God's existence and of the reliability of Scripture as a condition of faith in Christ. Such a demand will never—can never—be met, not within the time-and-space boundaries God has set for this life, for this time-and-space-bound "school of faith" He designed for us.

Absolute proof lies beyond human reach. That kind of proof requires complete knowledge, and no human being can acquire complete knowledge of anything in the universe because we humans are within and part of the universe.

What scientists demand, and rightly so, is adequate evidence, also referred to as practical proof. Scientists and the rest of us accept the truth of gravity, for example, based on sufficient practical testing, not absolute knowledge. We observe this phenomenon we call gravity to operate so consistently and predictably in all circumstances through all observable space and time that we do not doubt its reality or reliability.

According to the book of Romans, God holds every human being accountable to discern fact from fantasy, truth from tall tale. Each of us recognizes, at some point in growing up, where a story like that of Santa Claus or the Easter bunny or the tooth fairy departs from reality and enters the realm of make-believe. Some question earlier, some question later, but eventually we all question the stories with which we have been raised. God expects us to test them. God wants us to test them. God even commands us to test them ("prove" them, in the King James Version).[3]

All through Scripture we see examples of God giving people the tangible evidence they needed to believe His words. Adam, Eve, and others heard from God directly, audibly. Others heard from Him through special messengers, the angels. Some heard from him through prophets, whose authenticity could be established via the accuracy of their predictions. Some walked and talked with God in human form, Jesus Christ, whose words also were subject to verification by His fulfillment of Old Testament prophecies and by His control over the forces of nature, far beyond the scope of "magic." Some of us, in the era since Christ, have access to His written Word. Some have examined "the word written on their hearts." According to Romans 1, nature itself provides a testing tool available to all people everywhere and through all generations.[4]

Two of the many dramatic changes that have occurred in human history since the time of Christ include the increasing availability of the Bible in written, audio, and even video form, and the exponential increase in human knowledge about the natural realm. Testing of God's revelation, in other words, has become at the same time easier and more difficult. We have more biblical material to test—sixty-six books in both ancient and modern languages, more manuscripts to examine, and greater understanding of ancient languages through archaeological research—and more knowledge of nature, human history, and natural history with which to compare it. The quantity and complexity of the testing tools can seem daunting.

Scientific testing proved especially disconcerting in the early days of scientific advance. Scientific "truths" seemed to change from year to year, discovery to discovery, and sometimes clashed with familiar, traditional understanding of biblical truth, particularly that of Genesis 1–11. As I described in the earlier chapters of this book, the challenges seemed to heighten dogmatism. One group decided, "Science is true; the Bible is not." Another group said, "The Bible is true; science is not." Others suggested, "Perhaps the Bible is true in parts, mythical or legendary in parts, and science can help us sift." Others have proposed, "The Bible is true, and the parts that clash with science must simply be excused." Many have decided, "The Bible (and all religions) teach one kind of truth, science teaches another, and never the two need meet." In other words, we can forget testing; it's irrelevant. We can believe whatever we want. We can "create our own reality."

Another group of people, whose voice is often drowned out, says, "The Bible reveals truth, and nature reveals truth, and wherever the two meet they agree." Members of this group, whom I encounter wherever I travel and among whom I belong, say that truth never contradicts truth. If God's Word in the Bible seems to clash with God's expression of Himself in nature, we must dig deeper to understand each. The problem typically lies not in the data, but in our understanding of it. Increasing our understanding of truth constitutes a large part of our assignment here on Earth. The first commandment is clear: "Love the Lord your God with all your heart and with all your soul *and with all your mind* and with all your strength" (emphasis added). Living by that commandment enables us to obey the rest, which Jesus summarized as "Love your neighbor as yourself" (Mark 12:30–31).

Testing Genesis 1–11 holds the potential to increase our understanding of both God and ourselves, and of the rest of God's creation, as well. If people can embrace the truth of these Genesis chapters, they can embrace the truth of all Scripture and of all the divine interventions or "miracles" the Bible describes, including the miracle of our salvation. We can begin to grasp the point of all God's creation: to bring us (who so choose) to live in His presence in the new creation He promised us. In that new creation, "the dwelling of God is with men,...and God himself will be with them and be their God" (Revelation 21:3). To be with us personally and to be our God is His ultimate purpose.

As scientists discover more and more about the realm of nature and everything within it, including ourselves and our beginnings, we can be certain that the evidence for its divine design as well as for the divine inspiration of Scripture will grow in quantity and quality. The basis for such certainty lies in the pattern observed over the centuries, decades, years, and days right up to the writing of this book: advancing research, both biblical and scientific brings an ever-increasing accumulation of evidence buttressing reasons to believe. Let's keep on learning.

# Appendix A

# BIBLICAL ORIGIN OF THE
# SCIENTIFIC METHOD

For a clear example of the misapplication of the scientific method, consider the case of Galileo, whose heliocentric (sun-centered) model of the solar system was rejected by the Roman Catholic Church. The tribunal rejected Galileo's model based on their (mis)interpretation of biblical statements about the Earth's foundations being "immovable."

In defending his findings Galileo pointed out that church scholars had failed to apply the proper interpretive method in their study of the Bible's words. Specifically, they had failed to establish the frame of reference (or vantage point) of the relevant passages.[1] Because the author (observer) revolves and rotates at the same rate as the ground on which he stands, those foundations are fixed, according to his frame of reference.

The heart of Galileo's defense was that certain theologians had ignored two biblical imperatives. First, they had overlooked multiple biblical commands to "test everything" by every means available.[2] Second, they had interpreted the immovability texts without identifying the frame of reference, or point of view, from which they were written. As he argued, such oversights led to critical errors.[3] Today, most people recall Galileo's challenging the clerics to "look through the telescope," but we would also do well to remember his additional challenge to apply proper (scientific) methodology—derived from the pages of Scripture—in interpreting biblical texts.

Once the printing press made the Bible more widely available, scholars noted that wherever it describes a sequence of physical events, it follows a particular pattern. The description begins with an indication of the frame of reference (point of view) and the initial conditions; then it tells what occurred and closes with a statement of the final conditions and concluding comments. Scottish theologian Thomas Torrance has written extensively and also edited a number of books describing how the Bible and the theological advances that arose from the Reformation played a critical role in the development of the scientific method.[4] Thus, it seems no accident that the scientific revolution exploded out from Reformation-era Europe.

The following is a brief overview of the method as it applies to observations, experiments, or biblical texts:

1. Identify the phenomenon to be investigated and explained.

2. Identify the frame of reference or point of view being used to study and describe the phenomenon.

3. Determine the initial condition(s) from which the phenomenon begins.

4. Make note of what takes place in what sequence as it proceeds.

5. Describe the final conditions.

6. Form a tentative explanation (hypothesis or interpretation) of what occurred.

7. Test that initial explanation with further observations/experiments/texts.

8. Revise or refine the explanation accordingly.

9. Determine how well the explanation fits with established understanding of related phenomena/texts.

10. Repeat all these steps for further insight and validation of the explanation.

# Appendix B

## WORD STUDIES IN GENESIS 1

The English translation of Genesis 1 presented below is taken from the New International Version, 1984. Superscripts to the right of certain words are keyed to the lexical definitions that follow. The definitions are all excerpted from the *Theological Wordbook of the Old Testament* (TWOT).

1. In the beginning God[1] created[2] the heavens[3] and the earth.[4]

2. Now the earth[4] was formless[5] and empty,[6] darkness was over the surface of the deep,[7] and the Spirit[8] of God[1] was hovering[9] over the waters.

3. And God[1] said, "Let there be[10] light," and there was light.

4. God[1] saw that the light was good, and he separated the light from the darkness.

5. God[1] called the light "day"[11] and the darkness he called "night." And there was evening,[12] and there was morning[13]—the first day.[11]

6. And God[1] said, "Let there be[10] an expanse[14] between the waters to separate water from water."

7. So God[1] made[15] the expanse[14] and separated the water under the expanse[14] from the water above it. And it was so.

8. God[1] called the expanse[14] "sky."[3] And there was evening,[12] and there was morning[13]—the second day.[11]

9. And God[1] said, "Let the water under the sky[3] be gathered to one place, and let dry ground appear."[16] And it was so.

10. God[1] called the dry ground "land"[4] and the gathered waters he called "seas." And God[1] saw that it was good.

11. Then God[1] said, "Let the land[4] produce[17] vegetation;[18] seed[19]-bearing plants[20] and trees[21] on the land[4] that bear fruit[22] with seed[19] in it, according to their various kinds."[23] And it was so.

12. The land[4] produced[24] vegetation:[18] plants[20] bearing seed[19] according to their kinds[23] and trees[21] bearing fruit[22] with seed[19] in it according to their kinds.[23] And God[1] saw that it was good.

13. And there was evening,[12] and there was morning[13]—the third day.[11]

14. And God[1] said, "Let there be[10] lights[25] in the expanse[14] of the sky[3] to separate the day[11] from the night, and let them serve as signs[26] to mark seasons and days[11] and years.

15. And let there be[10] lights[25] in the expanse[14] of the sky[3] to give light on the earth."[4] And it was so.

16. God[1] made[15] two great lights[25]—the greater light[25] to govern the day[11] and the lesser light[25] to govern the night. He also made[15] the stars.

17. God[1] set[27] them in the expanse[14] of the sky[3] to give light on the earth,[4]

18. to govern the day[11] and the night, and to separate light from darkness. And God[1] saw that it was good.

19. And there was evening,[12] and there was morning[13]—the fourth day.[11]

20. And God[1] said, "Let the water teem[28 & 29] with living creatures,[30] and let birds fly above the earth[4] across the expanse[14] of the sky."[3]

21. So God[1] created[2] the great creatures[31] of the sea and every living and moving thing[30] with which the water teems, according to their kinds,[23] and every

winged bird according to its kind.[23] And God[1] saw that it was good.

22. God[1] blessed them and said, "Be fruitful and increase in number and fill the water in the seas, and let the birds increase on the earth."[4]

23. And there was evening,[12] and there was morning [13]—the fifth day.[11]

24. And God[1] said, "Let the land[4] produce[24] living creatures[30] according to their kinds:[23] livestock,[32] creatures[33] that move along the ground, and wild[4] animals,[34] each according to its kind."[23] And it was so.

25. God[1] made[15] the wild[4] animals[34] according to their kinds,[23] the livestock[32] according to their kinds,[23] and all the creatures[33] that move along the ground according to their kinds.[23] And God[1] saw that it was good.

26. Then God[1] said, "Let us make[15] man[35] in our image, in our likeness, and let them rule over the fish of the sea and the birds of the air, over the livestock,[32] over all the earth,[4] and over all the creatures[33] that move along the ground."

27. So God[1] created[2] man[35] in his own image, in the image of God[1] he created[2] him; male and female he created[2] them.

28. God[1] blessed them and said to them, "Be fruitful and increase in number; fill the earth[4] and subdue[36] it. Rule over the fish of the sea and the birds of the air and over every living creature[34] that moves on the ground."

29. Then God[1] said, "I give you every seed[19]-bearing plant[20] on the face of the whole earth[4] and every tree[21] that has fruit[22] with seed[19] in it. They will be yours for food.

30. And to all the beasts[34] of the earth[4] and all the birds of the air and all the creatures[38] that move on the ground—everything that has the breath of life in it—I give every green[37] plant[20] for food." And it was so.

31. God[1] saw all that he had made,[15] and it was very good. And there was evening,[12] and there was morning[13]—the sixth day.[11]

Genesis 2:1. Thus the heavens[3] and the earth[4] were completed in all their vast array.

## Definitions[a]

1. *'ĕlōhîm*: God, gods, judges, angels. Generally viewed as the plural of *'ĕlōah*, and used far more freqently in Scripture than *'ēl* or *'ĕlōah* for the true God. The plural ending is not intended as a true plural when used of God, but is consistently used with singular verb forms. It occurs in the general sense of deity some 2,570 times in Scripture. This is the only word used for God throughout Genesis 1. TWOT 93c

2. *bārā'*: the basic meaning is "to create." It emphasizes the initiation of the object and is limited to divine activity. Since the primary emphasis is on the newness of the created object, it lends itself well to the concept of creation *ex nihilo*, although that concept isn't necessarily inherent in the word. Occurs in verses 1, 21, 27. TWOT 278

3. *shāmayim*: heaven, heavens, sky. Usage falls into two broad categories, 1) the physical heavens, which yield snow, dew, frost, and hold the sun, moon, planets, and stars; and 2) the heavens as the abode of God. Heaven and earth together constitute the universe (Gen. 1:1). Occurs in verses 1, 8, 9, 14, 15, 17, 20, and chapter 2:1. TWOT 2407a

4. *'ereṣ*: earth, land, city, world. In verses 1, 2, 10–12, 15, 17, 20, 22, 24–26, 28–30, 2:1. TWOT 167

5. *tōhû*: confusion, the empty place. The word refers to the formlessness of the earth before God's creative hand began the majestic acts described in the following verses. In verse 2. TWOT 2494a

6. *bōhû*: void, waste, emptiness. Always occurring with *tōhû*, it describes the primordial condition of earth, "void" at the beginning of creation (Gen. 1:2). In verse 2. TWOT 205a

7. *tᵉhôm*: deep, depths, deep places. A large body of water. In verse 2. TWOT 2495a

8. *rûaḥ*: wind, breath, mind, spirit. At most points, context approves and the analogy of the New Testament strongly suggest that the *rûaḥ* YHWH is the Holy Spirit. In verse 2. TWOT 2131a

9. *rāḥap*: hover. This verb (in this form) occurs only in Gen. 1:2 and Deut. 32:11. In verse 2. TWOT 2149

10. *hāyâ*: to be, become, exist, happen. In verses 3, 6, 14, 15. TWOT 491

11. *yôm*: day, time, year. It can denote the period of light, twenty-four hours, a general vague "time," a point of time, or a year. In verses 5, 8, 13, 14, 16, 18, 19, 23, 31. TWOT 852

12. *'ereb*: evening, night. In verses 5, 8, 13, 19, 23, 31. TWOT 1689a

13. *bōqer*: Morning, dawn. Denotes the breaking through of the daylight, and thus dawn or morning. In verses 5, 8, 13, 19, 23, 31. TWOT 274c

14. *rāqîa'*: firmament. Rendered more correctly as expanse. It identifies God's heavenly expanse where the birds fly and that further expanse of sky in which God placed the stars, sun, and moon, referring apparently to their becoming visible through the cloud cover; presumably having been created already in verse 3. In verses 6–8, 14, 15, 17, 20. TWOT 2217a

15. *'āśâ*: do, fashion, accomplish. The word is much broader in scope than *bārā'*, connoting primarily the fashioning of the object. In verses 7, 16, 25, 26, 31. TWOT 1708

16. *rā'â*: see, look at, inspect. In verse 9. TWOT 2095

17. *dāshā'*: sprout, shoot, grow green. In verse 11. TWOT 456

18. *deshe'*: young, new grass, green herb, vegetation. In verses 11, 12. TWOT 456a

19. *zera'*: sowing, seed, offspring. In verses 11, 12, 29. TWOT 582a

20. *'ēśeb*: grass, herb, vegetation, plants. In verses 11, 12, 29, 30. TWOT 1707a

21. *'ēṣ*: tree, wood, timber, stalk. In verses 11, 12, 30. TWOT 1670a

22. *p<sup>e</sup>rî*: fruit. In verses 11, 12. TWOT 1809a

23. *mîn*: kind. In verses 11, 12, 21, 24, 25. TWOT 1191a

24. *yāṣā'*: go out, come out, go forth. In verses 12, 24. TWOT 893

25. *mā'ôr*: light, luminary. In verses 14–16. TWOT 52f

26. *'ôt*: sign, mark, token, ensign, standard, proof, warning. In verse 14. TWOT 41a

27. *nātan*: give. The three broad areas of meaning are give, put or set, and make or constitute. In verse 17. TWOT 1443

28. *shāraṣ*: teem, swarm. A teeming swarming, prolific multitude. In verse 20. TWOT 2467

29. *shereṣ*: teeming, swarming things. In verse 20. TWOT 2467a

30. *nepesh*: life, soul, creature, person, appetite, mind. The same Hebrew expression is used in verses 20, 21, and 24; man is here being associated with other creatures as sharing in the passionate experience of life. In verses 20, 21, 24. TWOT 1395a

31. *tannîn*: dragon, sea monster, serpent, whale. In verse 21. TWOT 2528b

32. *b<sup>e</sup>hēmâ*: beast, animal, cattle. In verses 24–26. TWOT 208a

33. *remeś*: creeping organisms. The root encompasses all smaller animals. In verses 24–26. TWOT 2177a

34. *ḥayyâ*: living thing, animal. The term is used mostly of wild animals in contrast to domestic animals. In verses 24, 25, 28, 30. TWOT 644c

35. *'ādām*: man, mankind, Adam. In verses 26, 27. TWOT 25a

36. *kābash*: subdue, bring into bondage, keep under, force. *kābash* assumes that the party being subdued is hostile to the subduer, necessitating some sort of coercion. In Gen. 1:28 it implies that creation will not do man's bidding gladly or easily and that man must now bring creation into submission by main strength. In verse 28. TWOT 951

37. *yereq*: green, greenness. In verse 30. TWOT 918a

38. *rāmaś*: creep, walk on all fours. Apparently the verb emphasizes the scurrying of small four-footed mammals. In verse 30. TWOT 2177

[a] These definitions are all excerpted from R. Laird Harris, Gleason L. Archer Jr., and Bruce K. Waltke, eds., *Theological Wordbook of the Old Testament*, 2 vols. (Chicago: Moody Press, 1980). Previous versions drew from several sources for the definitions. This version has been simplified by drawing from one source. Entry numbers (not page numbers) of the TWOT are included so the reader can easily find them. The verses where each word is found in the Genesis creation account are also included.

# Appendix C

# SONS OF GOD AND SONS OF MEN

What follows is a complete listing of all biblical references to "sons of God" and "sons of men," or the equivalent "children of God" and "children of men" based on the King James Version and the New International Version 1984.

**Biblical references to "sons of God" or "God's children"**

| | |
|---|---|
| Genesis 6:2 | Romans 8:14 |
| Genesis 6:4 | Romans 8:19 |
| Job 1:6 | Galatians 3:26 |
| Job 2:1 | Philippians 2:15 |
| Job 38:7 | 1 John 3:1 |
| Matthew 5:9 | 1 John 3:2 |
| John 1:12 | |

**Biblical references to "children of God" or "God's children"**

| | |
|---|---|
| John 11:52 | Romans 9:8 |
| Romans 8:16 | 1 John 3:10 |
| Romans 8:21 | 1 John 5:2 |

**Biblical references to "sons [daughters] of men"**

| | |
|---|---|
| Psalm 4:2 | Psalm 58:1 |
| Psalm 31:19 | Psalm 145:12 |
| Psalm 33:13 | Proverbs 8:31 |
| Psalm 57:4 | Ecclesiastes 2:3 |

Ecclesiastes 2:8

Ecclesiastes 3:10

Ecclesiastes 3:18

Ecclesiastes 3:19

Ecclesiastes 8:11

Ecclesiastes 9:3

Ecclesiastes 9:12

Isaiah 52:14

Jeremiah 32:19

Daniel 5:21

Daniel 10:16

Joel 1:12

Micah 5:7

Mark 3:28

Ephesians 3:5

## Biblical references to "children of men" or "sons of men"

2 Chronicles 6:30

Psalm 11:4

Psalm 12:1

Psalm 14:2

Psalm 21:10

Psalm 36:7

Psalm 45:2

Psalm 53:2

Psalm 66:5

Psalm 90:3

Psalm 107:8

Psalm 107:15

Psalm 107:21

Psalm 107:31

Psalm 115:16

Proverbs 15:11

Lamentations 3:33

Ezekiel 31:14

Daniel 2:38

# NOTES

## Chapter 1 – Personal Journey

1. 2 Timothy 3:16.
2. 1 Thessalonians 5:21.
3. John 10:35.
4. 1 John 4:1.
5. Hugh Ross, *Cosmic Fingerprints* (Glendora, CA: Reasons to Believe, 2005), DVD; Hugh Ross, *An Astronomer's Quest* (Glendora, CA: Reasons to Believe, 2000), audio CD.
6. Ross, *An Astronomer's Quest.*

## Chapter 2 – Reasons for Resistance

1. N. Jarosik et al., "Seven-Year Wilkinson Microwave Anisotropy Probe (WMAP) Observations: Sky Maps, Systematic Errors, and Basic Results," *Astrophysical Journal Supplement* 192 (February 2011): id. 14; Hugh Ross, *Why the Universe Is the Way It Is* (Grand Rapids: Baker, 2008), 128–31.
2. Hugh Ross, *The Creator and the Cosmos: How the Latest Scientific Discoveries Reveal God*, 3rd ed. (Glendora, CA: Reasons to Believe, 2001), 145–67, 175–99; Hugh Ross, *More Than a Theory: Revealing a Testable Model for Creation* (Grand Rapids: Baker 2009), 101–40, 259–60; Hugh Ross, "RTB Design Compendium (2009) *Why the Universe Is the Way It Is* and *More Than a Theory*," Reasons to Believe, accessed August 29, 2013, http://www.reasons.org/fine-tuning.
3. Frederic B. Burnham, quoted in David Briggs, "Science, Religion Are Discovering Commonality in Big Bang Theory," *Los Angeles Times*, May 2, 1992, B6–B7.
4. Hugh Ross, Fuz Rana, Michael Shermer, Sahotra Sarkar, and Kenneth Diller, Skeptics Forum at the University of Texas–Austin, Gregory Gymnasium,

April 28, 2009.

5. Stephen Jay Gould, "Nonoverlapping Magisteria," *Natural History* 108 (March 1997): 16–22.

6. Stephen Jay Gould, *Rocks of Ages: Science and Religion in the Fullness of Life* (New York: Ballantine Books, 2002), 3.

7. Council of the National Academy of Sciences (1981), quoted in Committee on Science and Creationism, James D. Ebert (chairman), *Science and Creationism: A View from the National Academy of Sciences* (Washington, DC: National Academy Press, 1984), 6.

8. Richard Dawkins, "When Religion Steps on Science's Turf," *Free Inquiry* 18, no. 2 (Spring 1998): 19.

9. Francis S. Collins, *The Language of God: A Scientist Presents Evidence for Belief* (New York: Free Press, 2006), 60–67.

10. Johnny V. Miller and John M. Soden, *In the Beginning... We Misunderstood: Interpreting Genesis in its Original Context* (Grand Rapids: Kregel Publications, 2012).

11. John H. Walton, *The Lost World of Genesis One: Ancient Cosmology and the Origins Debate* (Downers Grove, IL: InterVarsity, 2009), 107.

12. Walton, *Lost World of Genesis One*, 19.

13. Peter Enns, *Inspiration and Incarnation: Evangelicals and the Problem of the Old Testament* (Grand Rapids: Baker Academic, 2005); Miller and Soden, *In the Beginning*, 71–72, 90, 101–2, 147, 160; Walton, *Lost World of Genesis One*, 16, 18. 21, 56–58, 94–95.

14. Thomas F. Torrance, *Theology in Reconstruction* (Grand Rapids: Eerdmans, 1965); Thomas F. Torrance, *Reality and Scientific Theology* (Edinburgh: Scottish Academic Press, 1985); Thomas F. Torrance, "Ultimate and Penultimate Beliefs in Science," in *Facets of Faith & Science* 1; *Historiography and Modes of Interaction*, ed. Jitse M. van der Meer (New York: University Press of America, 1996), 151–76.

15. For a listing, see Hugh Ross, "Creation Passages in the Bible," Reasons to Believe, last modified January 1, 2004, http://www.reasons.org/articles/creation-passages-in-the-bible.

16. 1 Peter 1:12a.

17. 1 Peter 1:10–12.

18. Isaiah 7:14–8:4.

19. Isaiah 7:1–9:7.

20. Matthew 28:18–20.

21. Friedrich Delitzsch, *Babel and Bible*, trans. by Thomas J. McCormack and W. H. Garruth (Chicago: Open Court, 1903), 45.

22. Miller and Soden, *In the Beginning*, 71–72, 90, 101–2, 147, 160; Walton,

*Lost World of Genesis One*, 16, 18, 21, 56–58, 94–95; Enns, *Inspiration and Incarnation*.

23. Frank J. Tipler, *The Physics of Immortality: Modern Cosmology, God and the Resurrection of the Dead* (New York: Doubleday, 1994), 5.
24. Ibid.
25. Michael Ruse, "Naturalistic Fallacy," *Reason* (October 1996): 56.
26. Frank Press, *Science and Creationism: A View from the National Academy of Sciences* (Washington, DC: National Academy Press, 1984): 6.
27. The first known proclamations of this often repeated assertion were made by Cardinal Cesar Baronio and Galileo Galilei.
28. 2 Corinthians 5:7.
29. Acts 17:11, 1 Thessalonians 5:21, 2 Timothy 3:15.

## Chapter 3 – Creation of the Cosmos

1. One example is Bruce K. Waltke, *Creation and Chaos: An Exegetical and Theological Study of Biblical Cosmogony* (Portland, OR: Western Conservative Baptist Seminary, 1974). Waltke has since prepared a 900-page manuscript on the first three verses of Genesis 1.
2. Hugh Ross, *The Fingerprint of God*, commemorative ed. (Glendora, CA: Reasons to Believe, 2010), 21–27.
3. Hermann Bondi and T. Gold, "The Steady-State Theory of the Expanding Universe," *Monthly Notices of the Royal Astronomical Society* 108 (1948): 252–270; Fred Hoyle, "A New Model for the Expanding Universe," *Monthly Notices of the Royal Astronomical Society* 108 (1948): 372–382; Ross, *Fingerprint of God*, 53–105.
4. Robert H. Dicke et al., "Cosmic Black-Body Radiation," *Astrophysical Journal* 142 (1965): 414–19; John Gribbin, "Oscillating Universe Bounces Back," *Nature* 259 (1976): 15–16.
5. Genesis 1:1; Psalm 33:6–9; Psalm 90:2; John 17:24; 2 Timothy 1:9; Titus 1:2; Revelation 21:1.
6. Job 37:23; Jeremiah 23:24; John 1:3; Ephesians 1:4; Colossians 1:15–16; 2 Timothy 1:9; Titus 1:2; Hebrews 11:3.
7. Thomas E. McComiskey in R. Laird Harris, Gleason L. Archer Jr., and Bruce K. Waltke, *Theological Wordbook of the Old Testament*, vol. 1 (Chicago: Moody Press, 1980), 127.
8. Ibid.
9. Ibid.
10. Genesis 2:3–4, Psalm 33:6, 102:25, 148:5, Isaiah 40:26, 42:5, 45:18, John 1:3, Colossians 1:15–17, 2 Timothy 1:9, Titus 1:2.
11. R. Laird Harris, Gleason L. Archer Jr., and Bruce K. Waltke, *Theological*

*Wordbook of the Old Testament*, vol. 2 (Chicago: Moody Press, 1980), 701–2.

12. Harris, Archer, and Waltke, *Theological Wordbook*, vol. 1, 213–14.
13. Ibid., 199.
14. Harris, Archer, and Waltke, *Theological Wordbook*, vol. 2, 608.
15. Ibid., 823.
16. Harris, Archer, and Waltke, *Theological Wordbook*, vol. 1, 393.
17. Harris, Archer, and Waltke, *Theological Wordbook*, vol. 1. There were no vowels in the oldest Hebrew biblical manuscripts. The later insertion of vowel sounds multiplied the 3,067 biblical Hebrew words (not including seldom used proper nouns) to 8,674 (including all proper nouns used in the Old Testament).
18. Ibid., 74–75.
19. Harris, Archer, and Waltke, *Theological Wordbook*, vol. 2, 935–36.
20. 2 Corinthians 12:2.
21. Waltke, *Creation and Chaos*, 20, 25–26. This point was also one of Waltke's central themes in his Kenneth S. Kantzer Lectures in Systematic Theology given January 8–10, 1991, at Trinity Evangelical Divinity School in Deerfield, Illinois; Allen P. Ross, *Creation & Blessing: A Guide to the Study and Exposition of Genesis* (Grand Rapids, MI: Baker, 1988), 721, 725–26.
22. Genesis 1:1; Psalm 33:6–9; Isaiah 40:26–28; 42:5; John 1:3; 17:24; Ephesians 1:4; Colossians 1:15–16; 2 Timothy 1:9; Titus 1:2; Hebrews 11:3; 1 Peter 1:20; Revelation 4:11.
23. Stephen Hawking and Roger Penrose, "The Singularities of Gravitational Collapse and Cosmology," *Proceedings of the Royal Society of London* A 314 (January 27, 1970): 529–48.
24. Arvind Borde, Alan H. Guth, and Alexander Vilenkin, "Inflationary Spacetimes Are Incomplete in Past Directions," *Physical Review Letters* 90 (April 18, 2003): 151301.
25. Psalm 119:160; Ecclesiastes 7:1–25; Acts 17:11; Romans 12:2; 1 Thessalonians 5:21; Hebrews 6:18; 1 John 4:1.
26. Isaiah 41:5–7; 44:9–20; Jeremiah 23:9–40; Colossians 2:4, 8.
27. David Toshio Tsumura, *The Earth and the Waters in Genesis 1 and 2: A Linguistic Investigation* (Sheffield: Sheffield Academic, 1989), 41–43.
28. C. John Collins, *Genesis 1–4: A Linguistic, Literary, and Theological Commentary* (Phillipsburg, NJ: P&R, 2006), 51.
29. Ibid.
30. Rodney Whitefield, *Genesis One and the Age of the Earth: What Does the Bible Say?* (San Jose, CA: R. Whitefield, 2011), 10–11. The entire booklet is available as a free download at http://www.creationingenesis.com/booklet.html.

31. Whitefield, *Genesis One*, 10–17.
32. Herbert W. Morris, *Work-Days of God; or Science and the Bible*, enlarged ed. (London: W. Nicholson & Sons, 1915), 21–106; John Cunningham Geikie, *Hours with the Bible*, vol. 1 (New York: James Pott, 1905), 40–42.
33. C. I. Scofield, *The Scofield Reference Bible* (New York: Oxford University Press, 1945), 3–4.
34. James Buswell, Hugh Ross, Robert Saucy, and Dallas Willard, *Round Table on Genesis One*, 120-minute video cassette (Pasadena, CA: Reasons to Believe, 1992). Four scholars, including gap theorist Robert Saucy, interact on their differing interpretations of Genesis 1.
35. Bernard Ramm, *The Christian View of Science and Scripture* (Grand Rapids, MI: Eerdmans, 1954), 195–210.
36. Barbara Ercolano, Antonia Bevan, and Thomas Robitaille, "The Spectral Energy Distribution of Protoplanetary Discs Around Massive Young Stellar Objects," *Monthly Notices of the Royal Astronomical Society* 428 (January 2013): 2714–22; S. T. Megeath et al., "The Spitzer Space Telescope Survey of the Orion A and B Molecular Clouds–Part I: A Census of Dusty Young Stellar Objects and a Study of Their Mid-infrared Variability," *Astronomical Journal* 144 (December 2012): id. 192; Matthew S. Povich et al., "A Pan-Carina Young Stellar Object Catalog: Intermediate-mass Young Stellar Objects in the Carina Nebula Identified Via Mid-infrared Excess Emission," *Astrophysical Journal Supplement* 194 (May 2011): id. 14; Woojin Kwon, *"Circumstellar Structure Properties of Young Stellar Objects: Envelopes, Bipolar Outflows, and Disks"* (PhD dissertation, University of Illinois at Urbana-Champaign, December 2009), publication number: AAT 3406767. Source: DAI-B 71/05, Nov 2010, https://www.ideals.illinois.edu/bitstream/handle/2142/14711/Kwon_Woojin.pdf?sequence=2; J. M. De Buizer, "Testing the Circumstellar Disc Hypothesis: A Search for $H_2$ Outflow Signatures from Massive Young Stellar Objects with Linearly Distributed Methanol Masers," *Monthly Notices of the Royal Astronomical Society* 341 (May 2003): 277–98; C. Bertout, "Occultation of Young Stellar Objects by Circumstellar Disks. I. Theoretical Expectations and Preliminary Comparison with Observations," *Astronomy and Astrophysics* 363 (November 2000): 984–90.
37. C. P. Dullemond and J. D. Monnier, "The Inner Regions of Protoplanetary Disks," *Annual Review of Astronomy and Astrophysics* 48 (2010): 205–39; Mark C. Wyatt, "Evolution of Debris Disks," *Annual Review of Astronomy and Astrophysics* 46 (2008): 339–83.
38. "Released Kepler Planetary Candidates," Barbara A. Mikulski Archive for Space Telescopes, last modified February 27, 2012, accessed January 9, 2013, http://archive.stsci.edu/kepler/planet_candidates.html; "Interactive Extra-

Solar Planets Catalog," *The Extrasolar Planets Encyclopedia*, last modified September 4, 2013, accessed June 25, 2013, http://exoplanet.eu/catalog.

39. Eliza Miller-Ricci and Jonathan J. Fortney, "The Nature of the Atmosphere of the Transiting Super-Earth GJ 1214b," *Astrophysical Journal Letters* 716 (June 10, 2010): L74–L79.

40. P. Jonathan Patchett, "Scum of the Earth After All," *Nature* 382 (August 29, 1996): 758.

41. Harris, Archer, and Waltke, *Theological Wordbook*, vol. 1 and 2. This book contains definitions for 3,067 Hebrew words including Old Testament names that have theological import such as Abraham, David, Jerusalem, Jordan, and Sinai.

42. Harris, Archer, and Waltke, *Theological Wordbook*, vol. 1, 370–371; William Wilson, *Old Testament Word Studies* (Grand Rapids, MI: Kregel, 1978), 109.

43. Harris, Archer, and Waltke, *Theological Wordbook*, vol. 1, 370–71, vol. 2, 672–73; H. W. F. Gesenius, *Gesenius' Hebrew-Chaldee Lexicon to the Old Testament* (Grand Rapids, MI: Baker, 1979), 612–13.

44. R. Monastersky, "Speedy Spin Kept Early Earth from Freezing," *Science News* 143 (June 12, 1993): 373; William R. Kuhn, J. C. G. Walker, and Hal G. Marshall, "The Effect on Earth's Surface Temperature from Variations in Rotation Rate, Continent Formation, Solar Luminosity, and Carbon Dioxide," *Journal of Geophysical Research: Atmospheres* 94 (August 20, 1989): 11, 129–31, 136; George E. Williams, "Geological Constraints on the Precambrian History of Earth's Rotation and the Moon's Orbit," *Reviews of Geophysics* 38 (February 2000): 37–60.

45. Kuhn, Walker, and Marshall, "The Effect on Earth's Surface Temperature," 11, 129–31, 136; Hubert P. Yockey, *Information Theory and Molecular Biology* (Cambridge, UK: Cambridge University Press, 1992), 222–23; Richard A. Kerr, "Fiery Io Models Earth's First Days," *Science* 280 (April 17, 1998): 382.

46. Yuichiro Ueno et al., "Ion Microprobe Analysis of Graphite from Ca. 3.8 Ga Metasediments, Isua Supracrustal Belt, West Greenland: Relationship Between Metamorphism and Carbon Isotopic Composition," *Geochimica et Cosmochimica Acta* 66 (2002): 1257–68; Minik T. Rosing, "$^{13}$C-Depleted Carbon Microparticles in >3700-Ma Sea-Floor Sedimentary Rocks from West Greenland," *Science* 283 (January 29, 1999): 674–76; Craig E. Manning et al., "Geology and Age of Supracrustal Rocks: Akilia Island, Greenland: New Evidence for a >3.83 Ga Origin of Life," *Astrobiology* 1 (2001): 402–3; C. M. Fedo, J. S. Meyers, and P. W. U. Appel, "Depositional Setting and Paleogeographic Implications of Earth's Oldest Supracrustal Rocks, the >3.7 Ga Isua Greenstone Belt, West Greenland," *Sedimentary Geology* 141–42

(2001): 61–77; J. O'Neil and R. W. Carlson, "A Glimpse of Earth's Primordial Crust: The Nuvvuagittug Greenstone Belt As a Vestige of Mafic Hadean Oceanic Crust," *American Geophysical Union, Fall Meeting 2010* (December 2010): abstract #V43D-04; Uffe Gråe Jørgensen et al., "The Earth-Moon System During the Late Heavy Bombardment Period," *Icarus* 204 (2009): 368–80.

### Chapter 4 – Creation Days One and Two

1. Job 36:25–37:23.
2. Fazale Rana with Hugh Ross, *Who Was Adam: A Creation Model Approach to the Origin of Man* (Colorado Springs, CO: NavPress, 2005), 55–197.
3. Hugh Ross, *Hidden Treasures in the Book of Job: How the Oldest Book in the Bible Answers Today's Scientific Questions* (Grand Rapids, MI: Baker, 2011), 30–32.
4. R. Laird Harris, Gleason L. Archer Jr., and Bruce K. Waltke, *Theological Wordbook of the Old Testament*, vol. 2 (Chicago: Moody, 1980), 843.
5. H. W. F. Gesenius, *Gesenius' Hebrew-Chaldee Lexicon to the Old Testament* (Grand Rapids, MI: Baker, 1979), 766.
6. J. William Schopf, *Cradle of Life: The Discovery of Earth's Earliest Fossils* (Princeton, NJ: Princeton University Press, 1999); J. William Schopf, "The Oldest Known Records of Life: Early Archaean Stromatolites, Microfossils, and Organic Matter," in *Early Life on Earth, Nobel Symposium* No. 84, ed. Stefan Bengtson (New York: Columbia University Press, 1994): 193–205; J. William Schopf et al., "Laser-Raman Imagery of Earth's Earliest Fossils," *Nature* 416 (March 7, 2002): 73–76.
7. Craig E. Manning et al., "Geology and Age of Supracrustal Rocks, Akilia Island, Greenland: New Evidence for a >3.83 Ga Origin of Life," *Astrobiology* 1 (2001): 402–3; Minik T. Rosing, "$^{13}$C-Depleted Carbon Microparticles in >3700-Ma Sea-Floor Sedimentary Rocks from West Greenland," *Science* 283 (January 29, 1999): 674–76; S. J. Mojzsis et al., "Evidence for Life on Earth Before 3,800 Million Years Ago," *Nature* 384 (November 7, 1996): 55–59; C. M. Fedo, J. S. Meyers, and P. W. U. Appel, "Depositional Setting and Paleogeographic Implications of Earth's Oldest Supracrustal Rocks, the >3.7 Ga Isua Greenstone Belt, West Greenland," *Sedimentary Geology* 141–42 (2001): 61–77.
8. Minik T. Rosing and Robert Frei, "U-Rich Archaean Sea-Floor Sediments from Greenland—Indications of >3700 Ma Oxygenic Photosynthesis," *Earth and Planetary Science Letters* 217 (January 15, 2004): 237–44.
9. Harris, Archer, and Waltke, *Theological Wordbook*, vol. 1, 213–14.
10. Thorsten Kleine et al., "Hf-W Chronometry of Lunar Metals and the Age

and Early Differentiation of the Moon," *Science* 310 (December 9, 2005): 1671–74.

11. Joel Baker et al., "Early Planetesimal Melting from an Age of 4.5662 Gyr for Differentiated Meteorites," *Nature* 436 (August 25, 2005): 1127–31.

12. Neil F. Comins, *What If the Moon Didn't Exist? Voyages to Earths That Might Have Been* (New York: HarperCollins, 1993), 53–65.

13. Comins, *What If the Moon Didn't Exist?* 4–5, 58; W. R. Kuhn, J. C. G. Walker, and H. G. Marshall, "The Effect on Earth's Surface Temperature from Variations in Rotation Rate, Continent Formation, Solar Luminosity, and Carbon Dioxide," *Journal of Geophysical Research* 94 (August 20, 1989): 11, 129–31, 136.

14. Robin M. Canup and Erik Asphaug, "Origin of the Moon in a Giant Impact Near the End of the Earth's Formation," *Nature* 412 (August 16, 2001): 708–12; Robin M. Canup, "Simulations of a Late Lunar-Forming Impact," *Icarus* 168 (April, 2004): 433–456; Robin M. Canup, "Lunar-Forming Collisions with Pre-Impact Rotation," *Icarus* 196 (August, 2008): 518–38.

15. Louis A. Codispoti, "The Limits to Growth," *Nature* 387 (May 15, 1997): 237; Kenneth H. Coale et al., "A Massive Phytoplankton Bloom Induced by an Ecosystem-Scale Iron Fertilization Experiment in the Equatorial Pacific Ocean," *Nature* 383 (October 10, 1996): 495–99.

16. P. Jonathan Patchett, "Scum of the Earth After All," *Nature* 382 (August 29, 1996): 758.

17. William R. Ward, "Comments on the Long-Term Stability of the Earth's Obliquity," *Icarus* 50 (1982): 444–48; Carl D. Murray, "Seasoned Travellers," *Nature* 361 (February 18, 1993): 586–87; Jacques Laskar and P. Robutel, "The Chaotic Obliquity of the Planets," *Nature* 361 (1993): 608–12; Jacques Laskar, F. Joutel, and P. Robutel, "Stabilization of the Earth's Obliquity by the Moon," *Nature* 361 (February 18, 1993): 615–17.

18. Hugh Ross, *The Creator and the Cosmos: How the Latest Scientific Discoveries Reveal God*, 3rd ed. (Colorado Springs, CO: NavPress, 2001), 175–99; Hugh Ross, "RTB Design Compendium (2009) for *Why the Universe Is the Way It Is* and *More Than a Theory*," Reasons to Believe, accessed September 6, 2013, http://www.reasons.org/links/hugh/research-notes.

19. Carl Sagan and George Mullen, "Earth and Mars: Evolution of Atmospheres and Surface Temperatures," *Science* 177 (July 7, 1972): 52–56; F. M. Walter and D. C. Barry, "Pre- and Main-Sequence Evolution of Solar Activity," in *The Sun in Time*, eds. Charles Philip Sonett, Mark S. Giampapa, and Mildred Shapley Matthews (Tuscon, AZ: University of Arizona Press, 1991): 651–52.

20. I.-Juliana Sackmann and Arnold I. Boothroyd, "Our Sun. V. A Bright Young

Sun Consistent with Helioseismology and Warm Temperatures on Ancient Earth and Mars," *Astrophysical Journal* 583 (February 1, 2003): 1024–39; Sylvaine Turck-Chièze, Laurent Piau, and Sébastien Couvidat, "The Solar Energetic Balance Revisited by Young Solar Analogs, Helioseismology, and Neutrinos," *Astrophysical Journal Letters* 731 (April 20, 2011): id. L29; I. Ribas et al., "Evolution of the Solar Activity Over Time and Effects on Planetary Atmospheres. II. $k^1$ Ceti, an Analog of the Sun When Life Arose on Earth," *Astrophysical Journal* 714 (May 1, 2010): 384–95; Alicia Aarnio and K. Stassun, "The Application of Solar Physics to Mass Loss and Angular Momentum Evolution of Solar-type Pre-Main Sequence Stars," *Bulletin of the American Astronomical Society* 42 (January 2010): 592; Joyce Ann Guzik and Katie Mussack, "Exploring Mass Loss, Low-z Accretion, and Convective Overshoot in Solar Models to Mitigate the Solar Abundance Problem" *Astrophysical Journal* 713 (April 20, 2010): 1108–19.

21. This subject is described in some detail in my book *More Than a Theory: Revealing a Testable Model for Creation* (Grand Rapids, MI: Baker, 2009), 149–71.

22. Ken Caldeira and James F. Kasting, "Susceptibility of the Early Earth to Irreversible Glaciation Caused by Carbon Dioxide Clouds," *Nature* 359 (September 17, 1992): 226–28.

23. For a detailed description of these processes, see my book *More Than a Theory*, 149–71.

24. Tobias C. Owen, "The Case for a Cometary Contribution to Terrestrial Volatiles," European Geophysical Society XXVII General Assembly, Nice, France, April 21–26, 2002: abstract #1067; Hidenori Genda and Masahiro Ikoma, "Origin of the Ocean on the Earth: Early Evolution of Water D/H in a Hydrogen-Rich Atmosphere," *Icarus* 194 (March 1, 2008): 42–52; Guillermo Gonzalez, "Mini-Comets Write New Chapter in Earth-Science," *Facts & Faith* 11, no. 3 (1997): 6–7; David Deming, "On the Possible Influence of Extraterrestrial Volatiles on Earth's Climate and the Origin of the Oceans," *Palaeogeography, Palaeoclimatology, Palaeoecololgy* 146 (February 15, 1999): 33–51; Richard A. Kerr, "Spots Confirmed, Tiny Comets Spurned," *Science* 276 (May 30, 1997): 1333–34; Susan Taylor, James H. Lever, and Ralph P. Harvey, "Accretion Rate of Cosmic Spherules Measured at the South Pole," *Nature* 392 (April 30, 1998): 899–903.

25. Harris, Archer, and Waltke, *Theological Wordbook*, vol. 2, 862; Harris, Archer, and Waltke, *Theological Wordbook*, vol. 2, 935.

26. Ross, *Hidden Treasures*, 76–78.

27. For "to manufacture" and "to fabricate," see H. W. F. Gesenius, *Gesenius' Hebrew-Chaldee Lexicon to the Old Testament* (Grand Rapids, MI: Baker, 1979), 657;

Harris, Archer, and Waltke, *Theological Wordbook*, vol. 2, 701–2.

## Chapter 5 – Creation Days Three and Four

1.   *Wikipedia*, s.v. "Rodinia," last modified August 7, 2013, http://en.wikipedia.org/wiki/Rodinia; *Wikipedia*, s.v. "Pangaea," last modified September 2, 2013, http://en.wikipedia.org/wiki/Pangaea.
2.   D. G. Pearson, S. W. Parman, and G. M. Nowell, "A Link Between Large Mantle Melting Events and Continent Growth Seen In Osmium Isotopes," *Nature* 449 (September 13, 2007): 202–5.
3.   Joel Baker et al., "Early Planetesimal Melting from an Age of 4.5662 Gyr for Differentiated Meteorites," *Nature* 436 (August 25, 2005): 1127–31; Claude J. Allègre, Gérard Manhès, and Christa Göpel, "The Age of the Earth," *Geochimica et Cosmochimica Acta* 59 (April 1995): 1445–56.
4.   Psalm 104:6.
5.   Psalm 104:7–8.
6.   Psalm 104:9.
7.   Peter D. Ward, *The Medea Hypothesis: Is Life on Earth Ultimately Self-Destructive?* (Princeton: Princeton University Press, 2009), 41–125; Peter D. Ward, *Out of Thin Air: Dinosaurs, Birds, and Earth's Ancient Atmosphere* (Washington, DC: Joseph Henry, 2006), 229–34; Peter D. Ward and Donald Brownlee, *Rare Earth: Why Complex Life Is Uncommon in the Universe* (New York: Copernicus, 2000), 191–220.
8.   R. Laird Harris, Gleason L. Archer Jr., and Bruce K. Waltke, *Theological Wordbook of the Old Testament*, vol. 1 (Chicago: Moody Press, 1980), 199.
9.   Harris, Archer, and Waltke, *Theological Wordbook*, vol. 1, 252–53.
10.  R. Laird Harris, Gleason L. Archer Jr., and Waltke, *Theological Wordbook of the Old Testament*, vol. 2 (Chicago: Moody Press, 1980), 688–89.
11.  Ibid., 734.
12.  Donald E. Canfield and Andreas Teske, "Late Proterozoic Rise in Atmospheric Oxygen Concentration Inferred from Phylogenetic and Sulfur-Isotope Studies," *Nature* 382 (July 11, 1996): 127–32; Donald E. Canfield, "A New Model for Proterozoic Ocean Chemistry," *Nature* 396 (December 3, 1998): 450–53; John M. Hayes, "Biochemistry: A Lowdown on Oxygen," *Nature* 417 (May 9, 2002): 127.
13.  Genesis 1:20.
14.  L. Paul Knauth and Martin J. Kennedy, "The Late-Precambrian Greening of the Earth," *Nature* 460 (August 6, 2009): 728–32.
15.  Paul K. Strother et al., "Earth's Earliest Non-Marine Eukaryotes," *Nature* 473 (May 26, 2011): 505–9.
16.  Ibid., 505.

17. Jared M. Diamond, "Daisy Gives an Evolutionary Answer," *Nature* 380 (1996): 103–4; Paul R. and Anne H. Ehrlich, *Extinction: The Causes and Consequences of the Disappearance of Species* (New York: Random House, 1981), 22–23.

18. Robert M. May, John H. Lawton, and Nigel E. Stork, "Assessing Extinction Rates," in *Extinction Rates*, eds. John H. Lawton and Robert M. May (New York: Oxford University Press, 1995), 2–16; Ehrlich and Ehrlich, *Extinction*, 166–69.

19. P. Jonathan Patchett, "Scum of the Earth After All," *Nature* 382 (August 29, 1996): 758.

20. Ibid.

21. Menahem Mansoor, *Biblical Hebrew Step by Step*, vol. 1, 2nd ed. (Grand Rapids: Baker, 1980), 69–84.

22. Henri Blocher, *In the Beginning: The Opening Chapters of Genesis* (Downers Grove, IL: InterVarsity, 1984), 45–46, 51–53; John C. Whitcomb Jr., *The Early Earth: An Introduction to Biblical Creationism* (Grand Rapids, MI: Baker, 1972), 47–60; Scott M. Huse, *The Collapse of Evolution*, 3rd ed. (Grand Rapids, MI: Baker, 1997), 77; Douglas F. Kelly, *Creation and Change: Genesis 1.1–2.4 in the Light of Changing Scientific Paradigms* (Fearn, Ross-shire, UK: Mentor, 1997), 201–4; D. Russell Humphreys, *Starlight & Time: Solving the Puzzle of Distant Starlight in a Young Universe* (Colorado Springs, CO: Master Books, 1994), 78, 126.

23. Exodus 34:29–35.

24. Matthew 17:1–8, Mark 9:2–6, Luke 9:28–36.

25. J. Flemming et al., "Forecasts and Assimilation Experiments of the Antarctic Ozone Hole 2008," *Atmospheric Chemistry and Physics* 11 (March 2011): 1961–77; Jianchun Bian, "Features of Ozone Mini-Hole Events Over the Tibetan Plateau," *Advances in Atmospheric Sciences* 26 (March 2009): 305–11; Paul A. Newman et al., "When Will the Antarctic Ozone Hole Recover?" *Geophysical Research Letters* 33 (June 30, 2006), doi: 10.1029/2005GL025232; Karl Hoppel et al., "A Measurement/Model Comparison of Ozone Photochemical Loss in the Antarctic Ozone Hole Using Polar Ozone and Aerosol Measurement Observations and the Match Technique," *Journal of Geophysical Research: Atmospheres* 110 (October 2005), doi: 10.1029/2004JD005651; M. Alvarez-Madrigal and J. Pérez-Peraza, "Analysis of the Evolution of the Antarctic Ozone Hole Size," *Journal of Geophysical Research: Atmospheres* 110 (January 2005), doi: 10.1029/2004JD004944; D. J. Hofmann, "Recovery of Antarctic Ozone Hole," *Nature* 384 (November 21, 1996): 222–23; Constance Holden, "Antarctic Ozone Hole Hits Record Depth," *Science* 254 (October 18, 1991): 373; "Ozone Hole Watch: Images, Data, and Information for the South-

ern Hemisphere," NASA, accessed August 15, 2011, http://ozonewatch.gsfc.
nasa.gov/.

26. J. Lorente et al., "Climatology of Ozone 'Mini-Hole' Events and Their Influ-
ence on UV Solar Radiation in Barcelona (Spain)," in *Current Problems in
Atmospheric Radiation: Proceedings of the International Radiation Sympo-
sium, AIP Conference Proceedings* 1100 (March 2009): 65–68; Youfei Zheng
et al., "Response of Different Crop Growth and Yield to Enhanced UV-B
Radiation Under Field Conditions," in *Ultraviolet Ground- and Space-Based
Measurements, Models, and Effects IV, Proceedings of the SPIE* 5545, eds.
James R. Slusser, Jay R. Herman, Wei Gao, and Germar Bernhard (October
2004): 102–10; J. F. Abarca and C. C. Casiccia, "Skin Cancer and Ultraviolet
B Radiation under the Antarctic Ozone Hole: Southern Chile, 1987–2000,"
*Photodermatology, Photoimmunology, and Photomedicine* 18 (December 2002):
294–302; S. K.West et al., "Sunlight Exposure and Risk of Lens Opacities in
a Population-Based Study: The Salisbury Eye Evaluation Project," *Journal of
the American Medical Association* 280 (August 26, 1998): 714–18; R. P. Sinha,
S. C. Singh, and D.-P. Häder, "Photoecophysiology of Cyanobacteria," *Recent
Research Developments in Photochemistry and Photobiology* 3 (1999): 91–101;
Harry Slaper et al., "Estimates of Ozone Depletion and Skin Cancer Incidence
to Examine the Vienna Convention Achievements," *Nature* 384 (November
21, 1996): 256–258.

27. W. L. Chameides, P. S. Kasibhatla, J. Yienger, and H. Levy II, "Growth of
Continental-Scale Metro-Agro-Plexes, Regional Ozone Pollution, and World
Food Production," *Science* 264 (April 1, 1994): 74–77.

28. Paul Crutzen and Mark Lawrence, "Atmospheric Chemistry: Ozone Clouds
Over the Atlantic," *Nature* 388 (August 14, 1997): 625.

29. Paul Crutzen, "Mesospheric Mysteries," *Science* 277 (September 26, 1997):
1951–52; M. E. Summers et al., "Implications of Satellite OH Observations
for Middle Atmospheric $H_2O$ and Ozone," *Science* 277 (September 26, 1997):
1967–70.

30. Crutzen and Lawrence, "Ozone Clouds," 625; K. Suhre et al., "Ozone-Rich
Transients in the Upper Equatorial Atlantic Troposphere," *Nature* 388 (August
14, 1997): 661–63.

## Chapter 6 – Creation Days Five and Six

1. R. Laird Harris, Gleason L. Archer Jr., and Bruce K. Waltke, *Theological Wordbook of the Old Testament*, vol. 2 (Chicago: Moody, 1980), 956–57.

2. Bing Shen et al., "The Avalon Explosion: Evolution of Ediacara Morpho-
space," *Science* 319 (January 4, 2008): 81–84.

3. D.-G. Shu et al., "An Early Cambrian Tunicate from China," *Nature* 411

(May 24, 2001): 472–73; D.-G. Shu et al., "Primitive Deuterostomes from the Chengjiang Lagerstätte (Lower Cambrian, China)," *Nature* 414 (November 22, 2001): 419–24; D.-G. Shu et al., "Lower Cambrian Vertebrates from South China," *Nature* 402 (November 4, 1999): 42–46; Jun-Yuan Chen, Di-Ying Huang, and Chia-Wei Li, "An Early Cambrian Craniate-like Chordate," *Nature* 402 (December 2, 1999): 518–22; Richard A. Kerr, "Evolution's Big Bang Gets Even More Explosive," *Science* 261 (September 3, 1993): 1274–75; Richard A. Bowring et al., "Calibrating Rates of Early Cambrian Evolution," *Science* 261 (September 3, 1993): 1293–99; J.-Y. Chen et al., "A Possible Early Cambrian Chordate," *Nature* 377 (October 26, 2002), 720–21; D. Shu, X. Zhang, and L. Chen, "Reinterpretation of *Yunnanozoon* as the Earliest Known Hemichordate," *Nature* 380 (April 4, 1996), 428–30; "The Cambrian 'Explosion' and Why It Means So Much for Christians: An Interview with Dr. Paul Chien," with Fazale R. Rana and Hugh Ross, *Facts for Faith* (Quarter 2, 2000): 15–17.

4.   R. D. K. Thomas, Rebecca M. Shearman, and Graham W. Stewart, "Evolutionary Exploitation of Design Options by the First Animals with Hard Skeletons," *Science* 288 (May 19, 2000): 1239–42.

5.   Donald E. Canfield and Andreas Teske, "Late Proterozoic Rise in Atmospheric Oxygen Concentration Inferred from Phylogenetic and Sulphur-Isotope Studies," *Nature* 382 (July 11, 1996): 127–32; Donald E. Canfield, "A New Model for Proterozoic Ocean Chemistry," *Nature* 396 (December 3, 1998): 450–53; John M. Hayes, "Biogeochemistry: A Lowdown on Oxygen," *Nature* 417 (May 9, 2002): 127; Hugh Ross, *More Than a Theory: Revealing a Testable Model for Creation* (Grand Rapids, MI: Baker, 2009), 158–62.

6.   Richard Dawkins, *The Blind Watchmaker: Why the Evidence of Evolution Reveals a Universe without Design* (New York: W. W.Norton, 1987), 229.

7.   Gregory A. Wray, "Rates of Evolution in Developmental Processes," *American Zoologist* 32 (January–February, 1992): 131.

8.   Kevin J. Peterson, Michael R. Dietrich, and Mark A. McPeek, "MicroRNAs and Metazoan Macroevolution: Insights into Canalization, Complexity, and the Cambrian Explosion," *BioEssays* 31 (July 2009): 737.

9.   Harris, Archer, and Waltke, *Theological Wordbook*, vol. 2, 587–91.

10.  J. G. M. Thewissen et al., "Evolution of Cetacean Osmoregulation," *Nature* 381 (May 30, 1996): 379–80.

11.  Carl Zimmer, *At the Water's Edge: Macroevolution and the Transformation of Life* (New York: The Free Press, 1998); Michael Behe et al., *Firing Line: A Debate on Creation and Evolution*, PBS, moderator Michael Kinsley

(December 19, 1997).

12. Annalisa Berta, "What Is a Whale?" *Science* 263 (January 14, 1994): 180–81.

13. J. G. M. Thewissen, S. I. Madar, and S. T. Hussain, "Whale Ankles and Evolutionary Relationships," *Nature* 395 (October 1, 1998): 452.

14. Emmanuel Paradis, "Statistical Analysis of Diversification with Species Traits," *Evolution* 59 (January 2005): 1–12; Andrew P. Martin and Stephen R. Palumbi, "Body Size, Metabolic Rate, Generation Time, and the Molecular Clock," *Proceedings of the National Academy of Sciences, USA* 90 (May 1, 1993): 4087–91; James F. Gillooly et al., "The Rate of DNA Evolution: Effects of Body Size and Temperature on the Molecular Clock," *Proceedings of the National Academy of Sciences, USA* 102 (January 4, 2005): 121–29.

15. Marcel Cardillo et al., "Multiple Causes of High Extinction Risk in Large Mammal Species," *Science* 309 (August 19, 2005): 1239.

16. Ibid.

17. Konstantin Popadin et al., "Accumulation of Slightly Deleterious Mutations in Mitochondrial Protein-Coding Genes of Large Versus Small Mammals," *Proceedings of the National Academy of Sciences, USA* 104 (August 14, 2007): 13390.

18. Jason M. Kamilar and Lisa M. Paciulli, "Examining the Extinction Risk of Specialized Folivores: A Comparative Study of Colobine Monkeys," *American Journal of Primatology* 70 (September 2008): 816–27.

19. Aaron Clauset and Sidney Redner, "Evolutionary Model of Species Body Mass Diversification," *Physical Review Letters* 102 (January 23, 2009), doi: 10.1103/PhysRevLett.102.038103.

20. Aaron Clauset, David J. Schwab, and Sidney Redner, "How Many Species Have Mass M?" *American Naturalist* 173 (February 2009): 256–63; A. H. Harcourt and M. W. Schwartz, "Primate Evolution: A Biology of Holocene Extinction and Survival on the Southeast Asian Sunda Shelf Islands," *American Journal of Physical Anthropology* 114 (January 2001): 4–17; Ella Tsahar et al., "Distribution and Extinction of Ungulates During the Holocene of the Southern Levant," *PLoS ONE* 4, 4 (April 29, 2009), doi:10.1371/journal.pone.0005316; Samuel T. Turvey and Susanne A. Fritz, "The Ghosts of Mammals Past: Biological and Geographical Patterns of Global Mammalian Extinction Across the Holocene," *Philosophical Transactions of the Royal Society of London B Biological Sciences* 366 (September 12, 2011): 2564–76; Susanne A. Fritz, Olaf R. P. Bininda-Emonds, and Andy Purvis, "Geographical Variation in Predictors of Mammalian Extinction Risk: Big Is Bad, But Only in the Tropics," *Ecology Letters* 12 (June 2009): 538–49.

21. Trish J. Lavery et al., "Iron Defecation by Sperm Whales Stimulates Carbon Export in the Southern Ocean," *Proceedings of the Royal Society B* 277 (November 22, 2010): 3527–31; Hugh Ross, "Thank God for Whales," *Today's New Reason to Believe* (blog), August 23, 2010, http://www.reasons.org/thank-god-whales; Hugh Ross, *Hidden Treasures in the Book of Job: How the Oldest Book in the Bible Answers Today's Scientific Questions* (Grand Rapids, MI: Baker, 2011), 65–68.

22. The popular claim that human footprints were found next to trails of dinosaur footprints in the Paluxy Riverbed (in Texas) has been overturned. No credible evidence suggests that humans or any other primate species coexisted with the Triassic, Jurassic, or Cretaceous dinosaurs. For further details and documentation see my book, *A Matter of Days: Resolving a Creation Controversy* (Colorado Springs, CO: NavPress, 2004), 198–200.

23. Harris, Archer, and Waltke, *Theological Wordbook*, vol. 2, 850–851.

**Chapter 7 – The Final Act (For Now)**

1. R. Laird Harris, Gleason L. Archer Jr., and Bruce K. Waltke, *Theological Wordbook of the Old Testament*, vol. 1 (Chicago: Moody, 1980), 10.

2. Genesis 2:7.

3. Colossian 2:9.

4. Hebrews 1:3.

5. Fazale Rana and Hugh Ross, *Origins of Life: Biblical and Evolutionary Models Face Off* (Colorado Springs, CO: NavPress, 2004), 81–105.

6. Rana and Ross, *Origins*, 109–208; Fazale Rana, *Creating Life in the Lab: How New Discoveries in Synthetic Biology Make a Case for the Creator* (Grand Rapids, MI: Baker, 2011).

7. Johan J. Bolhuis and Clive D. L. Wynne, "Can Evolution Explain How Minds Work?" *Nature* 458 (April 16, 2009): 832–33; Thomas Nagel, "What Is It Like To Be a Bat?" *Philosophical Review* 83 (October 1974): 435–50; C. B. Campbell and William Hodos, "The *Scala Naturae* Revisited: Evolutionary Scales and Anagenesis in Comparative Psychology," *Journal of Comparative Psychology* 105 (September 1991): 211–21.

8. C. R. Raby and N. S. Clayton, "Prospective Cognition in Animals," *Behavioural Processes* 80 (March 2009): 314–24; Derek C. Penn, Keith J. Holyoak, and Daniel J. Povinelli, "Darwin's Mistake: Explaining the Discontinuity Between Human and Nonhuman Minds," *Behavioral and Brain Sciences* 31 (April 2008): 109–30; Esther Herrmann et al., "Humans Have Evolved Specialized Skills of Social Cognition: The Cultural Intelligence Hypothesis," *Science* 317 (September 7, 2007): 1360–66; Keith Jensen, Josep Call, and Mi-

chael Tomasello, "Chimpanzees Are Vengeful But Not Spiteful," *Proceedings of the National Academy of Sciences, USA* 104 (August 7, 2007):13046–50; Alexandra Horowitz, "Disambiguating the 'Guilty Look': Salient Prompts to a Familiar Dog Behaviour," *Behavioural Processes* 81 (July 2009): 447–52; Mark Petter et al., "Can Dogs (*Canis familiaris*) Detect Human Deception?" *Behavioural Processes* 82 (October 1, 2009):109–18.

9.  Richard G. Klein with Blake Edgar, *The Dawn of Human Culture: A Bold New Theory on What Sparked the "Big Bang" of Human Consciousness* (New York: Wiley, 2002), 230–237. There is some evidence suggesting that late Neanderthals may have stolen and attempted to use tools manufactured by humans in the same manner that monkeys today frequently steal and attempt to use humanly-manufactured implements.

10. M. V. Anikovitch et al., "Early Upper Paleolithic in Eastern Europe and Implications for the Dispersal of Modern Humans," *Science* 315 (January 12, 2007): 223–226; Richard G. Klein, *The Human Career: Human Biological and Cultural Origins*, 2nd ed. (Chicago: University of Chicago Press, 1999), 520–29; *Encyclopedia of Human Evolution and Prehistory*, 2nd ed., Eric Delson et al. (New York: Garland, 2000), s.vv. "Later Stone Age," "Late Paleolithic."

11. Eliso Kvavadze et al., "30,000-Year-Old Wild Flax Fibers," *Science* 325 (September 11, 2009): 1359; Ralf Kittler, Manfred Kayser, and Mark Stoneking, "Molecular Evolution of *Pediculus humanus* and the Origin of Clothing," *Current Biology* 13 (August 19, 2003): 1414–17; John Travis, "The Naked Truth? Lice Hint at a Recent Origin of Clothing," *Science News* 164 (August 23, 2003): 118; Irene Good, "Archaeological Textiles: A Review of Current Research," *Annual Review of Anthropology* 30 (October 2001): 209–26.

12. M. V. Anikovitch et al., *Encyclopedia of Human Evolution and Prehistory*, 2nd ed., s.v. "Late Paleolithic" (London: Routledge, 1999); Klein with Edgar, *Dawn of Human Culture*, 11–15; Klein, *Human Career*, 512–15; Steven L. Kuhn et al., "Ornaments of the Earliest Upper Paleolithic: New Insights from the Levant," *Proceedings of the National Academy of Sciences, USA* 98 (June 19, 2001): 7641–46.

13. O. Soffer, J. M. Adovasio, and D. C. Hyland, "The 'Venus' Figurines: Textiles, Basketry, Gender, and Status in the Upper Paleolithic," *Current Anthropology* 41 (August–October 2000): 511–37; Roger Lewin, *Principles of Human Evolution: A Core Textbook* (Malden, MA: Blackwell Science, 1998), 469–74; Rex Dalton, "Lion Man Takes Pride of Place as Oldest Statue," *Nature News*, September 4, 2003, http://www.nature.com/news/2003/030901/full/030901-6.html; Nicholas J. Conard, "Paleolithic Ivory Sculptures from Southwestern Germany and the Origins of Figurative Art," *Nature* 426 (December 18,

2003): 830–32; M. V. Anikovitch et al., *Encyclopedia of Human Evolution and Prehistory*, 2nd ed., s.v. "Late Paleolithic" (London: Routledge, 1999); Achim Schneider, "Ice-Age Musicians Fashioned Ivory Flute," *Nature News*, December 17, 2004, http://www.nature.com/news/2004/041217/full/news041213-14.html; Tim Appenzeller, "Evolution or Revolution?" *Science* 282 (November 20, 1998): 1451; Klein, *The Human Career*, 550–53.

14. Michael Balter, "Radiocarbon Dating's Final Frontier," *Science* 313 (September 15, 2006): 1560–63; H. Valladas et al., "Palaeolithic Paintings: Evolution of Prehistoric Cave Art," *Nature* 413 (October 4, 2001): 479.

15. Nicholas J. Conard, "A Female Figurine from the Basal Aurignacian of Hohle Fels Cave in Southwestern Germany," *Nature* 459 (May 14, 2009): 248–52.

16. Pierre-Jean Texier et al., "A Howiesons Poort Tradition of Engraving Ostrich Eggshell Containers Dates to 60,000 Years Ago at Diepkloof Rock Shelter, South Africa," *Proceedings of the National Academy of Sciences, USA* 107 (April 6, 2010): 6180–85.

17. Christopher S. Henshilwood et al., "Middle Stone Age Shell Beads from South Africa," *Science* 304 (April 16, 2004): 404; Christopher S. Henshilwood et al., "Emergence of Modern Human Behavior: Middle Stone Age Engravings from South Africa," *Science* 295 (February 15, 2002): 1278–80; Kyle S. Brown et al., "Fire as an Engineering Tool of Early Modern Humans," *Science* 325 (August 14, 2009): 859–62; Vincent Mourre, Paola Villa, and Christopher S. Henshilwood, "Early Use of Pressure Flaking on Lithic Artifacts at Blombos Cave, South Africa," *Science* 330 (October 29, 2010): 659–62.

18. Henshilwood et al., "Emergence of Modern Human Behavior," 1278.

19. Harris, Archer, and Waltke, *Theological Wordbook*, vol. 1, 5–6.

20. Ibid.

21. Ibid., 113.

22. Daniel 5:9–11, 18–22.

23. Luke 3:35–36.

24. Phillip Endicott et al., "Evaluating the Mitochondrial Timescale of Human Evolution," *Trends in Ecology & Evolution* 24 (August 13, 2009): 515–21.

25. Alwyn Scally and Richard Durbin, "Revising the Human Mutation Rate: Implications for Understanding Human Evolution," *Nature Reviews Genetics* 13 (October 2012): 745–53.

26. Qiaomei Fu et al., "A Revised Timescale for Human Evolution Based on Ancient Mitochondrial Genomes," *Current Biology* 23 (March 21, 2013): 553–59.

27. Lois A. Tully et al., "A Sensitive Denaturing Gradient-Gel Electrophoresis Assay Reveals a High Frequency of Heteroplasmy in Hypervariable Region 1 of the Human mtDNA Control Region," *American Journal of Human Genet-

*ics* 67 (August 2000): 432–43; Ann Gibbons, "Calibrating the Mitochondrial Clock," *Science* 279 (January 2, 1998): 28–29.

28. Russell Thomson et al., "Recent Common Ancestry of Human Y Chromosomes: Evidence from DNA Sequence Data," *Proceedings of the National Academy of Sciences, USA* 97 (June 20, 2000): 7360–65; Daniel Garrigan et al., "Inferring Human Population Sizes, Divergene Times, and Rates of Gene Flow from Mitochondrial, X and Y Chromosome Resequencing Data," *Genetics* 177 (December 2007): 2195–2207; L. Simon L. Whitfield, John E. Sulston, and Peter N. Goodfellow, "Sequence Variation of the Human Y Chromosome," *Nature* 378 (November 23, 1995): 379–80; Jonathan K. Pritchard et al., "Population Growth of Human Y Chromosomes: A Study of Y Chromosome Microsatellites," *Molecular Biology and Evolution* 16 (December 1999): 1791–98; Peter A. Underhill et al., "Y Chromosome Sequence Variation and the History of Human Populations," *Nature Genetics* 26 (November 2000): 358–361; Ornelia Semino et al., "Ethiopians and Khoisan Share the Deepest Clades of the Human Y-Chromosome Phylogeny," *The American Journal of Human Genetics* 70 (January 1, 2002): 265–68.

29. Wei Wei et al., "A Calibrated Human Y-Chromosomal Phylogeny Based on Resequencing," *Genome Research* 23 (February 2013): 388–95.

30. Fulvio Cruciani et al., "A Revised Root for the Human Y Chromosomal Phylogenetic Tree: The Origin of Patrilineal Diversity in Africa," *The American Journal of Human Genetics* 88 (May 19, 2011): 814–18.

31. Fernando L. Mendez et al., "An African American Paternal Lineage Adds an Extremely Ancient Root to the Human Y Chromosome Phylogenetic Tree," *The American Journal of Human Genetics* 92 (February 28, 2013): 454–59.

32. Scott A. Elias et al., "Life and Times of the Bering Land Bridge," *Nature* 382 (July 4, 1996): 61–63; Heiner Josenhans et al., "Early Humans and Rapidly Changing Holocene Sea Levels in the Queen Charlotte Islands-Hecate Strait, British Columbia, Canada," *Science* 277 (July 4, 1997): 71.

33. Genesis 1:28–30, Job 37–39.

34. Genesis 3:17, 9:2, Isaiah 24.

35. Genesis 9:3.

36. Genesis 9:2.

37. Acts 2:23, Romans 8:28–30.

38. *American Megafaunal Extinctions at the End of the Pleistocene*, ed. Gary Haynes (New York: Springer Science, 2009); Barry W. Brook and David M. J. S. Bowman, "One Equation fits Overkill: Why Allometry Underpins Both Prehistoric and Modern Body Size-Biased Extinctions," *Population Ecology* 47 (August 2005): 137–41; David A. Burney and Timothy F. Flannery, "Fifty Millennia of Catastrophic Extinctions after Human Contact," *TRENDS in*

*Ecology and Evolution* 20 (July 2005): 395–401; Gary K. Meffe, C. Ronald Carroll, and contributors, *Principles of Conservation Biology*, 2nd ed. (Sunderland, MA: Sinauer Associates, 1997), 87–156; John Alroy, "A Multispecies Overkill Simulation of the End-Pleistocene Megafaunal Mass Extinction," *Science* 292 (June 8, 2001): 1893–96; Richard G. Roberts et al., "New Ages for the Last Australian Megafauna: Continent-Wide Extinction about 46,000 Years Ago," *Science* 292 (June 8, 2001): 1888–92; Paul R. and Anne H. Ehrlich, *Extinction: The Causes and Consequences of the Disappearance of Species* (New York: Random House, 1981), 20–21; Jeffrey K. McKee et al., "Forecasting Global Biodiversity Threats Associated with Human Population Growth," *Biological Conservation* 115 (January 2004): 161–64; Leigh Dayton, "Mass Extinctions Pinned on Ice Age Hunters," *Science* 292 (June 8, 2001): 1819; Gerardo Ceballos and Paul R. Ehrlich, "Mammal Population Losses and the Extinction Crisis," *Science* 296 (May 3, 2002): 904–7; David W. Steadman, "Prehistoric Extinctions of Pacific Island Birds: Biodiversity Meets Zooarchaeology," *Science* 267 (February 24, 1995): 1123–31.

39. Christopher Stringer and Robin McKie, *African Exodus: The Origins of Modern Humanity* (New York: Henry Holt, 1997): 165–66; *Quaternary Extinctions: A Prehistoric Revolution*, eds. Paul S. Martin and Richard G. Klein (Tuscon: University of Arizona Press, 1984); *Wikipedia*, s.v. "Quaternary Extinction Event," last modified September 11, 2013, http://en.wikipedia.org/wiki/Quaternary_extinction_event.

40. Kenneth R. Miller, *Only a Theory: Evolution and the Battle for America's Soul* (New York: Viking, The Penguin Group, 2008), 52.

41. Hugh Ross, *Why the Universe Is the Way It Is* (Grand Rapids, MI: Baker, 2008), 27–191; Hugh Ross, *Beyond the Cosmos: What Recent Discoveries in Astrophysics Reveal about the Glory and Love of God*, 3rd ed. (Kissimmee, FL: Signalman, 2010), 193–98, 200–1, 210–13.

42. Ibid.

43. Paul G Falkowski et al., "The Rise of Oxygen Over the Past 205 Million Years and the Evolution of Large Placental Mammals," *Science* 309 (September 30, 2005): 2202–2204; Hugh Ross, *The Creator and the Cosmos: How the Latest Scientific Discoveries Reveal God*, 3rd ed. (Colorado Springs, CO: NavPress, 2001), 145–67, 175–212; Hugh Ross, "RTB Design Compendium (2009) for *Why the Universe Is the Way It Is* and *More Than a Theory*," Reasons to Believe, accessed January 13, 2013, http://www.reasons.org/fine-tuning.

44. Hugh Ross, *More Than a Theory: Revealing a Testable Model for Creation* (Grand Rapids, MI: Baker, 2009), 149–71; Hugh Ross, *Hidden Treasures in the Book of Job: How the Oldest Book in the Bible Answers Today's Scientific Questions* (Grand Rapids, MI: Baker, 2011), 63–68; Hugh Ross, "Resolving Faint

Sun Paradoxes, Parts 1, 2, and 3," *Today's New Reason to Believe* (blog), http://www.reasons.org/resolving-faint-sun-paradoxes-part-1, http://www.reasons.org/articles/resolving-faint-sun-paradoxes-part-2, http://www.reasons.org/articles/resolving-faint-sun-paradoxes-part-3, accessed August 23, 2011.
45.   Psalm 104:24–30.

## Chapter 8 – Source Controversy

1.   Allen P. Ross, *Creation and Blessing: A Guide to the Study and Exposition of Genesis* (Grand Rapids, MI: Baker, 1988), 24–35; Ronald Youngblood, *How It All Began: Genesis I–II A Bible Commentary for Laymen* (Ventura, CA: Regal, 1980), 13–15; Josh McDowell, *More Evidence that Demands a Verdict: Historical Evidences for the Christian Scriptures* (San Bernardino, CA: Campus Crusade for Christ, 1975), 91–116.
2.   Ellen van Wolde, *Stories of the Beginning: Genesis 1–11 and Other Creation Stories*, trans. John Bowden (Ridgefield, CT: Morehouse, 1997), 188–94.
3.   Don J. Wiseman, "Babylonia," *International Standard Bible Encyclopedia*, vol. 1, (A–D), revised, ed. G. W. Bromiley (Grand Rapids, MI: Eerdmans, 1979), 398.
4.   Edith Hamilton, *Mythology: Timeless Tales of Gods and Heroes* (New York: Mentor, 1969); Marie-Louise Von Franz, *Patterns of Creativity Mirrored in Creation Myths* (Zurich: Spring, 1972); Albert R. Kitzhaber, *Myths, Fables, and Folktales* (New York: Holt, Rinehart, and Winston, 1974); Van Wolde, *Stories of the Beginning*.
5.   Cunningham Geikie, *Hours with the Bible: The Scriptures in the Light of Modern Knowledge*, vol. 1. (New York: James Pott & Company, 1905), 21–32; Alexander Heidel, *The Babylonian Genesis* (Chicago: University of Chicago Press, 1951), 1–140; Howard F. Vos, *Genesis and Archaeology* (Chicago: Moody, 1963), chapters 2–4.
6.   Exodus 19:3–25; 24:9–18; 32:1; 33:11; 34:28.
7.   Hugh Ross, *Hidden Treasures in the Book of Job: How the Oldest Book in the Bible Answers Today's Scientific Questions* (Grand Rapids, MI: Baker, 2011), 30–32.
8.   Not all of the scriptures undergirding the different religions of the world are independent of the Bible. The *Qur'an* and the Mormon scriptures (*The Book of Mormon*, *The Doctrine and Covenants*, and *The Pearl of Great Price*) both written during the Christian era do incorporate substantial creation material from the Bible. Thus, technically they are not non-biblical creation texts. However, both the *Qur'an* and the Mormon scriptures also add creation material that contradicts, at least in part, biblical creation texts.
9.   Heidel, *Babylonian Genesis*, 1–140.

10.  Ibid.

**Chapter 9 – Message of Day Seven**
1.  Exodus 20:8–10; Deuteronomy 5:12–15.
2.  Leviticus 25:1–7.
3.  Paul R. Ehrlich and Anne H. Ehrlich, *Extinction: The Causes and Consequences of the Disappearance of Species* (New York: Ballantine, 1981), 19–38, 123–247; Robert M. May, John H. Lawton, and Nigel E. Stork, "Assessing Extinction Rates," in *Extinction Rates*, eds. John H. Lawton and Robert M. May (New York: Oxford University Press, 1995): 10–21; Paul R. Ehrlich, "The Scale of the Human Enterprise and Biodiversity Loss," in *Extinction Rates*, eds. John H. Lawton and Robert M. May (New York: Oxford University Press, 1995), 214–24; David W. Steadman, "Human-Caused Extinction of Birds," in *Biodiversity II: Understanding and Protecting Our Biological Resources*, eds. Marjorie L. Reaka-Kudla, Don E. Wilson, and Edward O. Wilson (Washington, DC: Joseph Henry Press, 1997), 139–58.
4.  Ehrlich and Ehrlich, *Extinction: The Causes and Consequences of the Disappearance of Species*, 23.
5.  Kevin de Queiroz, "Ernst Mayr and the Modern Concept of Species," *Proceedings of the National Academy of Sciences, USA* 102 (May 3, 2005): 6600–6607.
6.  Jared M. Diamond, "Daisy Gives an Evolutionary Answer," *Nature* 380 (March 14, 1996): 103–4; Ehrlich and Ehrlich, *Extinction: The Causes and Consequences of the Disappearance of Species*, 23.
7.  Zachary D. Blount, Christina Z. Borland, and Richard E. Lenski, "Historical Contingency and the Evolution of a Key Innovation in an Experimental Population of *Escherichia coli*," *Proceedings of the National Academy of Sciences, USA* 105 (June 10, 2008): 7899–7906.
8.  Ibid.; Hugh Ross, *More Than a Theory: Revealing a Testable Model for Creation* (Grand Rapids, MI: Baker, 2009), 169–70; Fazale Rana, "Inability to Repeat the Past Dooms Evolution," *Today's New Reason to Believe* (blog), Reasons to Believe, August 7, 2008, http://www.reasons.org/inability-repeat-past-dooms-evolution.
9.  Angus Buckling et al., "The Beagle in a Bottle," *Nature* 457 (February 12, 2009): 824–29; Tim Connallon and L. Lacey Knowles, "Recombination Rate and Protein Evolution in Yeast," *BioMed Central Evolutionary Biology* 7 (November 27, 2007): doi:10.1186/1471-2148-7-235; Gail W. T. Wilson et al., "Soil Aggregation and Carbon Sequestration Are Tightly Correlated with the Abundance of Arbuscular Mycorrhizal Fungi: Results from Long-Term Field Experiments," *Ecology Letters* 12 (May 2009): 452–61; Molly K. Burke et al., "Genome-Wide Analysis of a Long-Term Evolution Experiment with

*Drosophila*," *Nature* 467 (September 30, 2010): 587–90.

10. Revelation 21:1–22:5. See also Hugh Ross, *Why the Universe Is the Way It Is* (Grand Rapids, MI: Baker, 2009), 95–206.

11. R. Laird Harris, Gleason L. Archer Jr., and Bruce K. Waltke, *Theological Wordbook of the Old Testament*, vol. 1 (Chicago: Moody, 1980), 370–71; William Wilson, *Old Testament Word Studies: Hebrew English and Chaldee Lexicon and Concordance* (Grand Rapids, MI: Kregel, 1978), 109.

12. Harris, Archer, and Waltke, *Theological Wordbook*, vol. 1, 370–71; R. Laird Harris, Gleason L. Archer Jr., and Bruce K. Waltke, *Theological Wordbook*, vol. 2, 672–73; *Gesenius' Hebrew-Chaldee Lexicon to the Old Testament*, trans. Samuel P. Tregelles (Grand Rapids, MI: Baker, 1979), 612–13.

13. Hugh Ross, *A Matter of Days: Resolving a Creation Controversy* (Colorado Springs, CO: NavPress, 2004), 21–23, 54–56, 73–76.

14. Ibid., 23–26, 139–206.

15. Ibid., 41–49.

16. *The Genesis Debate: Three Views on the Days of Creation*, ed. David G. Hagopian (Mission Viejo, CA: Crux Press, 2001), 47, 68–69, 89–90, 99–102, 203–206, 291–292.

17. Henry Morris III, *After Eden: Understanding Creation, the Curse, and the Cross*, eds. Henry M. Morris and John D. Morris (Green Forest, AR: Master Books, 2003), 103–24; Ken Ham, Jonathan Sarfati, and Carl Wieland, *The Revised and Expanded Answer Book: The 20 Most Asked Questions About Creation, Evolution, and the Book of Genesis, Answered!* ed. Don Batten (Green Forest, AR: Master Books, 2000), 256–57; Douglas F. Kelly, *Creation and Change: Genesis 1.1–2.4 in the Light of Changing Scientific Paradigms* (Geanies House, Fearn, Ross-shire, Scotland, U K: Mentor, 1997), 97–98, 228–31; Jonathan Sarfati, *Refuting Compromise: A Biblical and Scientific Refutation of "Progressive Creationism" (Billions of Years) as Popularized by Astronomer Hugh Ross*, 2nd ed. (Powder Springs, GA: Creation Book Publishers, 2011), 191–96; James Stambaugh, "Whence Cometh Death? A Biblical Theology on Physical Death and Natural Evil" in *Coming to Grips with Genesis: Biblical Authority and the Age of the Earth*, eds. Terry Mortenson and Thane H. Ury (Green Forest, AR: Master Books, 2008), 373–74.

18. Ross, *More Than a Theory*, 149–71.

19. Hugh Ross, *Why the Universe Is the Way It Is* (Grand Rapids, MI: Baker, 2008), 95–106, 147–92.

20. 1 Corinthians 15:55–56.

**Chapter 10 – Spiritual Perspective on Creation: Genesis 2**

1.  R. Laird Harris, Gleason L. Archer Jr., and Bruce K. Waltke, *Theological Word-*

*book of the Old Testament*, vol. 1 (Chicago: Moody, 1980), 500–1.
2. Ibid., 17.
3. Sanjoy M. Som et al., "Air Density 2.7 Billion Years Ago Limited to Less than Twice Modern Levels by Fossil Raindrop Imprints," *Nature* 484 (April 19, 2012): 359–362.
4. Genesis 2:8.
5. Genesis 2:10–14.
6. Genesis 2:11–13.
7. Douglas Phillips, "An Urgent Appeal to Pastors," *Back to Genesis*, no. 119 (November 1998): c; Henry M. Morris, "The Wolf and the Lamb," *Back to Genesis*, no. 69 (September 1994): a–c; John C. Whitcomb Jr., *The Early Earth: An Introduction to Biblical Creationism* (Grand Rapids, MI: Baker, 1972), 65, 116, 131; John D. Morris, "Evolution and the Wages of Sin," *Impact*, no. 209 (November 1990): ii–iii.
8. Jeffrey I. Rose, "New Light on Human Prehistory in the Arabo-Persian Gulf Oasis," *Current Anthropology* 51 (December 2010): 849–83.
9. Jeffrey I. Rose, quoted in Jeanna Bryner, "Lost Civilization May Have Existed Beneath the Persian Gulf," *LiveScience*, published December 9, 2010, accessed September 9, 2011, http://www.livescience.com/history/lost-civilization-possibly-existed-beneath-persian-gulf-101209.html.
10. Hans-Peter Uerpmann with Margarethe Uerpmann, *The Capital Area of Northern Oman. Pt. 3: Stone Age Sites and Their Natural Environment* (Weisbaden, Germany: Reichert, 2003); *The Archaeology of Jebel al-Buhais, Sharjah, United Arab Emirates. Vol. 1: Funeral Monuments and Human Remains From Jebel al-Buhais*, eds. Hans-Peter Uerpmann, Margarethe Uerpmann, and Sabah A. Jasim (Tubingen, Germany: Kerns, 2006).
11. Simon J. Armitage et al., "The Southern Route 'Out of Africa:' Evidence for an Early Expansion of Modern Humans into Arabia," *Science* 331 (January 28, 2011): 453–56.
12. *The Interlinear Bible: Hebrew/Greek/English*, vol. 1, ed. and trans. Jay P. Green Sr. (Lafayette, IN: Associated Publishers and Authors, 1982), 6.
13. Genesis 6:3.
14. Judith Campisi, "Aging, Chromatin, and Food Restriction—Connecting the Dots," *Science* 289 (September 22, 2000): 2062–63; Su-ju Lin, Pierre-Antoine Defossez, and Leonard Guarente, "Requirement of NAD and *SIR2* for Life-Span Extension by Calorie Restriction in *Saccharomyces cerevisiae*," *Science* 289 (2000), 2126–2128.
15. Simon Melov et al., "Extension of Life-Span with Superoxide Dismutase/Cata-

lase Mimetics," *Science* 289 (September 1, 2000): 1567–69.

16. Camilo Mora et al., "How Many Species Are There on Earth and in the Ocean?" *PLoS Biology* 9, no. 8 (August 23, 2011), doi:10.1371/journal. pbio.1001127.

17. Robert M. May, John H. Lawton, and Nigel E. Stork, "Assessing Extinction Rates," in *Extinction Rates*, eds. John H. Lawton and Robert M. May (New York: Oxford University Press, 1995), 11.

18. Gary K. Meffe, C. Ronald Carroll, and contributors, *Principles of Conservation Biology*, 2nd ed. (Sunderland, MA: Sinauer Associates, 1997), 90–112, 131–39.

19. Genesis 1:11, 12, 21, 24, 25.

20. 20 Henry M. Morris, "Adam and the Animals," *Impact*, no. 212 (February 1991): ii; Ken Ham, "Revelation: Key to the Past," *Back to Genesis*, no. 39 (March 1992): b; William J. Spear Jr., "Could Adam Really Name All Those Animals?" *Impact*, no. 265 (July 1995): i–iv; Henry M. Morris, *Biblical Creationism*, 25.

21. 21 Hugh Ross, *A Matter of Days: Resolving a Creation Controversy* (Colorado Springs, CO: NavPress, 2004), 80–81.

22. 22 R. Laird Harris, Gleason L. Archer Jr., and Bruce K. Waltke, *Theological Wordbook of the Old Testament*, vol. 2 (Chicago: Moody, 1980), 768.

23. Harris, Archer, and Waltke, *Theological Wordbook, vol. 1*, 503–4.

24. Henry M. Morris, *Biblical Creationism: What Each Book of the Bible Teaches about Creation and the Flood* (Green Forest, AR: Master Books, 2000), 36; Ken Ham, "*One Race One Blood: A Biblical Answer to Racism*, Chapter 3: The True Origin of Species," Answers in Genesis article archives, published December 26, 2008, accessed September 28, 2011, http://www.answersingenesis.org/ articles/orob/true-origin-of-species; Georgia Purdom and Bodie Hodge, "Zonkeys, Ligers, and Wolphins, Oh My!" Answers in Genesis article archives, published August 6, 2008, accessed September 28, 2011, http://www.answers-ingenesis.org/articles/aid/v3/n1/zonkeys-ligers-wholphins.

25. Harris, Archer, Waltke, *Theological Wordbook*, vol. 1, 438.

26. Harris, Archer, and Waltke, *Theological Wordbook*, vol. 2, 660–61.

27. Genesis 2:9, 3:22.

28. Hugh Ross, *Why the Universe Is the Way It Is* (Grand Rapids, MI: Baker, 2009); Hugh Ross, *Beyond the Cosmos: What Recent Discoveries in Astrophysics Reveal about the Glory and Love of God*, 3rd ed. (Orlando: Signalman, 2010), 187–220; Revelation 21:1–22:5.

## Chapter 11 – How Far the Fall? Genesis 3

1.  Job 38:4–7.

2.  Revelation 1:20; 12:3–4.

3.  Genesis 2:17.

4.  Numbers 22:21–33.

5.  Genesis 3:22–24

6.  Romans 5:12–6:14.

7.  Victor J. Stenger, *God: The Failed Hypothesis* (Amherst, NY: Prometheus, 2007), 219, 241.

8.  Genesis 3:17.

9.  Jeremiah 33:25.

10. Ecclesiastes 1:1–11.

11. Mark W. Zemansky, *Heat and Thermodynamics*, 4th ed. (New York: McGraw-Hill, 1957), 42–60, 157–94.

12. Romans 8:20–22.

13. J. H. Taylor et al., "Experimental Constraints on Strong-Field Relativistic Gravity," *Nature* 355 (January 9, 1992): 132–36; Roger Penrose, *Shadows of the Mind: A Search for the Missing Science of Consciousness* (New York: Oxford University Press, 1994), 229–31.

14. Roger Penrose, "An Analysis of the Structure of Space-Time," *Adam Prize Essay* (Cambridge University, 1966); Stephen W. Hawking, "Singularities and the Geometry of Space-Time," *Adam Prize Essay* (Cambridge University, 1966); Stephen W. Hawking and George F. R. Ellis, "The Cosmic Black-Body Radiation and the Existence of Singularities in Our Universe," *Astrophysical Journal* 152 (April 1968): 25–36; Stephen W. Hawking and Roger Penrose, "The Singularities of Gravitational Collapse and Cosmology," *Proceedings of the Royal Society of London*, Series A 314 (January 27, 1970): 529–48; Hugh Ross, *Beyond the Cosmos: What Recent Discoveries in Astrophysics Reveal about the Glory and Love of God*, 3rd ed. (Orlando: Signalman, 2010), 24–33.

15. Hugh Ross, "Part 1. Fine-Tuning for Life in the Universe," Reasons to Believe, 2008, accessed 10/1/11, http://www.reasons.org/files/compendium/compendium_part1.pdf.

16. Hugh Ross, *The Creator and the Cosmos: How the Latest Scientific Discoveries Reveal God*, 3rd ed. (Colorado Springs, CO: NavPress, 2001), 36, 81, 97, 99–100, 153, 155.

17. Genesis 1:31.

18. Revelation 21:1–5.

19. The universe's laws and characteristics optimize the training and the new

physics of the new creation maximizes future rewards, relationships, and careers in my book. I discuss each of these things and how they work in my book *Why the Universe Is the Way It Is* (Grand Rapids, MI: Baker, 2008).

20. Ken Ham and Terry Mortenson, "What's Wrong with Progressive Creation?" in *War of the Worldviews*, eds. Becky Stelzer, Stacia McKeever, and Michael Matthews (Hebron, KY: Answers in Genesis, 2005), 95–110; Ken Ham and Terry Mortenson, "Chapter 12: What's Wrong with Progressive Creation?" Answers in Genesis, *The Answers Book 2*, accessed September 26, 2011, http://www.answersingenesis.org/articles/nab2/whats-wrong-with-progressive-creation.

21. Psalm 104:21.

22. Job 38:39–41.

23. Trish J. Lavery et al., "Iron Defecation by Sperm Whales Stimulates Carbon Export in the Southern Ocean," *Proceedings of the Royal Society B* 277 (June 16, 2010): 3527–31; Hugh Ross, *Hidden Treasures in the Book of Job: How the Oldest Book in the Bible Answers Today's Scientific Questions* (Grand Rapids, MI: Baker, 2011), 65–68.

24. Philippians 1:20–23.

## Chapter 12 – Cain's Story: Genesis 4

1. *The Works of Josephus*, new updated ed., trans. William Whiston (Peabody, MA: Hendrickson Publications, 1987), 31.

2. Genesis 4:16.

3. Genesis 4:25.

4. Genesis 20:2–16.

5. Thomas Virgil Peterson, *Ham & Japheth: The Mythic World of Whites in the Antebellum South*, American Theological Library Association Monograph 12 (Metuchen, NJ: Scarecrow/American Theological Library Association, 1978).

6. "U. S. Abortion Statistics: Facts and Figures Relating to the Frequency of Abortion in the United States," Abort73, last modified June 21, 2013, accessed September 11, 2013, http://www.abort73.com/abortion_facts/us_abortion_statistics/.

7. Abortion TV: Tune Into the Truth, http://www.abortiontv.com/Misc/Abortion-Statistics.htm, accessed October 3, 2011.

## Chapter 13 – Possibility of Long Life Spans: Genesis 5–6

1. Genesis 4:19–22.

2. A. D. Erlykin, "Around and Above the Knee," *Nuclear Physics B–Proceedings Supplements* 39 (February 1995): 215–27.

3.  A. D. Erlykin and A. W. Wolfendale, "A Single Source of Cosmic Rays in the Range $10^{15}$–$10^{16}$ eV," *Journal of Physics G: Nuclear and Particle Physics* 23 (August 1997): 979.

4.  Ibid.; A. D. Erlykin and A. W. Wolfendale, "Recent Progress in EAS Measurements and the Single SNR Model of the Knee," *Nuclear Physics B Proceedings Supplements* 75 (March 1999): 305–8; A. D. Erlykin and A. W. Wolfendale, "Spectral Features and Masses in the PeV Region," *Nuclear Physics B Proceedings Supplements* 122 (July 2003): 209–12.

5.  A. D. Erlykin and A. W. Wolfendale, "Further Evidence Favouring the Single Source Model for Cosmic Rays," *Astroparticle Physics* 23 (February 2005): 1–9.

6.  Anatoly D. Erlykin and A. W. Wolfendale, "Can One See Gamma Rays from the Single Source Responsible for the Knee?" *Proceedings of the 28th International Cosmic Ray Conference. July 31–August 7, 2003, Trukuba, Japan*, eds. T. Kajita et al. (International Union of Pure and Applied Physics, 2003): 2349.

7.  A. D. Erlykin and A. W. Wolfendale, "Cosmic Rays and the Monogem Supernova Remnant," *Astroparticle Physics* 22 (October 2004): 47–63.

8.  S. E. Thorsett, et al., "Pulsar PSR B0656+14, The Monogem Ring, and the Origin of the 'Knee' in the Primary Cosmic Ray Spectrum," *Astrophysical Journal Letters* 592 (August 1, 2003): L71–L73.

9.  S. E. Thorsett et al., L71.

10.  Ibid.

11.  Douglas Hanahan, "Benefits of Bad Telomerase," *Nature* 406 (August 10, 2000): 573–74; Steven E. Artandi et al., "Telomere Dysfunction Promotes Non-Reciprocal Translocations and Epithelial Cancers in Mice," *Nature* 406 (August 10, 2000): 641–645.

12.  Elizabeth H. Blackburn, "Telomere States and Cell Fates," *Nature* 408 (November 2, 2000): 53–56.

13.  Su-Ju Lin, Pierre-Antoine Defossez, and Leonard Guarente, "Requirement of NAD and *SIR2* for Life-Span Extension by Calorie Restriction in *Saccharomyces cerevisiae*," *Science* 289 (September 22, 2000): 2126–28; Simon Melov et al., "Extension of Life-Span with Superoxide Dismutase/Catalase Mimetics," *Science* 289 (September 1, 2000): 1567–69.

14.  Genesis 9:29; 11:10–25.

15.  Romans 1:29–32; 2 Peter 2:13–19.

16.  Stephen T. Sherry et al., "*Alu* Evolution in Human Populations: Using the Coalescent to Estimate Effective Population Size," *Genetics* 147 (December 1, 1997): 1977–82; A. Tenesa et al., "Recent Human Effective Population Size Estimated from Linkage Disequilibrium," *Genome Research* 17 (March 9, 2007):

520–26.

17. Darrel Falk and Dennis Venema, "Does Genetics Point to a Single Primal Couple?" The BioLogos Foundation Forum, published April 5, 2010, February 28, 2012, http://biologos.org/blog/does-genetics-point-to-a-single-primal-couple.

18. Fazale Rana, "Were They Real? The Scientific Case for Adam and Eve," *Today's New Reason to Believe* (blog), published October 1, 2010, accessed September 13, 2013, http://www.reasons.org/articles/were-they-real-the-scientific-case-for-adam-and-eve; Patricia Fanning, "Assumptions, Circular Reasoning, and a Literal Adam and Eve," *Today's New Reason to Believe* (blog), published November 28, 2011, accessed September 13, 2013, http://www.reasons.org/articles/assumptions-circular-reasoning-and-a-literal-adam-and-eve.

**Chapter 14 – Sons of God and the Nephilim: Genesis 6**

1.  Genesis 6:4.
2.  Gleason L. Archer, *Encyclopedia of Bible Difficulties* (Grand Rapids, MI: Zondervan, 1982), 79–80; J. Sidlow Baxter, "Who Were Those 'Sons of God?'" *Studies in Problem Texts* (Grand Rapids, MI: Zondervan, 1960), 147–92; James Boice, "The Gathering Storm: Genesis 6:1–22," *Bible Studies*, vol. 12, no. 10 (October 1980), 4–12; Ellen van Wolde, *Stories of the Beginning: Genesis 1–11 and Other Creation Stories*, trans. John Bowden (Ridgefield, CT: Morehouse, 1997), 112–16; Trevor J. Major, "Genesis 6:1–4 and the 'Sons of God,'" *Reasons & Revelation* 13, no. 7 (July 1993), 54.
3.  Ezra 9:1–10:44; 2 Corinthians 6:14–18.
4.  1 Samuel 17:4–7; 21:9; 1 Chronicles 20:5.
5.  Deuteronomy 3:11.
6.  *The International Standard Bible Encyclopedia*, vol. 2, eds. James Orr et al. (Grand Rapids, MI: Eerdmans, 1956), 765; Ezekiel 40:5.
7.  1 Samuel 17:4–16, 25, 33; 2 Samuel 21:16, 18–22.
8.  2 Samuel 21:20.
9.  Norris McWhirter and Ross McWhirter, *Guinness Book of World Records*, 1975 ed. (New York: Sterling, 1975), 13.
10. 1 Samuel 9:2.
11. Numbers 13:32–33.
12. *The New Bible Dictionary*, ed. J. D. Douglas (Grand Rapids, MI: Eerdmans, 1962), 1206.
13. Deuteronomy 14:1.
14. Deuteronomy 32:5.

15. Isaiah 43:6.
16. Matthew 22:30.
17. Revelation 21:2–7; 22:2–5.
18. Some of the best documentation comes from the nonprofit organization Spiritual Counterfeits Projects (P.O. Box 4308, Berkeley, CA 94704, hotline number: 510-540-0300), which makes available for the public scholarly articles, journals, and papers on occult practices and organizations.
19. Craig S. Hawkins, *Witch Craft: Exploring the World of Wicca* (Grand Rapids, MI: Baker, 1996), 60, 79–81; Hugh Ross, Kenneth Samples, and Mark Clark, *Lights in the Sky and Little Green Men* (Colorado Springs, CO: NavPress, 2002), 68, 131, 137.
20. Baxter, "Who Were Those 'Sons of God?'" 152.
21. Genesis 18:1–8,16; 19:1–22; Joshua 5:13–15; 1 Kings 19:5–8; Daniel 9:21–23; 10:4–21; Luke 1:11–20; Luke 24:4–8; Acts 1:10–11; 10:2–8; 12:4–11; 27:23; Hebrews 13:2; Revelation 21:9–22:11.
22. Genesis 18:2–8; 19:3–8; Joshua 5:13–15; Daniel 3:25; 9:21–23; Luke 24:4–8; Acts 1:10–11; Hebrews 13:2.
23. Genesis 19:4–11.
24. Matthew 8:28–33; Mark 1:23–26.
25. Genesis 6:12, 5.

**Chapter 15 – Boundaries of God's Wrath: Genesis 6**
1. Romans 5:12–14.
2. Job 4:8; Proverbs 5:22; 11:5; Isaiah 57:20–21; Jeremiah 5:25; Romans 7:5; Galatians 5:19–21; 6:7–8.
3. Genesis 18:20–21; 19:13; Exodus 20:4–6; Joshua 6:22–7:26; 1 Corinthian 6:12–20.
4. 1 Corinthians 6:12–20.
5. Genesis 19:4–5.
6. 2 Corinthians 1:21–22; 5:5; Ephesians 1:13–14.
7. Matthew 5:13.
8. 2 Peter 2:14, 18–19.
9. 2 Timothy 2:26; 3:2–8.
10. Romans 1:32; 2 Peter 2:18–19.
11. R. Laird Harris, Gleason L. Archer Jr., and Bruce K. Waltke, *Theological Wordbook of the Old Testament*, vol. 2 (Chicago: Moody, 1980), 917–18; H. W. F. Gesenius, *Gesenius' Hebrew-Chaldee Lexicon to the Old Testament* (Grand Rapids, MI: Baker, 1979), 815–16.

12. R. Laird Harris, Gleason L. Archer Jr., and Bruce K. Waltke, *Theological Wordbook of the Old Testament*, vol. 1 (Chicago: Moody, 1980), 297; Gesenius, *Hebrew-Chaldee Lexicon*, 288.
13. Luke 17:26–37; 2 Timothy 3:1–8.
14. Exodus 21:28–29; Leviticus 20:15–16.
15. Genesis 15:13–16; 18:16–33.
16. 1 Thessalonians 1:10; 5:9; 2 Peter 2:9; Revelation 3:10.
17. Genesis 15:13–16.

**Chapter 16 – Global or Worldwide Flood? Biblical Evidence**

1.  Simon G. Southerton, *Losing a Lost Tribe: Native Americans, DNA, and the Mormon Church* (Salt Lake City: Signature Books, 2004).
2.  Romans 1:8.
3.  Colossians 1:6.
4.  Jonathan Sarfati, *Refuting Compromise: A Biblical and Scientific Refutation of "Progressive Creationism,"* 2nd ed. (Atlanta: Creation Book Publishers, 2011), 249.
5.  Job 38:8–10.
6.  Psalm 104:9.
7.  *The Greek New Testament*, 3rd ed., eds. Kurt Aland et al. (New York, NY: United Bible Societies, 1975), 811.
8.  Sarfati, *Refuting Compromise*, 241; Henry Morris, *Biblical Creationism: What Each Book of the Bible Teaches about Creation and the Flood* (Green Forest, AR: Master Books, 2000), 187–88.
9.  *The Greek New Testament*, 808.
10. Kenneth S. Wuest, *Wuest's Word Studies From the Greek New Testament: In These Last Days*, vol. 2 (Grand Rapids, MI: Eerdmans, 1973), 51.
11. Ibid.
12. Genesis 11:1–9.
13. R. Laird Harris, Gleason L. Archer, Jr. and Bruce K. Waltke, *Theological Wordbook of the Old Testament*, vol. 1 (Chicago: Moody Press, 1980), 449.
14. Harris, Archer, and Waltke, *Theological Wordbook*, vol. 1, 224–25.
15. Ibid., 146; Gesenius, *Hebrew-Chaldee Lexicon*, 153.
16. *The Interlinear Hebrew/Greek English Bible*, vol. 1, ed. and trans. Jay P. Green (Lafayette, IN: Associated Publishers and Authors), 16.
17. Gesenius, *Hebrew-Chaldee Lexicon*, 295, 733, 807–9, 821; Harris, Archer, and Waltke, *Theological Wordbook*, vol. 1, 309; R. Laird Harris, Gleason L. Archer Jr., and Bruce K. Waltke, *Theological Wordbook of the Old Testament*, vol. 2

(Chicago: Moody, 1980), 800, 909, 923.

18. *The Encyclopedia of Ancient Civilizations*, ed. Arthur Cotterell (New York, NY: Mayflower Books, 1980), 117–122; *The International Standard Bible Encyclopedia*, vol. 1, eds. James Orr and Melvin Grove Kyle (Grand Rapids, MI: Eerdmans, 1956), 224–225; *The New Bible Dictionary*, eds. J. D. Douglas et al. (Grand Rapids, MI: Eerdmans, 1962), 56–60.

19. Victor P. Hamilton in Harris, Archer, and Waltke, *Theological Wordbook*, vol. 1, 74–75.

20. Ibid., 319.

21. Ibid., 10.

22. Leonard J. Coppes in Harris, Archer, and Waltke, *Theological Wordbook*, vol. 1, 10–11.

## Chapter 17 – Global or Worldwide Flood? Scientific Evidence

1. There are three cubit measures: the common or short cubit (18 inches), the royal cubit (20 inches), and the long cubit (22 inches).

2. Genesis 7:19, 24, 8:1–5.

3. T. C. Mitchell, "Geology and the Flood," in *New Bible Dictionary*, 2nd ed., eds. J. D. Douglas et al. (Downers Grove, IL: InterVarsity Press, 1982), 382–83.

4. Stephen Jay Gould, *The Historical Atlas of the Earth: A Visual Exploration of Earth's Physical Past*, eds. Roger Osborne and Donald Tarling (New York: Henry Holt, 1996), 130–31.

5. *Radioisotopes and the Age of the Earth: A Young-Earth Creationist Research Initiative*, eds. Larry Vardiman, Andrew A. Snelling, and Eurgene F. Chaffin (El Cajon, CA and St. Joseph, MO: Institute for Creation Research and Creation Research Society, 2000), 343–44. This book is also available as a free PDF at http://www.icr.org/i/pdf/research/rate-all.pdf.

6. Jeremiah 33:25.

7. Hugh Ross, *A Matter of Days: Resolving a Creation Controversy* (Colorado Springs, CO: NavPress, 2004), 163–67.

8. Ibid.

9. Daniel M. Sigman, Mathis P. Hain, and Gerald H. Haug, "The Polar Ocean and Glacial Cycles in Atmospheric $CO_2$ Concentration," *Nature* 466 (July 1, 2010): 47–55; EPICA community members, Laurent Augustin et al., "Eight Glacial Cycles from an Antarctic Ice Core," *Nature* 429 (June 10, 2004): 623–28; Hideaki Motoyama, "The Second Deep Ice Coring Project at Dome Fuji, Antarctica," *Scientific Drilling* 5 (October 28, 2007): 41–43.

10. North Greenland Ice Core Project members, K. K. Andersen et al., "High-

Resolution Record of Northern Hemisphere Climate Extending into the Last Interglacial Period," *Nature* 431 (September 9, 2004): 147–51.

11. Carl Wieland, "The Lost Squadron: Deeply Buried Missing Planes Challenge 'Slow and Gradual' Preconceptions" *Creation* 19, no. 3 (June–August 1997): 10–14.

12. Robert M. Carter and Paul Gammon, "New Zealand Maritime Glaciation: Millennial-Scale Southern Cloimate Change Since 3.9 Ma," *Science* 304 (June 11, 2004): 1659–62.

13. J. S. Dean, "Dendrochronology," in *Dating and Age Determination of Biological Materials*, eds. Michael R. Zimmerman and John Lawrence Angel (London: Croom Helm, 1986), 126–65.

14. M. G. L Baillie and J. R. Pilcher, "The Belfast 'Long Chronology' Project" in ed. R. G. W. Ward, *Applications of Tree-Ring Studies: Current Research in Dendrochronology and Related Subjects*, BAR International Series 333 (Oxford: British Archaeological Reports, May 1987), 203–14; B. Becker, "An 11,000-Year German Oak and Pine Dendrochronology for Radiocarbon Calibration," *Radiocarbon* 35:1 (1993): 201–13.

15. Michael R. May et al., "A Pleistocene Clone of Palmer's Oak Persisting in Southern California," *PLoS ONE* 4 (December 23, 2009): e8346.

16. Larry Vardiman, "RATE in Review: Unresolved Problems," *Acts & Facts* 36, no. 12 (December 2007): 6; also available at Institute of Creation Research, accessed January 18, 2013, http://www.icr.org/article/rate-review-unresolved-problems/.

17. Donald L. Turcotte and Gerald Schubert, *Geodynamics*, 2nd ed. (Cambridge, UK: Cambridge University Press, 2002), 136–37.

18. Henry N. Pollack, Suzanne J. Hunter, and Jeffrey R. Johnson, "Heat Flow from the Earth's Interior: Analysis of the Global Data Set," *Reviews of Geophysics* 31, no. 3 (August 1993): 267–280. The heat flow figures are on pages 272–73.

19. J. Brian Pitts, "Nonexistence of Humphreys' 'Volume Cooling' for Terrestrial Heat Disposal by Cosmic Expansion," *Perspectives on Science and Christian Faith* 61, no. 1 (March 2009): 23–28.

20. Jonathan Sarfati, *Refuting Compromise: A Biblical and Scientific Refutation of "Progressive Creationism,"* 2nd ed. (Atlanta: Creation Book Publishers, 2011), 257–60.

21. "Earth Movements from Japan Earthquake Seen from Space," RedOrbit, last modified March 30, 2011, accessed December 24, 2011, http://www.redorbit.com/news/space/2020961/earth_movements_from_japan_earth-

quake_seen_from_space/.

22. K. E. Bullen, *An Introduction to the Theory of Seismology* (Cambridge, UK: Cambridge University Press, 1963), 259–62; Hiroo Kanamori, "Shaking without Quaking," *Science* 279 (March 27, 1998): 2063–64.

23. "Global Petroleum Resources: A View to the Future," Thomas S. Ahlbrandt and Peter J. McCabe, *Geotimes*, last modified November 2002, http://www.geotimes.org/nov02/feature_oil.html; "USGS Reassesses Potential World Petroleum Resources: Oil Estimates Up, Gas Down," USGS Newsroom, last modified March 22, 2000, http://www.usgs.gov/newsroom/article.asp?ID=636; *Wikipedia*, s.v. "Oil Reserves," last modified September 5, 2013, http://en.wikipedia.org/wiki/Oil_reserves; Nick A. Owen, Oliver R. Inderwildi, and David A. King, "The Status of Conventional World Oil Reserves—Hype or Cause for Concern?" *Energy Policy* 38 (August 2010): 4743–49, http://www.ceunes.ufes.br/downloads/2/monicatognella-htreserva%20petróleo.pdf; "Energy Publications," Center for Energy Studies Rice University's Baker Institute, http://www.rice.edu/energy/publications/EF-pub-WorldOilReserves-101911.pdf; U. S. Energy Information Administration, last modified 2012, www.eia.gov/emeu/international/oilconsumption.html; "Total World Petroleum Consumption," last modified June 2008, accessed December 30, 2011, http://www.docstoc.com/docs/878819/Total-World-Petroleum-Consumption.

24. Paul Averitt, *Coal Resources of the United States, January 1, 1974*, U. S. Geological Survey Bulletin 1412 (Washington: U.S. Government Printing Office, 1975); "Coal Terminology: Resource & Reserve," Ground Truth Trekking, last modified September 25, 2012, http://groundtruthtrekking.org/Issues/AlaskaCoal/CoalTerminology.html; "Coal Reserves," last modified February 12, 2013, http://sourcewatch.org/index.php?title=Coal_reserves; "World Coal Consumption by Region," US Energy Information Administration, last modified March 2011, http://www.eia.gov/oiaf/aeo/tablebrowser/#release=IEO2011&subject=0-IEO2011&table=7-IEO2011&region=0-0&cases=Reference-0504a_1630; "World Coal Consumption by Year," IndexMundi, last modified 2011, http://www.indexmundi.com/energy.aspx?product=coal&graph=consumption; "Coal Statistics," World Coal Association, http://www.worldcoal.org/resources/coal-statistics.

25. *Wikipedia*, s.v. "List of Countries by Natural Gas Proven Reserves," last modified September 13, 2013, http://en.wikipedia.org/wiki/List_of_countries_by_natural_gas_proven_reserves; Thomas S. Ahlbrandt and Peter J. McCabe, "Global Petroleum Resources: A View to the Future," *Geotimes*,

last modified November 2002, http://www.geotimes.org/nov02/feature_oil.html; "World Natural Gas-Consumption," IndexMundi, last modified February 21, 2013, http://www.indexmundi.com/world/natural_gas_con-sumption.html; "Energy Publications," Center for Energy Studies Rice University's Baker Institute, http://www.rice.edu/energy/publications/EF-pub-WorldOilReserves-101911.pdf.

26. Paul Averitt, *Coal Resources*; "Coal Terminology: Resource Reserve," Ground Truth Trekking, last modified September 25, 2012, http://groundtruthtrek-king.org/Issues/AlaskaCoal/CoalTerminology.html; "Coal Reserves," last modified February 12, 2013, http://sourcewatch.org/index.php?title=Coal_reserves.

27. *Natural Gas 1998: Issues and Trends* (Washington, DC: Energy Information Administration, 1998): 73, accessed January 1, 2012, http://www.eia.gov/pub/oil_gas/natural_gas/analysis_publications/natural_gas_1998_issues_trends/pdf/chapter3.pdf.

28. Amy Myers Jaffe, Kenneth B. Medlock III, and Ronald Soligo, *The Status of World Oil Reserves: Conventional and Unconventional Resources in the Future Supply Mix* (Houston: James A. Baker III Institute for Public Policy, Rice University, October 2011): 11–12; "Energy Publications," Center for Energy Studies Rice University's Baker Institute, accessed January 1, 2012, http://www.rice.edu/energy/publications/EF-pub-WorldOilReserves-101911.pdf.

29. Richard Nehring, "Traversing the Mountaintop: World Fossil Fuel Production to 2050," *Philosophical Transactions of the Royal Society B, Biological Sciences* 364 (October 27, 2009): 3077.

30. Leslie Mullen, "Eating Kerogen," *Astrobiology Magazine*, published November 28, 2001, http://www.astrobio.net/exclusive/74/eating-kerogen.

31. "Future Supply Potential of Natural Gas Hydrates," in *Natural Gas 1998: Issues and Trends* (Washington, DC: Energy Information Administration, 1998): 74, accessed January 1, 2012, http://www.eia.gov/pub/oil_gas/natu-ral_gas/analysis_publications/natural_gas_1998_issues_trends/pdf/chap-ter3.pdf.

32. Ibid.

33. C. Michael Hogan et al., "Limestone," *The Encyclopedia of Earth*, ed. Andy Jorgenson, last modified August 21, 2012, accessed January 7, 2012, http://www.eoearth.org/article/Limestone?topic=49478.

34. Kurt Bucher and Rodney Grapes, *Petrogenesis of Metamorphic Rocks*, 8th ed. (Berlin: Springer, 2011), 24.

35. Ibid.

36. "Earth's Crust," British Antarctic Survey: Natural Environment Research Council, accessed January 8, 2012, http://www.antarctica.ac.uk/about_antarctica/geography/rock/earths_crust.php.

37. "Limestone," Naturalstone.com, accessed January 8, 2012, http://www.natural-stone.com/limestone.html.

38. Brian Groombridge and Martin Jenkins, *World Atlas of Biodiversity: Earth's Living Resources in the 21st Century* (Berkeley and Los Angeles: University of California Press, 2002), 10–11.

39. Romans 8:21.

40. Romans 8:20–22.

41. Walter T. Brown, *In the Beginning*, 5th ed. (Phoenix: Center for Scientific Creation, 1989), 58–84; Jonathan Sarfati, *Refuting Compromise: A Biblical and Scientific Refutation of "Progressive Creationism,"* 2nd ed. (Atlanta: Creation Book Publishers, 2011), 273–74, 279–80, 368–70.

42. Minik T. Rosing, "$^{13}$C-Depleted Carbon Microparticles in >3700-Ma Sea-Floor Sedimentary Rocks from West Greenland," *Science* 283 (January 29, 1999): 674–76; S. Flögel et al., "Simulating the Biogeochemical Effects of Volcanic $CO_2$ Degassing on the Oxygen-State of the Deep Ocean During the Cenomanian/Turonian Anoxic Event (OAE2)," *Earth and Planetary Science Letters* 305 (May 15, 2011): 371–74; David B. Finkelstein, Lisa M. Pratt, and Simon C. Brassell, "Can Biomass Burning Produce a Globally Significant Carbon-Isotope Excursion in the Sedimentary Record," *Earth and Planetary Science Letters* 250 (October 30, 2006): 501–10; Denis Lacelle et al., "Geomicrobiology and Occluded $O_2$-$CO_2$-Ar Gas Analyses Provide Evidence of Microbial Respiration in Ancient Terrestrial Ground Ice," *Earth and Planetary Science Letters* 306 (June 1, 2011): 46–54; Jennifer L. Macalady et al., "Dominant Microbial Populations in Limestone-Corroding Stream Biofilms, Frasassi Cave System, Italy," *Applied and Environmental Microbiology* 72 (August 2006): 5596–5609; Katja Meyer et al., " $^{13}$C Evidence That High Primary Productivity Delayed Recovery from End-Permian Mass Extinction," *Earth and Planetary Science Letters* 302 (February 1, 2011): 378–84.

43. "Proof of Noah's Flood at the Black Sea," Answers in Genesis Information Department, published November 22, 1999, http://answersingenesis.org/articles/1999/11/22/proof-of-Noahs-flood; Frank Lorey, "Tree Rings and Biblical Chronology," *Acts & Facts* 23, no. 6 (1994).

44. Martyn Bramwell, *Glaciers and Ice Caps* (Belgium: Franklin Watts, 1986), 19.

45. David G. Vaughan et al., "Reassessment of Net Surface Mass Balance in

Antarctica," *Journal of Climate* 12 (April 1999): 933–46.

46. Camilo Mora et al., "How Many Species Are There on Earth and in the Ocean?" *PLoS Biology* 9, no. 8 (August 23, 2011), doi:10.1371/journal.pbio.1001127.

47. John C. Whitcomb Jr. and Henry M. Morris, *The Genesis Flood: The Biblical Record and Its Scientific Implications* (Phillipsburg, NJ: Presbyterian and Reformed Publishing, 1961), 66.

48. Ibid.

49. Whitcomb and Morris, *The Genesis Flood*, 66–69 (in particular figure 4 on page 67 shows zebras and horses evolving from a single horse-like pair aboard Noah's ark).

50. Don Batten, "Ligers and Wholphins? What's Next?" *Creation Ex Nihilo* 22 (2000): 28–33.

51. Philip Kitcher, "Born-Again Creationism" in *Intelligent Design Creationism and Its Critics: Philosophical, Theological, and Scientific Perspectives*, ed. Robert T. Pennock (Cambridge, MA: A Bradford Book, MIT Press, 2001), 259.

52. 2 Kings 6:4–7, Matthew 8:23–27, 14:16–21, 14:25–31, John 11:38–44, 20:3–9, Hebrews 11:3.

**Chapter 18 – The Ark's Passengers: Genesis 6–9**

1. Robert A. Moore, "The Impossible Voyage of Noah's Ark," *Creation/Evolution* 11 (1983): 3–36.

2. Moore, 1–5; R. G. Elmendorf et al., "The Voyage of Noah's Ark—An Epilogue," *Creation/Evolution* 13 (1983): 39–48.

3. Genesis 19:12–29.

4. 2 Peter 2:5.

5. Hebrews 11:7.

6. 1 Peter 3:20.

7. Genesis 19:1, 6–9.

8. R. Laird Harris, Gleason L. Archer Jr., and Bruce K. Waltke, *Theological Wordbook of the Old Testament*, vol. 1 (Chicago: Moody, 1980), 135–36.

9. Ibid., 92–93.

10. Ibid., 281.

11. R. Laird Harris, Gleason L. Archer Jr., and Bruce K. Waltke, *Theological Wordbook of the Old Testament*, vol. 2 (Chicago: Moody, 1980), 587–91.

12. Ibid., 654–655.

13. Ibid., 850–851.

14. Ibid., 775.

15. Hugh Ross, *Hidden Treasures in the Book of Job: How the Oldest Book in the Bible Answers Today's Scientific Questions* (Grand Rapids: Baker, 2011), 131–73.
16. Harris, Archer, and Waltke, *Theological* Wordbook, vol. 2, 956–57.
17. Ibid., 793.
18. Genesis 6:21.
19. Genesis 6:16.
20. Richard A. Fox, "The Incredible Discovery of Noah's Ark: An Archaeological Quest?" *Free Inquiry* 13, no. 3 (1993), 43–48; Gerald A. Larue, "More on 'The Incredible Discovery of Noah's Ark'; Sun International Pictures, Inc., Responds to Critics," *Free Inquiry* 13, no. 4 (1993), 10–13, 61–63; John Cole, "Noah's Ark on CBS," *National Center for Science Education Reports* 13, no. 1 (1993), 4, 6; Bret A. Corum, "Dan Quayle on Noah's Ark?" *National Center for Science Education Reports* 13, no. 3 (1993), 6; Paul Kurtz, "Exploring the Television Wasteland," *Skeptical Inquirer* 17, no. 4 (1993), 354.
21. Genesis 10:11.
22. Alexander Heidel, *The Babylonian Genesis: The Story of Creation*, 2nd ed. (Chicago & London: University of Chicago Press, 1951), 1–140; John Cunningham Geikie, *Hours with the Bible*, vol. 1 (New York: James Pott, 1905), 174–81.
23. Ellen van Wolde, *Stories of the Beginning: Genesis 1–11 and Other Creation Stories*, trans. John Bowden (Ridgefield, CT: Morehouse, 1997), 116–18.

**Chapter 19 – Origin of Nations and Races: Genesis 9 –11**

1. John Keegan, *The Second World War* (New York: Penguin Books, 1989), 590; Stephen E. Ambrose and C. L. Sulzberger, *New History of World War II*, rev. ed. (New York: Viking, 1997), x.
2. Keegan, *Second World War*, 590.
3. Carroll Quigley, *The World Since 1939: A History* (New York: Collider, 1968), 167; Pete du Pont, "When Nations Snuff Out Their Own Citizens," *Insight on the News* 13, no. 39 (October 27, 1997), 30.
4. Isaiah 59:8–9.
5. Daniel 2:28–45; 7:2–18; 8:2–22; 10:13, 20; 11:2–35.
6. Luke 12:51.
7. Luke 2:14.
8. John 14:27a.
9. Genesis 10:8–12.
10. Genesis 11:1–6.
11. Genesis 11:4.

12. Genesis 1:28; 9:1.
13. Genesis 11:6.
14. Genesis 11:7, 9.
15. Scott A. Elias et al., "Life and Times of the Bering Land Bridge," *Nature* 382 (July 4, 1996): 61–63.
16. Elias et al, "Bering Land Bridge," 63.
17. Heiner Josenhans et al., "Early Humans and Rapidly Changing Holocene Sea Levels in the Queen Charlotte Islands—Hecate Strait, British Columbia, Canada," *Science* 277 (July 4, 1997): 71.
18. Ibid., 71, 73.
19. Ibid., 73.
20. Ibid., 71.
21. Ibid., 74.
22. Ibid., 71, 73.
23. Ibid., 73.
24. Ibid., 74.
25. Genesis 10:25a.
26. Josenhans et al., "Early Humans," 73.
27. Numbers 12:1.
28. Jeremiah 13:23.
29. Genesis 9:25–27.
30. K. A. Kitchen, "Canaan, Canaanites," in *The New Bible Dictionary*, 2nd ed., ed J. D. Douglas (Wheaton, IL: Tyndale House/ Leicester, UK: InterVarsity, 1982), 165.
31. Henry M. Morris, *The Genesis Record:A Scientific and Devotional Commentary on the Book of Beginnings* (Grand Rapids, MI: Baker, 1976), 234.
32. John 2:1–10.
33. 1 Timothy 5:23.
34. Manfred Heun et al., "Site of Einkorn Wheat Domestication Identified by DNA Fingerprinting," *Science* 278 (November 14, 1997): 1312–14; Jared Diamond, "Location, Location, Location: The First Farmers," *Science* 278 (November 14, 1997): 1243–44.
35. Melinda A. Zeder and Brian Hesse, "The Initial Domestication of Goats (*Capra hircus*) in the Zagros Mountains 10,000 Years Ago," *Science* 287 (March 24, 2000): 2254–57.
36. Michael Butler, "Did Plaster Hold Neolithic Society Together?" *Science* 294 (December 14, 2011): 2278–81.
37. Hugh Ross, *Why the Universe Is the Way It Is* (Grand Rapids, MI: Baker, 2008).

## Chapter 20 – Higher Criticism

1. D. C. Simpson, *Pentateuchal Criticism* (London: Oxford University Press, Humphrey Milford, 1924), 23–24.
2. William Henry Green, *The Higher Criticism of the Pentateuch* (New York: Scribner, 1895), 61.
3. Howard Osgood, "Jean Astruc," *The Presbyterian and Reformed Review* 3 (1892): 97–101.
4. Osgood, "Jean Astruc," 87; Jean Astruc, *Conjectures sur les* mémoirs *originaux dont il paraît que Moise s'est servi pour composer la Genèse, avec des remarques qui appuient ou éclaircissens ces conjectures* (Bruxelles, Fricx, 1753), 378, 439; Eamonn O'Doherty. "The Conjectures of Jean Astruc, 1753," *Catholic Biblical Quarterly*, 15 (1953): 300–4.
5. Johann Gottfried Eichhorn, *Einleitung in das Alte Testament*, vols. 1–5. (Göttingen, Netherlands: C. E. Rosenbusch, 1823–1824). Most of the relevant material can be found in volume 1.
6. S. R. Driver, *The Book of Genesis*, 3rd ed. (London: Methuen, 1904), 3–43.
7. *The Fundamentals: A Testimony to the Truth*, vol. 1, eds. R. A. Torrey et al. (Grand Rapids, MI: Baker, 1993), 16–88.
8. *The Interpreter's Bible*, vol. 1, eds. George A. Buttrick et al. (New York: Abingdon, 1952), 462–500; Louis Berkhof, *Systematic Theology*, 4th ed. (Grand Rapids, MI: Eerdmans, 1941), 150–60.
9. Eta Linnemann, "Higher Criticism and Systematic Theology," transcript of lecture given at Grace Valley Christian Center in Davis, CA on November 10, 2001, http://www.gracevalley.org/sermon_trans/Special_Speakers/Higher_Criticism_and_Systematic_Theology.html.
10. Franklin Johnson, "Fallacies of the Higher Criticism," in *The Fundamentals: A Testimony to the Truth*, vol. 4, eds. R. A. Torrey et al. (Grand Rapids, MI: Baker, 1994), 56–61.
11. David N. Livingstone, *Darwin's Forgotten Defenders* (Grand Rapids, MI: Eerdmans, 1987), 57–145.
12. Larry L. Walker, "Some Results and Reversals of the Higher Criticism of the Old Testament," *Criswell Theological Review* 1.2 (1987): 281–94; Gleason L. Archer Jr., *A Survey of Old Testament Introduction* (Chicago: Moody, 1974); Walter C. Kaiser Jr., "The Literary Form of Genesis 1–11," in *New Perspectives on the Old Testament*, ed. J. Barton Payne (Waco, TX: Word, 1970); Josh McDowell, *More Evidence That Demands a Verdict* (San Bernardino, CA: Campus Crusade for Christ, 1975).

## Chapter 21 – "Creation Science"

1. George McCready Price, *The New Geology* (Mountain View, CA: Pacific Press, 1923).
2. Ronald L. Numbers, *The Creationists: The Evolution of Scientific Creationism* (New York: Alfred A. Knopf, 1992), 87.
3. Ibid., 111.
4. Ibid., 75.
5. Ibid., 90.
6. Bernard Ramm, *The Christian View of Science and Scripture* (Grand Rapids, MI: Eerdmans, 1954).
7. Ibid., 180.
8. Ibid., 9. The phrase "narrow bibliolatry" appeared only in the paperback edition. In the cloth editions, page 9, Ramm used the phrase "narrow evangelical Biblicism."
9. Ibid., 115–17, 271–80.
10. Ibid., 220–22.
11. Ibid., 308–28.
12. Ibid., 220–21.
13. Ibid., 221–22.
14. Numbers, *Creationists*, 187–89, 196–97.
15. John C. Whitcomb Jr., and Henry M. Morris, *The Genesis Flood: The Biblical Record and Its Scientific Implications* (Phillipsburg, NJ: Presbyterian and Reformed Publishing, 1961).
16. Ronald L. Numbers, "Creating Creationism: Meanings and Usage Since the Age of Agassiz, Part Three," *Facts & Faith*, vol. 10, no. 2 (1996): 13.
17. John 12:24, 1 Corinthians 15:36.
18. Whitcomb and Morris, *Genesis Flood*, 66.
19. Henry Morris, *Biblical Creationism: What Each Book of the Bible Teaches about Creation and the Flood* (Green Forest, AR: Master Books, 2000), 36; Whitcomb and Morris, *Genesis Flood*, 66–69, 80–87. In particular, figure 4 on p. 67 shows, for example, zebras and horses evolving from a single horse-like pair on board Noah's ark.
20. Philip Kitcher, "Born-Again Creationism," in *Intelligent Design Creationism and Its Critics: Philosophical, Theological, and Scientific Perspectives*, ed. Robert T. Pennock (Cambridge, MA: MIT Press, 2001), 259.
21. James S. Stambaugh, "Death before Sin," *Impact*, no. 191 (The Institute for Creation Research: May 1989): i–iv; Whitcomb and Morris, *Genesis Flood*, 461–466; John D. Morris, "If All Animals Were Created as Plant Eaters, Why

Do Some Have Sharp Teeth?" *Acts & Facts* 26, no. 4 (April 1997): d.

22. Whitcomb and Morris, *Genesis Flood*, 66.

23. John D. Morris, "If All Animals Were Created as Plant Eaters," d.

24. As visitors enter the hall of Culture in Crisis at the Answers in Genesis Creation Museum they are greeted by a huge wrecking ball smashing into the foundation of a church. The only words on the ball, lettered over half a foot high, are "millions of years." Such an image also appears as a slide in many of the public lectures presented by young-earth creationist speakers.

25. Paul S. Taylor and Mark Van Bebber, "Fact Sheet on Hugh Norman Ross," *Progressive Creation Attack Pack* (Florence, KY: Answers in Genesis, 1995): 1; Henry M. Morris and John D. Morris, *Science, Scripture, and the Young Earth* (El Cajon, CA: Institute for Creation Research, 1989), 67; Kenneth Ham, "What Is a Creationist?" *Acts & Facts* 20, no. 6 (June 1991): b; Creationists.org, "Refuting the Heresies of Dr. Hugh Ross," The Young Earth Creation Club, accessed September 29, 2011, http://www.creationists.org/hugh-ross-heresies-and-bad-science.html.

26. Hugh Ross, *A Matter of Days: Resolving a Creation Controversy* (Colorado Springs: NavPress, 2004), 97–220.

## Chapter 22 – New Criticism

1. Lee Irons with Meredith G. Kline, "The Framework View," in *The Genesis Debate: Three Views on the Days of Creation*, ed. David G. Hagopian (Mission Viejo, CA: CruxPress, 2001), 220.

2. Henri Blocher, *In the Beginning: The Opening Chapters of Genesis*, trans. David G. Preston (Downers Grove, IL: InterVarsity, 1984), 50.

3. Some examples would be Richard T. Wright, *Biology through the Eyes of Faith* (San Francisco: Harper & Row, 1989), 141–159; Francis S. Collins, *The Language of God: A Scientist Presents Evidence for Believe* (New York: Free Press, 2006), 206–210; E. K. Victor Pearce, *Who Was Adam?* 3rd paperback ed. (Walkerville, Republic of South Africa: Africa Centre for World Mission, 1987); Ray L. Elliott, *The Third Adam: God's Scripture Written in the Fossil Record* (Neosho, MO: New Leaf, 1989), 24–30.

4. Genesis 1:26–27.

5. Matthew 19:1–6, Mark 10:1–9, Romans 5:12–21, 1 Corinthians 15:20–22, 44–49, 1 Timothy 2:13.

6. Romans 5:12–21, 1 Corinthians 15:20–22.

7. Fazale Rana with Hugh Ross, *Who Was Adam?* (Colorado Springs, CO: NavPress, 2005), 55–75, 123–37, 179–243; Fazale Rana, "Orangutan Ge-

netic Diversity Sheds Light on Humanity's Origin," *Today's New Reason to Believe* (blog), published March 16, 2011, http://www.reasons.org/articles/orangutan-genetic-diversity-sheds-light-on-humanitys-origin; Fazale Rana, Hugh Ross, and Kenneth Samples, "Ancient DNA Shows Interbreeding between Homo Sapiens and Neanderthal," *Science News Flash* (podcast), published May 10, 2010, http://www.reasons.org/podcasts/science-news-flash/ancient-dna-shows-interbreeding-between-homo-sapiens-and-neanderthal; Jeff Zweerink, "Does New Date for Neanderthal Extinction Mean the End of Human-Neanderthal Interbreeding?" *Today's New Reasons to Believe* (blog), published June 15, 2011, http://www.reasons.org/articles/does-new-date-for-neanderthal-extinction-mean-the-end-of-human-neanderthal-interbreeding.

8.  Fazale Rana with Hugh Ross, *Who Was Adam?* 139–83; Fazale Rana, Hugh Ross, and Steve Scheele, "Evidence From the Fossil Record," *Adam: Miracle, Myth, or Monkey,* January 10,2012, http://www.reasons.org/audio/evidence-from-the-fossil-record.

9.  Hugh Ross, *Hidden Treasures in the Book of Job: How the Oldest Book in the Bible Answers Today's Scientific Questions* (Grand Rapids, MI: Baker, 2011), 105–17, 124–28, 140–42.

10. Rana with Ross, *Who Was Adam?* 77–95; Fazale Rana, "New Statue Figures into Biblical Case for Human Origins," *Today's New Reason to Believe* (blog), published July 30, 2009, http://www.reasons.org/articles/new-statue-figures-into-biblical-case-for-human-origins; Fazale Rana, "New Flute Plays into Biblical Case for Human Origins," *Today's New Reason to Believe* (blog), published August 27, 2009, http://www.reasons.org/articles/new-flute-plays-into-biblical-case-for-human-origins; Hugh Ross, "New Date for First Aussies," *Today's New Reason to Believe* (blog), published April 1, 2004, http://www.reasons.org/articles/new-date-for-first-aussies.

11. Examples include J. Daniélou, *In the Beginning…Genesis I–III,* trans. Julien L. Randolf (Baltimore-Dublin: Helicon, 1965); Bernard Ramm, *The Christian View of Science and Scripture* (Grand Rapids: Eerdmans, 1954), 96–102; Gerhard F. Hasel, "The Polemic Nature of the Genesis Cosmology," *The Evangelical Quarterly* 46 (April–June, 1974): 81–102; Gerhard F. Hasel, "The Significance of the Cosmology of Genesis 1 in Relation to Ancient Near Eastern Parallels," *Andrews University Seminary Studies* 10 (1972): 1–20; John H. Stek, "What Says the Scripture?" in *Portraits of Creation: Biblical and Scientific Perspectives on the World's Formation,* ed. Howard J. Van Till (Grand Rapids: Eerdmans, 1990), 226–35.

12. Ellen van Wolde, *Stories of the Beginning: Genesis 1–11 and Other Creation Stories*, trans. John Bowden (Ridgefield, CT: Morehouse, 1997).

13. 1 Corinthian 2:12–13, Ephesians 6:17, Colossians 3:16, 1 Thessalonians 2:13, 2 Timothy 3:16, Hebrews 1:1–2, Hebrews 4:12.

14. 1 Peter 1:12a.

15. John H. Walton, *The Lost World of Genesis One: Ancient Cosmology and the Origins Debate* (Downers Grove, IL: InterVarsity, 2009), 113.

16. Walton, *Lost World of Genesis One*, 107.

17. Ibid., 113.

18. Ibid.

19. Johnny V. Miller and John M. Soden, *In the Beginning…We Misunderstood: Interpreting Genesis 1 in Its Original Context* (Grand Rapids: Kregel, 2012), 189.

20. Ibid., 189–90.

21. Walton, *Lost World of Genesis One*, 93.

22. Ibid., 118.

23. Ibid., 91, 93, 109.

24. Ibid., 92.

25. Ibid., 93.

26. Ibid., 115.

27. Ibid., 127.

28. Ibid., 116.

29. Ibid.

30. Stephen J. Gould, "Nonoverlapping Magisteria," *Natural History* 106 (March 1997): 19–22.

31. 1 Peter 3:15.

32. Walton, *Lost World of Genesis One*, 21.

33. Walton, *Lost World of Genesis One*, 16.

34. Stephen Hawking and Roger Penrose, "The Singularities of Gravitational Collapse and Cosmology," *Proceedings of the Royal Society of London A* 314 (January 27, 1970): 529–48; Arvind Borde, Alan H. Guth, and Alexander Vilenkin, "Inflationary Spacetimes Are Incomplete in Past Directions," *Physical Review Letters* 90 (April 18, 2003): 151301.

35. Fang Li Zhi and Li Shu Xian, *Creation of the Universe* (Singapore: World Scientific, 1989), 173.

36. Arno Penzias quoted in *Cosmos, Bios, and Theos: Scientists Reflect on Science, God, and the Origins of the Universe, Life, and Homo Sapiens*, eds. Henry Margenau and Roy Abraham Varghese (La Salle, IL: Open Court, 1992), 83.

37. Edward Harrison, *Masks of the Universe* (New York: Collier Books, Macmillan, 1985), 252.
38. Documentation of these discoveries are summarized in my book, *More Than a Theory: Revealing a Testable Model for Creation* (Grand Rapids: Baker, 2009) and presented in more detail in the following Reasons to Believe books: Fazale Rana and Hugh Ross, *Origins of Life: Biblical and Evolutionary Models Face Off* (Colorado Springs, CO: NavPress, 2004); Rana with Ross, *Who Was Adam?*; Fazale Rana, *The Cell's Design: How Chemistry Reveals the Creator's Artistry* (Grand Rapids, MI: Baker, 2008); Fazale Rana, *Creating Life in the Lab: How New Discoveries in Synthetic Biology Make a Case for the Creator* (Grand Rapids, MI: Baker, 2011); Hugh Ross, *Why the Universe Is the Way It Is* (Grand Rapids, MI: Baker, 2008); Hugh Ross, *Beyond the Cosmos: What Recent Discoveries in Astrophysics Reveal About the Glory and Love of God*, revised and updated ed. (Colorado Springs, CO: NavPress, 2010); Ross, *Hidden Treasures in the Book of Job*; Hugh Ross, *A Matter of Days: Resolving a Creation Controversy* (Colorado Springs, CO: NavPress, 2004); and Hugh Ross, *The Creator and the Cosmos: How the Greatest Scientific Discoveries of the Century Reveal God* (Colorado Springs, CO: NavPress, 1995).
39. Antony Flew and Roy Abraham Varghese, *There Is a God: How the World's Most Notorious Atheist Changed His Mind* (San Francisco: HarperOne, 2007); Antony Flew and Gary Habermas, "My Pilgrimage from Atheism to Theism: A Discussion Between Antony Flew and Gary Habermas," *Philosophia Christi* 6, no. 2 (2004): 197–211.
40. The classic text on the early history of astronomy is a 522-page book: Arthur Berry, *A Short History of Astronomy* (New York: Charles Scribner's Sons, 1898). The relevant material to my point can be found on pages 3–61. The book can be read online for free at http://archive.org/stream/shorthistoryofas025511mbp#page/n13/mode/2up. For an abbreviated history of astronomy previous to the time of Christ see George Abell, *Exploration of the Universe*, 2nd ed. (New York: Holt, Rinehart, and Winston, 1964): 7–23.
41. L. Jetsu et al., "Did the Ancient Egyptians Record the Period of the Eclipsing Binary Algol—The Raging One?" *Astrophysical Journal* 773 (August 10, 2013): id. 1.
42. Hebrews 11:24.
43. Walton, *Lost World of Genesis One*, 17.
44. Ibid.

45. Ibid., 105.
46. Christian Reformed Church, *Ecumenical Creeds and Reformed Confessions* (Grand Rapids: CRC Publications, 1988), 79.
47. Ecclesiastes 1, 3, 9; Romans 8:18–23.
48. I relate this history in my book, *Fingerprint of God*, commemorative ed. (Glendora,CA: Reasons to Believe, 2010), 15–39.
49. Ibid.
50. Robert Jastrow, *God and the Astronomers*, 2nd ed. (New York: W. W. Norton, 1992), 106–7.
51. Walton, *Lost World of Genesis One*, 105.
52. For a summary of ancient Christian discernment, see Etienne Gilson, *The Christian Philosophy of St. Thomas Aquinas* (Notre Dame, IN: Notre Dame Press, 1956), 130–59. For a summary of ancient Jewish discernment, see Gerald L. Schroeder, *Genesis and the Big Bang: The Discovery of Harmony between Modern Science and the Bible* (New York: Bantam books, 1990), 58–69, 84–95.
53. Walton, *Lost World of Genesis One*, 171. Here, in his answer to the question, "If this is the 'right' reading, why didn't we know about it until now?" Walton, in part, responded, "It was only with the decipherment of the ancient languages and the recovery of their texts that windows were again opened to an understanding of an ancient worldview that was the backdrop of the biblical world."
54. See, for example, Psalm 119:160; Isaiah 45:18–19; John 8:31–32, 10:35b; Titus 1:2, Hebrews 6:18, 1 John 5:6.

**Chapter 23 – More Than Myth**

1. "Definition of 'myth' in English," Oxford Dictionaries, www.oxforddictionaries.com/definition/american_english/myth.
2. Ellen van Wolde, *Stories of the Beginning: Genesis 1–11 and Other Creation Stories*, trans. John Bowden (Ridgefield, CT: Morehouse, 1997), 1.
3. 1 Thessalonians 5:21.
4. Romans 1:18–20.

**Appendix A – Biblical Origin of the Scientific Method**

1. 1 Chronicles 16:30; Psalm 93:1; Psalm 96:10; Psalm 104:5.
2. Job 34:4, Acts 17:11, Romans 12:2, 1 Thessalonians 5:21, 1 John 4:1, Revelation 2:2.
3. James Brodrick, *Galileo: The Man, His Work, His Misfortunes* (New York: Harper & Row, 1964), 75–78.

4.  Thomas F. Torrance, *Theology in Reconstruction* (Grand Rapids: Eerdmans, 1965); Thomas F. Torrance, *Reality and Scientific Theology* (Edinburgh: Scottish Academic Press, 1985); Thomas F. Torrance, "Ultimate and Penultimate Beliefs in Science," in *Facets of Faith & Science* 1; *Historiography and Modes of Interaction*, ed. Jitse M. van der Meer (New York: University Press of America, 1996), 151–76.

# INDEX

# ACKNOWLEDGMENTS

I began working on this book more than thirty-five years ago, before the publication of any of my other books. It holds special significance for me because my investigation of the Bible and of the possibility that God had something to do with it started with my first look into Genesis. The opening verse grabbed my attention and never let go. It pulled me to the next, the next, and the next, and I'm still studying, ever amazed at the accuracy with which the Bible describes the natural realm and anticipates scientific discovery.

When I live with a book in my head, Kathy, my wife, lives with that book too. So I'd like to express my thanks to her for helping me think it through, organize it, and choose its words.

Joe Aguirre, Krista Bontrager, Sandra Dimas, Linda Kloth, Fuz Rana, Dave Rogstad, Kenneth Samples, and Jeff Zweerink, my colleagues at Reasons to Believe (RTB), invested many hours in reviewing the manuscript and providing helpful recommendations and improvements. I also benefitted much from Vern Poythress' review of the manuscript and his suggested additions and clarifications. I owe much to their insight and study. My friend Marj Harman helped track down elusive references. Maureen Moser did the painstaking and essential fact-checking, and Elissa Emoto helped create the index and fact-checked endnotes. Sandra Dimas also did an amazing job of coordinating the editorial process, proofreading the text, and creating the index.

Finally, I would like to express my thanks to RTB's ministry care and advancement teams. Their support and encouragement and extra work allow me to focus on writing and editing. Their service goes far beyond the call of duty. I'm blessed to work with men and women who share my passion for providing new reasons to believe in our Creator and Savior.

# ABOUT THE AUTHOR

 **Hugh Ross** is founder and president of Reasons to Believe, an organization that researches and communicates how God's revelation in the words of the Bible harmonizes with the facts of nature.

With a degree in physics from the University of British Columbia and a grant from the National Research Council of Canada, Dr. Ross earned a PhD in astronomy from the University of Toronto. For several years he continued his research on quasars and galaxies as a postdoctoral fellow at the California Institute of Technology. His writings include journal and magazine articles and numerous books—*The Fingerprint of God, The Creator and the Cosmos, Beyond the Cosmos, Why the Universe Is the Way It Is*, and more. He has spoken on hundreds of university campuses as well as at conferences and churches around the world.

He lives in Southern California with his wife, Kathy and two sons, Joel and David.

# ABOUT REASONS TO BELIEVE

Uniquely positioned within the science-faith discussion since 1986, Reasons to Believe (RTB) communicates that science and faith are, and always will be, allies, not enemies. Distinguished for integrating science and faith respectfully and with integrity, RTB welcomes dialogue with both skeptics and believers. Addressing topics such as the origin of the universe, the origin and history of life, and the origin, history, and destiny of humanity, RTB's website offers a vast array of helpful resources. Through their books, blogs, podcasts, and speaking events, RTB scholars present powerful reasons from science to trust in the reliability of the Bible and the message it conveys about creation and redemption.

For more information, contact us via:
www.reasons.org
818 S. Oak Park Rd.
Covina, CA 91724
(855) REASONS